College Algebra

Student Workbook

Fourth Edition

Dr. Marilyn P. Carlson

Professor, Mathematics Education

Arizona State University

Phoenix

Pathways College Algebra – Student Workbook, Fourth Edition

Published by Rational Reasoning, LLC., 477 N Mondel Dr, Gilbert, AZ 85233.

This book was typeset in 11/12 Times Roman

ISBN 978-1-7326111-0-8

Printed in the United States of America

10 9 8 7 6 5 4 3 2 1

www.rationalreasoning.net

To: The College Algebra Student

Welcome!

You are about to begin a new mathematical journey that we hope will lead to your choosing to continue studying mathematics. Even if you don't currently view yourself as a math person, it is very likely that these materials and this course will change your perspective. The materials in this workbook are designed with student learning and success in mind and are based on decades of research on student learning. In addition to becoming more confident in your mathematical abilities, the reasoning patterns, problem solving abilities and content knowledge you acquire will make more advanced courses in mathematics, the sciences, engineering, nursing, and business more accessible. The worksheets and homework will help you see a purpose for learning and understanding the ideas of algebra, while also helping you acquire critical knowledge and ways of thinking that you will need for learning mathematics in the future. To assure your success, we urge you to advantage of the many resources we have provided to support your learning. We also ask that you make a strong effort to make sense of the questions and ideas that you encounter. This will assure that your mathematical journey through this course is rewarding and transformational.

Wishing you much success!

Dr. Marilyn P. Carlson

Table of Contents

This investigation contains review and practice with important skills and procedures you may need in this module and future modules. Your instructor may assign this investigation as an introduction to the module or may ask you to complete select exercises "just in time" to help you when needed. Alternatively, you can complete these exercises on your own to help review important skills.

Order of Operations
Use this section prior to the module or with/after Investigation 1.

The order of operations is an agreed-upon convention that ensures expressions are evaluated the same way by everyone. The commonly accepted order is as follows.

    i. *Simplify any expressions contained within parentheses or brackets. If there are nested sets of parentheses, then work from the inside to the outside.*

    ii. *Evaluate any parts of the expression containing exponents.*

    iii. *Negate any terms with a negation symbol in front of them.*

    iv. *Perform all multiplication and division, working from left to right.*

    v. *Perform all addition and subtraction, working from left to right.*

In Exercises #1-3, use the order of operations to simplify each expression.

1. $3 + 6(4) \div 12 - 1$
        2. $4(3 + 2)^2 - 10$
        3. $-(16 - 2^3) + 4$

When an expression is written as a fraction, we think of the entire numerator and denominator as having parentheses around them. Thus, we simplify the entire numerator as much as possible and the entire denominator as much as possible before reducing or evaluating the quotient.

In Exercises #4-6, use the order of operations to simplify each expression.

4. $\dfrac{13 - 3^2}{2^3}$
        5. $\dfrac{4 - 6 \div 2}{10 + 3 \cdot (-3)}$
        6. $\dfrac{-5 + (9 - 5(4)) + 3}{5(-2) - 1}$

In Exercises #7-9, place parentheses to guide the order of operations so the expressions evaluate to the indicated value. For example, if we want the expression $3 + 6 \cdot 4 - 2$ to evaluate to 18 we need parentheses as follows: $(3 + 6) \cdot (4 - 2)$. Any other way of placing the parentheses, or evaluating it as its written, will produce a different result.

7. $3 + 6 \cdot 4 - 2$ so that its value is 34
        8. $5 - 4 \cdot 2^2 + 18$ so that its value is 22

9. $5 - 4 \cdot 2^2 + 18$ so that its value is –41

The Distributive Property
Use this section prior to the module or with/after Investigation 2.

The distributive property is stated as follows. For real numbers a, b, and c,

$a(b + c) = ab + ac$ [can also be written $ab + ac = a(b + c)$]

$6(2 + 3)$

The distributive property is all about grouping. Suppose six friends each bring two bags of tortilla chips and three bags of pretzels to stock the snack bar at a dorm movie night. How many bags of snacks did they bring?

We can think of this in two ways. The first method is to count the number of bags of snacks each person brings [(2 + 3), or 5] and multiply this by the number of people [6]. So the total number of bags of snacks [30] can be represented as shown to the right (top).

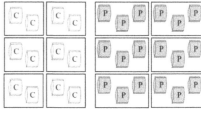

$6(2) + 6(3)$

The second method is to count the number of bags of tortilla chips [6(2), or 12] and the number of bags of pretzels [6(3), or 18] and add them together [12 + 18]. So the total number of bags of snacks [30] can be represented as shown to the right (bottom).

Therefore, we can understand why the expressions $6(2 + 3)$ and $6(2) + 6(3)$ are equivalent (beyond the fact that they evaluate to the same number).

In Exercises #10-12, use the distributive property to rewrite the expression in expanded form. For example, we can rewrite $3(6 + x)$ as $3(6) + 3x$ or $18 + 3x$.

10. $2(5 + r)$

11. $7(3x + 2)$

12. $x(7 + 4y)$

When subtraction is involved, you might choose to change the expression to involve addition. This may help you avoid sign errors (including forgetting about the negative). For example, you can rewrite $2(x - 5)$ as $2(x + (-5))$. Then applying the distributive property yields $2x + 2(-5)$, or $2x + (-10)$, or $2x - 10$.

In Exercises #13-15, use the distributive property to rewrite the expression in expanded form.

13. $6(x - 4)$

14. $4(3 - 2y)$

15. $-x(6y - 5)$

Note that the distributive property works "both directions" (we usually call one direction *distribution* and the other direction *factoring* – but they are both applications of this equality). So just as we can rewrite $3(x + 5)$ as $3(x) + 3(5)$ or $3x + 15$, we can rewrite $3x + 15$ as $3(x + 5)$.

In Exercises #16-21, use the distributive property to rewrite the expression in factored form. For example, we can rewrite $3x + 15$ as $3(x + 5)$.

16. $4x + 36$

17. $2x + 14$

18. $5x - 20$

19. $3x - 27$

20. $-2x + 30$

21. $-6x - 24$

Evaluating Expressions
Use this section prior to the module or with/after Investigation 2.

Given that $a = 2$, $b = -3$, $c = 0$, and $d = -5$, evaluate each of the expressions in Exercises #22-24.

22. $b(2a - 3d)$

23. $d^2 - 25 + c$

24. $6 - \dfrac{b}{ad}$

Given that $r = 3$, $t = 5$, $u = -2$, and $w = -12$, evaluate each of the expressions in Exercises #25-27.

25. $2(rt - w)$

26. $\dfrac{w}{3u} - r$

27. $r^2 + u^3 - t$

Formulas and Equations
Use this section prior to the module or with/after Investigation 3.

Formulas show how the values of two (or more quantities) are related as they change together. For example, the formula $A = lw$ represents how the area of a rectangle (in some square unit) is related to its length and width (measured in some units). Or, $y = 2x - 8$ represents how the values of x and y are related as they change.

Evaluating a formula involves substituting value(s) into the expression on one side of the formula (the side that contains operations and perhaps multiple terms).

In Exercises #28-30, evaluate each formula for the given input.

28. $y = (x + 5)^2 - 6$ for $x = -1$

29. $c = \frac{1}{3}(d - 4) + 7$ for $d = 12$

30. $y = \dfrac{1}{x} + x^2$ for $x = 10$

Solving an equation involves fixing the value of one side of the formula (usually the side that only contains one variable) and determining the value of the other variable(s) that produce that value.

In Exercises #31-33, use the given information to write an equation and then solve it.

31. solve $4x + 15 = y$ for x if $y = 38$

32. solve $r = 2(p - 3) + 5$ for p if $r = 17$

33. solve $z = \dfrac{x + 3}{x}$ for x if $z = 7$

Writing a formula involves representing a relationship between two (or more) quantities that change together using mathematical expressions connected by an equal sign.

34. a. Indicate on the figure and describe the attribute of the rectangle below that represents the following quantities.
    l = length of the side of the rectangle (measured in inches)
    w = width of the side of the rectangle (measured in inches)
    p = perimeter of the rectangle (measured in inches)
    A = area of the rectangle (measured in square inches)

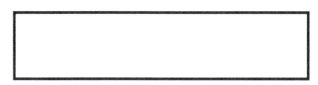

   a. Write the formula that determines the perimeter of a rectangle, given its width and length.

   b. Determine the width w of a rectangle when $p = 21$ and $l = 7$. Show your work.

35. a. Describe the attribute of the cube below that represents the following quantities.
    x = length of the sides of the cube (measured in centimeters)
    S = surface area of the cube measured in square centimeters
    V = volume of the cube measured in cubic centimeters

   b. Write the formula to express the volume of a cube V in terms of its side length x. Then determine the volume of a cube that has a side length of $4\frac{5}{8}$ centimeters.

   c. Write the formula to express the surface area of a cube S in terms of its side length x. Then determine the surface area of a cube when the cube's side length is $2\frac{2}{3}$ centimeters.

In this course, you will learn to represent how two varying quantities in dynamic situations change together. We begin the course by helping you acquire methods for identifying quantities as a first step to visualizing and representing (with formulas and graphs) how two quantities are related and change together.

Prior to defining a formula and graph to represent how two quantities in a problem context are related and change together you must first:

- Notice which two varying quantities you are being asked to relate (e.g., a sphere's volume and its radius length or the remaining length of a candle and the number of hours the candle has been burning).
- Make sense of how the two varying quantities are related and change together.

*1. Arizona State University graduate Desiree Linden won the 2018 Boston marathon. She began the 26.2-mile race with a slow pace due to the wind and rain. After the halfway point of the race she was feeling strong and increased her pace, completing the marathon in in a total time of 2:39:54 (2 hours, 39 minutes and 54 seconds).

  a. Identify at least two distances in this situation that are varying. *Be specific in your descriptions.*

  b. Identify at least two distances in this situation that are constant (do not vary).

  c. As the number of miles Desiree ran since starting the race increases, how does her distance from the finish line change?

  d. As Desiree's distance from the finish line decreases how does her distance from the start of the race change? Draw a diagram to support your answer.

Quantities

Quantities are the attributes of an object or situation that you can imagine measuring. To clearly describe a quantity, we must include:

- the object or description of the situation and what attribute we are measuring
- where we are measuring the quantity from
- the units used in the measurement

If the value of a quantity does not change then the quantity is called a ***fixed quantity*** and its value is a constant.

If the value of the quantity changes then the quantity is called a ***varying quantity*** and the quantity can assume more than one value.

Examples of *fixed quantities*: the height of a water bottle (in inches), the weight of a table (in pounds), and the distance between two fixed points (in miles).

In the first situation, *height* is a measurable attribute of the water bottle. The unit being used to measure the water bottle's height is inch. In the second situation, *weight* is an attribute of the table. The unit being used to measure the table's weight is a pound.

*2. Discuss with your classmates how you can recognize a quantity in a problem situation.

*3. a. List two fixed quantities by stating the measurable attribute of some object in your classroom that you can imagine measuring. *Include the unit of measurement in your description.*

   b. Determine if each of the following describes a fixed quantity. If not, modify the statement so that it does represent a fixed quantity.
      i. the surface area in square inches

      ii. the distance (in miles) from mile marker 204 to mile marker 210

      iii. the volume (in gallons)

Examples of *varying quantities*: the distance (in miles) of your car from home as you drive to work, the height (in feet) of a ball above the top of a 15-foot tall building, the number of gallons of water in a filling tank.

Prior to trying to write formulas or construct graphs to represent how two varying quantities are changing together, it is useful to visualize how the relevant quantities are changing in the situation.

Example: If we want to represent the height of a flying ball above the top of a 15-foot tall building, we can assume that the building's height is being measured from the ground and that the ball can be both above and below the top of the 15-foot high building.

Here is a number line with 0 representing the top of the 15-foot tall building. We labeled the number line so that numbers to the right of 0 represent the ball's height **above** the top of the building (number of feet).

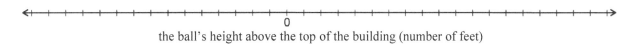

the ball's height above the top of the building (number of feet)

Notice that negative values indicate that the ball is below the top of the building. For example, a value of –5 conveys that the ball is –5 feet *above the top of the building* or 5 feet below the top of the building.

*4. a. If the ball is thrown downward from the top of the 15-foot building, where on the number line would we plot points to represent the ball's position? Why?

    b. Place (and label) points on the number line to represent that the ball is:
      i. 5 feet above the top of the building
      ii. 4 feet below the top of the building
      iii. 9 feet above the ground
      iv. 23 feet above the ground

Note that in each description of a varying quantity you must have a starting point for your measurement in mind. "The distance of a car in miles" does not describe a quantity, but "The distance traveled in miles since the car left the parking lot" does.

5. We can represent the distance (in miles) of Laura's car north of a stop sign using a number line.

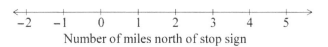

Number of miles north of stop sign

    a. What does 0 on the number line represent?

    b. Using a dashed line, illustrate on the number line above that Laura has traveled 4 miles north of the stop sign.

    c. Laura is now 2 miles south of the stop sign. Illustrate this on the number line if the number line still represents "number of miles north of the stop sign".

*6. As Desiree Linden is running the marathon her distance from the starting line is varying and her distance from the finish line is varying.

    a. When Desiree has run 5 miles from the starting line, how far is she from the finish line? Indicate Desiree's approximate position on this illustration.

    b. When Desiree has run 22 miles from the starting line, how far is she from the finish line? Indicate Desiree's approximate position on this illustration.

    c. If we let x represent the varying number of miles that Desiree has run from the starting line of the Boston Marathon to the finish line of the Boston Marathon, how does the value of x vary in this situation?

    d. What are the restrictions on the values that x can assume in this situation?

Variables

Instead of representing a quantity's values with words it is more concise to **define a variable** by designating some letter (or other symbol) to represent the values that a specific varying quantity can assume.

When defining a variable we must be precise in describing the quantity and how it is being measured, by saying:

    i. what quantity we are measuring
    ii. where we are measuring the quantity from, and
    iii. the measurement unit.

Using Exercise #6, let the variable x represent Desiree's varying number of miles from the starting line of the race. In doing so, we write:

Let x represent Desiree's distance (in miles) from the starting line.

We then think of x as representing the varying number of miles that Desiree runs from the starting line of the race toward the finish line of the race.

---

e. If our goal is to represent Desiree's distance from the finish line *in terms of* her distance from the starting line, x, we need to determine how to combine the fixed quantity 26.2 miles and the varying quantity x to represent this quantity.

In this figure illustrate:
   i. The fixed length of the race of 26.2 miles.
   ii. Desiree's varying distance from the starting line, using a dashed line that has an arrow at the end (or vector), to indicate the direction Desiree is running. Place the variable x above this dashed line.
   iii. The varying distance that is represented with the expression $26.2 - x$.

*7. a. Discuss the usefulness of a variable (symbol) for representing all the values that a quantity can assume.

b. It is important when defining variables that we are specific in describing the varying quantity whose values are being represented by the variable (designated symbol). Is the statement, "d = Erin's distance (in miles)" an adequate definition of a variable? If not, what is missing and how might you modify this statement so that it defines a variable?

c. When defining a variable, why is it important to describe where the quantity is being measured from <u>and</u> the measurement unit?

8. Jenny's gas tank has 2.5 gallons of gasoline remaining when she pulls into a gas station to fill her 22-gallon tank.
   a. Represent the quantities in this situation by:
      i. drawing a solid line to represent the fixed quantity of 2.5 gallons
      ii. drawing a dashed line with an arrow to represent the varying number of gallons of gasoline added to the tank

   b. If n represents the varying number of gallons of gasoline added to the tank, write an expression to represent the varying number of gallons of gasoline in the tank.

9. The city's water tank holds 20,500 gallons of water. After the tank is full, water begins draining from the tank.
    a. Define a variable d to represent the varying amount of water that has drained from the tank. Use the variable d to write an expression that represents the varying number of gallons of water remaining in the tank.

    b. As the number of gallons of water that have drained from the tank d increases, how does the number of gallons of water remaining in the tank change?

*10. Bob starts running. Bill starts running 5 seconds later. If t represents the varying number of seconds Bill has been running, write an expression using (or in terms of) t to represent the number of seconds Bob has been running.

11. Jim and Juan are 120 feet apart and start walking toward one another at that same time and the same speed.
    a. When Jim has walked x feet, how many feet has Juan walked?

    b. Illustrate the situation. Use a solid line for the fixed quantity (the original 120 feet between Jim and Juan), a dashed line with an arrow (vector) to represent the varying distance Jim has walked, and another dashed line with an arrow to represent the varying distance Juan has walked.

    c. Using x, label the fixed quantity of 120 feet and the varying distances Jim and Juan have walked.

    d. Write an expression to represent the combined distance that Jim and Juan have walked since they started walking toward one another.

    e. Write an expression to represent the varying distance between Jim and Juan as they are walking toward one another. Then place this expression on your illustration in part (b).

*1. Becky and Wendy are 45 feet apart and start walking toward one another at the same time. Since Wendy is walking twice as fast as Becky, Wendy travels $2x$ feet whenever Becky travels x feet.

   a. Illustrate this situation with a drawing, given that x represents the distance Becky has walked since she started walking toward Wendy. (*Use a solid line to represent the fixed distance between Becky and Wendy, and dashed lines with arrows (vectors) to represent the varying distances that Becky and Wendy have walked.*)

   b. Label the expressions x, $2x$ and $45 - 3x$ on your drawing in part (a). Then describe in your own words what each expression represents.

   c. If we let d represent the varying distance (in feet) between Becky and Wendy, then $d = 45 - 3x$. What is the benefit of representing the varying distance between Becky and Wendy using a single variable such as d, in addition to representing it using the expression $45 - 3x$?

"… in terms of …"

When we write $d = 45 - 3x$, we say that we have defined a formula that expresses the distance between Becky and Wendy ***in terms of*** x, the number of feet that Becky has walked toward Wendy.

This formula conveys how d, the distance (in feet) between Becky and Wendy, and x, the distance (in feet) Becky has walked toward Wendy, change together. In particular, we write it with the assumption that we are using values of x to determine values of d.

Additional examples include:
   - The formula $y = 2x - 8$ represents values of y in terms of x.
   - The formula $5(c + 1)^2 + 3 = w$ represents values of w in terms of c.

In addition to representing how two varying quantities change together with expressions and formulas, we can also represent how these values change together with graphs. The two axes on a graph can be thought of as number lines with a point simultaneously representing the values of two quantities represented on the number lines. The curve we draw then represents all corresponding pairs of values for the quantities as they change together.

It is a mathematical convention to let the x-axis (or horizontal axis) represent the values of the independent quantity—in this case x, and the vertical axis to represent the values of the dependent quantity—in this case d or $45 - 3x$.

---

*2. Continuing with the context from Exercise #1, complete the following.

a. Which axis should be labeled, "the distance in feet Becky has traveled since she started walking toward Wendy"?

b. Which axis should be labeled, "the distance in feet between Becky and Wendy since they started walking toward one another"?

c. Label the axes and plot the points (0, 45), (7, 9) and (15, 45) on this grid. What does the point (7, 9) represent in this context?

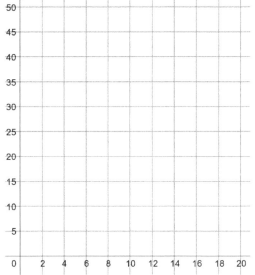

d. i. Determine two other points on the graph that represent how x and $45 - 3x$ are related.

   ii. When $x = 5.2$, what is the value of $45 - 3x$?

   iii. When x has a value of 9.87, what is the value of d?

   iv. When the distance Becky has walked increases from 0 to 5 feet, how does the distance between Becky and Wendy vary?

*3. A candle is 18 inches tall before it's lit.
   • Let x represent the number of inches burned from the candle.
   • Let y represent the number of inches of candle remaining.

a. What does the expression $18 - x$ represent?

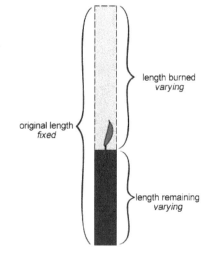

length burned
varying

original length
fixed

length remaining
varying

b. Label x, y, 18, and $18 - x$ on the diagram.

c. Write a formula that represents y in terms of x.

d. Is it possible to write your formula in part (b) without using a constant quantity? What role do constant quantities play in helping you define a formula that describes how two varying quantities change together? Discuss this with a partner or as a class.

e. Construct a graph to represent the remaining length of the candle (in inches) y in terms of the number of inches that have burned from the candle, x. Label both axes.

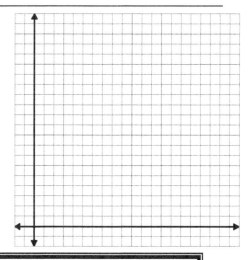

Formulas

A formula defines how two varying quantities change together. Consider two varying quantities with their varying values represented by the variables x and y.

- If we write a formula that expresses y in terms of x, we say that y is the dependent variable and x is the independent variable. The formula's structure is "y = [some expression with x]".
- Likewise, if we write a formula that expresses x in terms of y, we say that x is the dependent variable and y is the independent variable. The formula's structure is "x = [some expression with y]".

---

*4. Sam boards a Ferris wheel from the bottom and rides around several times before getting off. This graph represents Sam's height above the ground (in feet) with respect to the amount of time (in seconds) since the Ferris wheel began moving for one complete rotation of the wheel.

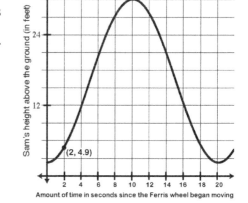

a. The point (2, 4.9) is plotted on the graph. Explain what this point conveys in the context of the Ferris wheel situation.

b. Complete the sentence, "As the number of seconds since the Ferris wheel began moving increases from 0 to 20 seconds, Sam's height above the ground…

c. As the *number of seconds since the Ferris wheel began moving* **increases** from 2 to 8 seconds, how does *Sam's height in feet above the ground* **change**? Represent this change in height on the graph.

d. As the *number of seconds since the Ferris wheel began moving* **increased** from 10 to 16 seconds, what was the **change** in *Sam's height in feet above the ground*? Represent this change on the graph and with a mathematical expression.

---

e. Let *t* represent the values of the quantity *the number of minutes since the Ferris wheel began moving*. Write a complete sentence that correctly defines the variable *t*.

f. Define the variable *h* so that it represents the varying values of the dependent quantity in this situation. *Remember that you must ALWAYS say where the measurement begins (for example, "since 10 am" or "since Becky started walking") and include units (seconds, feet, square inches, etc.) when defining variables.*

Changes in Quantities

Once we have defined a variable *x* to represent the varying values of a quantity we can write Δx (read as "delta *x*") to represent *changes* in that quantity's value.

The change in a quantity's value is a new quantity itself, and if the value of *x* changes from x_1 to x_2 then the amount of change can be represented as $x_2 - x_1$.

For example, if *x* changes from $x = 6$ to $x = 19$, then $\Delta x = 19 - 6$, or the value of *x* changed by 13 units.

---

5. The temperature in Phoenix *T* in degrees Fahrenheit varies during the day. On May 1st the temperature was 65 degrees Fahrenheit at 6 am and 90 degrees Fahrenheit at 11 am.
    a. What was the change in temperature ΔT over the time period from 6am to 11 am?

    b. Represent the change in temperature ΔT determined in part (a) on the number line.

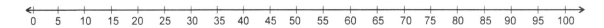

    c. Assuming that $t = 0$ corresponds to 12 am (midnight), what was the change in time Δt from 6 am to 11 am on May 1st?

    d. Represent Δt on the number line.

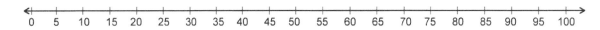

    e. Represent a change of temperature of 5 degrees Fahrenheit. Discuss with your classmates how many ways you can represent this change of 5 degrees as the temperature in Phoenix varied from 60 degrees Fahrenheit to 90 degrees Fahrenheit on May 1st.

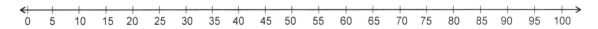

    f. Represent a change of −7 degrees Fahrenheit from 90 degrees Fahrenheit on the number line.

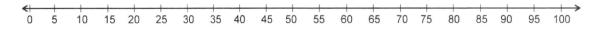

---

*6. A 7-quart glass container weighs 4 pounds when empty. The weight of water is 2 pounds per quart. Let *x* represent the varying number of quarts of water that are in the container.

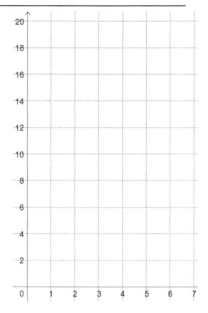

   a. Label the axes on the grid and plot the points (0, 4), (1, 6) and (4, 12). What do these points represent in this context?

   b. If *x* increases from *x* = 1 to *x* = 4,
     i. What is the change in the value of *x* and what does this change represent in this context?

     ii. Represent the change you computed in (i) on the number line.

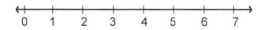

     iii. What is the corresponding change in the weight of the container and water (in pounds)?

     iv. Represent this change on the number line.

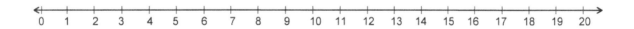

   c. On the grid in part (a), use vectors to represent the simultaneous changes in the number of quarts of water and the weight of the water as the number of quarts of water increases from 1 to 4.

   d. i. Write a formula to represent the total weight of the container and water *y* (in pounds) in terms of the number of quarts of water that have been added to the container, *x*.

     ii. What does the constant in front of *x* represent?

     iii. What does the constant **term** represent?

7. The given graph relates the depth of water in a reservoir to the number of months since January 1, 1990.

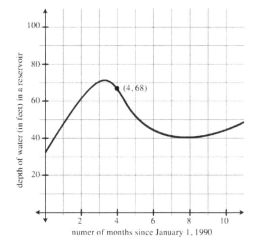

a. Define variables to represent the values of the varying quantities in this situation.

b. Interpret the meaning of the point (4, 68).

c. Label 3 other points on the graph and describe what they represent.

d. The number of months since January 1, 1990 increases from 1 to 3 months.
   i. What is the change in the number of months since January 1, 1990?

   ii. Represent this change on the graph.

e. As the number of months since January 1, 1990 increases from 1 to 3 months.
   i. How does the depth of the water in the reservoir vary?

   ii. What is the change in the depth of the water?

   iii. Represent the change from 1 to 3 months since January 1, 1990 and the corresponding change of the water depth of the reservoir on the graph.

f. Estimate the depth of the water in the reservoir 7 months after January 1, 1990.

g. How does the depth of the water in the reservoir vary as the number of months since January 1, 1990 increases from 4 to 7 months? Illustrate this variation on the graph.

You have been studying linear relationships and the idea of constant rate of change since your first course in algebra. You learned that any formula that can be written or simplified to the form $y = mx + b$ describes a linear relationship between x and y, and that x and y vary together at a constant rate of change. In this formula m represents the constant rate at which y changes with respect to x, and b represents the *y-intercept* or value of y when $x = 0$.

We can speak of how the value of one quantity varies and how the value of a second quantity varies, but if we want to consider how the values of two quantities are varying together, we need to think about how the ordered pair (x, y) varies under specific constraints imposed by a dynamic context, formula, or graph.

*1. Benny walks to school at a constant speed and travels 8 feet in 3 seconds.
   a. If Benny walks 2 times as long as 3 seconds (that is, he walks for 6 seconds), how far will Benny walk, given that he is walking at a constant rate of change and travels 8 feet in 3 seconds?

   b. If Benny walks 1/3 of 3 seconds (that is, he walks for 1 second), what part of 8 feet must he walk, given he is walking at a constant speed and travels 8 feet in 3 seconds?

   c. With a partner or as a class, discuss the reasoning used to determine your answers to parts (a) and (b).

   d. When answering parts (a) and (b) what relationship remained constant?

   e. What constant rate of change describes how Benny is walking?

   f. If Benny continues at this constant rate of change for another 4 seconds after reaching school, what distance did he travel in those 4 seconds?

Constant Rate of Change

Given that two values x and y are changing together at a ***constant rate of change*** and we know (or can find) **any** two pairs of values (x_1, y_1) and (x_2, y_2) in the relationship, then $\dfrac{y_2 - y_1}{x_2 - x_1} = m$ (where m is some constant). We say that y **is changing at a constant rate of change of m with respect to x.**

For any pairs of values (x_1, y_1) and (x_2, y_2) in the relationship, the ratio of $y_2 - y_1$, (read as the change in y) to $x_2 - x_1$ (read as the change in x) remains constant (or always has the constant value m). We can also say that if two quantities are related by a constant rate of change, the corresponding changes in the two quantities are proportional.

Using this definition, if we let $\Delta x = x_2 - x_1$ and $\Delta y = y_2 - y_1$, for any pairs of values (x_1, y_1) and (x_2, y_2) in the constant rate of change relationship between x and y, then we can also write $\dfrac{\Delta y}{\Delta x} = m$.

---

*2. The owner of a swimming pool wants to know the rate at which his swimming pool is filling. He knows that the water in the pool is 18 inches deep when it is 2 pm. Water continues flowing in at what appears to be a constant rate of change and he wants to determine its value.

   a. The pool owner notes that when it is 5 pm the water is 32 inches deep. What is the change in depth of the water over the time period from 2 pm to 5 pm?

   b. What is the change in time elapsed between 2 pm and 5 pm?

   c. What is the rate of change of the water's depth (in inches) with respect to time (in hours)?

   d. If the pool continues filling for another 6 hours (after 2 pm),
      i. what is the change in the height of water in the pool?

      ii. what is the new height of the water in the pool when it is 5 pm?

*3. Porter received a remote-control car as a gift for his birthday. 6 meters after Porter's car began to move it reached top speed. His car continued at this constant speed for 5 more seconds and traveled a distance of 3 meters every 1 second.

   a. What total distance had Porter's car traveled when it reached top speed (that is, 0 seconds since reaching top speed)? What total distance had Porter's car traveled 4 seconds after it reached top speed?

   b. What constant rate of change did Porter's car travel after it reached top speed?

   c. Write a linear formula to define the distance *d* (in meters) Porter's car traveled *since it started to move* in terms of the number of seconds *t since Porter's car reached top speed.*

   d. How far did Porter's car travel at top speed over any:
      i.   ½ second interval after it reached top speed?

      ii. 3-second interval after it reached top speed?

      iii. 3.5-second interval after it reached top speed?

      iv. 3.2-second interval after it reached top speed?

   e. How far did Porter's car travel at top speed over any *k* second interval ($0 < k < 5$) after Porter's car reached top speed?

f. When Porter's car travels at its top speed of 3 meters per second, describe how the car's *distance traveled* and *elapsed time* change together. *Hint: For any change in time Δt since Porter's car started moving, the distance Porter's car traveled changes by_____.*

g. Construct a graph to represent the distance *d* (in meters) Porter's car traveled since it started to move, in terms of the number of seconds *t* since Porter's car reached top speed. *Be sure to label the axes.*

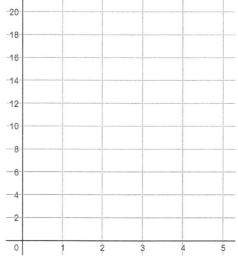

h. How is *m*, the constant rate that Porter's car traveled after reaching top speed, represented on the graph? How is *b* (the vertical intercept) represented on the graph?

i. In the ratio $m = \frac{18-9}{4-1}$, what does 18 − 9 represent in the context? What does 4 − 1 represent in the context?

j. What does the ratio $m = \frac{18-9}{4-1}$ represent in the context?

*4. Review your responses to Exercises #1 and 3. Describe what it means for an object to move at a constant speed. (*Note: Say something more than "The speed doesn't change" – be descriptive and reference specific quantities.*)

Constant Rate of Change Revisited

If *y* changes at a constant rate with respect to *x*, then we know that $\frac{\Delta y}{\Delta x} = m$, or $\frac{y_2 - y_1}{x_2 - x_1} = m$ when (x_1, y_1) and (x_2, y_2) represent any two pairs of corresponding values in the relationship.

Note that $\Delta y = m \cdot \Delta x$ is another way to express the relationship $\frac{\Delta y}{\Delta x} = m$. This form emphasizes that Δy is always *m* times as large as Δx when *x* and *y* change together. Note that we can also write this as follows.

$$\Delta y = m \cdot \Delta x$$
$$y_2 - y_1 = m \cdot (x_2 - x_1)$$

© 2018 Carlson, Oehrtman, and Moore

*5. Each of the following represents a situation with a constant rate of change. Use the definition above to explain what these statements mean:

a. $\Delta y = 6 \cdot \Delta x$ (*Hint: As the values of x and y change together, the change in y is always...*)

b. $\Delta y = -2 \cdot \Delta x$

c. $\Delta y = \frac{1}{2} \cdot \Delta x$

*6. a. Illustrate the meaning of $\Delta y = -2 \cdot \Delta x$ on a graph that passes through the point (1, 7).

b. As x varies from 1 to 5.5, how does y vary? Illustrate these variations on your graph.

c. Does x take on all values between 1 and 5.5? If so, how is this illustrated on your graph?

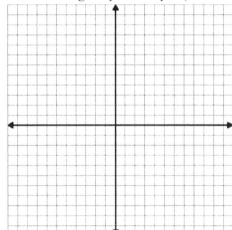

In your high school Algebra classes you learned that the constant rate of change of y with respect to x can be determined if you know any two points in the relationship in which x and y are changing together at a constant rate of change (also referred to as a linear relationship). We reviewed this in our definition boxes on constant rate of change, but restate here that if (x_1, y_1) and (x_2, y_2) are **any two pairs of values in a linear relationship**, then we can determine the change from x_1 to x_2 and the corresponding changes from y_1 to y_2. The ratio of these changes $\frac{y_2 - y_1}{x_2 - x_1} = m$ is the constant rate of change of y with respect to x.

7. The given graph represents a linear relationship between y, Bob's distance (in miles) to the finish line of a race, and x, the amount of time (in minutes) since Bob passed the final water station.

a. What does the point (–22, 8.2) represent in this situation?

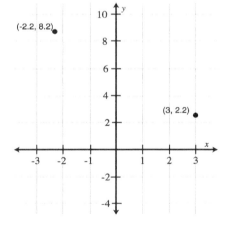

b. Determine the value of m, the constant rate of change of y with respect to x, in this linear relationship and say what this value represents.

c. Use the general formula $y_2 - y_1 = m \cdot (x_2 - x_1)$ to relate the values of x and y in the linear relationship depicted in the given graph.

d. For the point (30, 2.2) we have that $x_1 = 30$ and $y_1 = 2.2$.

   i. Since y represents the varying distances that Bob is from the finish line of the race, what does $y - 2.2$ represent?

   ii. Since x is the varying number of minutes since Bob passed the final water station in the race, what does $x - 30$ represent in this situation?

Point-Slope Form of a Linear Function

The general formula $y - y_1 = m(x - x_1)$ defines a linear relationship where m is the constant rate of change of y with respect to x and (x_1, y_1) is an ordered pair in the relationship.

---

8 a.   What do x and y represent in the point-slope form of a linear function?

b.   Describe situations in which the point-slope form of a linear function is useful.

*9. Given that the x and y axes have the same scale for both of these graphs, answer the following questions.

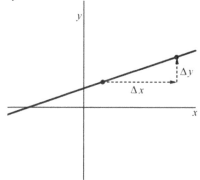

Graph of linear function A

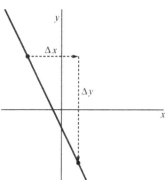

Graph of linear function B

a.   What is the approximate constant rate of change of y with respect to x for the linear functions?

Linear function A: Linear function B:

b.   Write a formula that expresses Δy in terms of Δx.

Linear function A: Linear function B:

c.   Write a formula that expresses y in terms of x given the y-intercept of the graph of function A is 3 and the y-intercept of the graph of function B is -3.

Formula for linear function A: Formula for linear function B:

---

10. A candle is 8.5 inches tall when it has been burning for 6 hours at a rate of ¼ in. per hour.
    a. How tall was the candle when it had been burning for 2.4 hours? (*Hint: Think about how the change in the remaining length of the candle is related to the change in the number of hours the candle has been burning.*)

    b. How tall was the candle before it was lit (when it had been burning for 0 hours)?

11. a. Graph the line $y = 4x$ and plot 3 points on your graph, then illustrate Δy and Δx between (0, 0) and each of these points.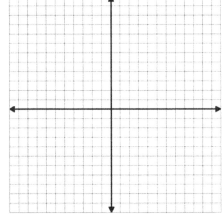

    b. Consider the graph that you constructed in (a). For each point (x, y) on your graph, compare the values of x and y to the values of Δx and Δy between (0, 0) and (x, y). What do you notice?

    c. Given that $\frac{\Delta y}{\Delta x} = 4$ for some linear function, under what conditions does $\frac{y}{x}$ also equal 4?

12. Calvin uses a slow-running hose to fill an empty wading pool. The graph represents the volume of water (in gallons) in the pool, v, in terms of the amount of time elapsed, t, (in minutes) since Calvin began filling the pool.
    a. Write a formula that determines the volume of water, v, (in gallons) in terms of the time elapsed, t, (in minutes) since the pool began filling.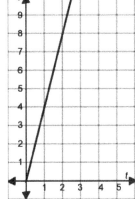

    b. Δv is how many times as large as Δt? Express this relationship with a formula.

    c. How are the formulas you wrote in parts (a) and (b) related?

    d. Write a formula that determines the elapsed time, t, (in minutes) since the pool began filling in terms of the volume of water, v, (in gallons) of water in the pool.

    e. Δt is how many times as large as Δv? Express this relationship with a formula and explain how it relates to the formula you wrote in part (d).

    f. What do you notice about how your formulas in part (a) and part (d) are related? Do they represent the same relationship? Explain.

*1. The perimeter P of a square (measured in inches) is expanding in size at a constant rate of change of 4 inches per inch with respect to the square's side length s (measured in inches).
   a. If the length of the side of the square changes from
      i. 0 to 2.5 inches, how does the square's perimeter P change?

      ii. 1 to 3 inches, how does the square's perimeter P change?

   b. Express the ***change*** in the square's perimeter P in terms of the ***change*** in the square's side length s.

     $\Delta P = \underline{\hspace{1cm}} \cdot \Delta s$

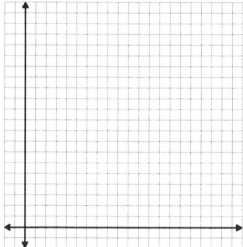

   c. Write a formula and construct a graph that represents the perimeter of the square P (in inches) in terms of the square's side length s (in inches).

   d. Illustrate the solution to $12 = 4s$ (that is, solve $12 = 4s$ for s) on your graph and describe what this solution represents.

   e. If $P = 4s$ represents the square's perimeter in terms of the square's side length (in inches), write a formula that represents the perimeter's side length s in terms of the square's perimeter P.

   f. How is the formula you determined in part (e) related to the formula $P = 4s$?

   g. i. Represent the changes you computed in part (a) as vectors on the axes.

     ii. What does the length of each vector represent?

     iii. What must be true about the end points of the vectors? Explain.

> ### Proportional Relationships
>
> If y varies with x in a linear relationship so that $y = m \cdot x$ (that is, the value of y is m times as large as the value of x), then we can think of any value of x or y as a change away from 0.
>
> In this instance, we say that y **is proportional to** x (and also that x is proportional to y).
>
> Note that if $y = m \cdot x$, then it's also true that $\Delta y = m \cdot \Delta x$ (that is, the change in y is m times as large as the change in x as the quantities co-vary). We can say that Δy is proportional to Δx and that Δx is proportional to Δy.

*2. Here are two cylinders: one wide and one narrow. Both cylinders have equally spaced marks for measurement. Water is poured into the wide cylinder up to the 4th mark (see A). This water rises to the 6th mark when poured into the narrow cylinder (see B).

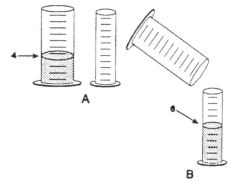

a. Both cylinders are emptied, and water is poured into the narrow cylinder up to the 11th mark. How high would this water rise if it were poured into the empty wide cylinder?

b. Imagine pouring water into the narrow cylinder and let x represent the varying mark-number the water reaches in the narrow cylinder as you pour. Let y represent the mark-number the water would reach if we poured the same volume of water into the wide cylinder.

   i. What is the meaning of $\frac{y}{x} = \frac{2}{3}$ in this context?

   ii. What is the meaning of $y = \frac{2}{3}x$ in this context?

   iii. What is the meaning of $\Delta y = \frac{2}{3}\Delta x$ in this context?

c. i. When $x = 1$, what is the value of y?

   ii. When $x = 3$, what is the value of y?

   iii. When $x = 4.5$, what is the value of y?

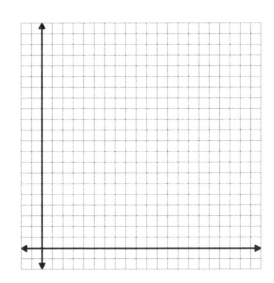

d. Plot the three points (x, y) you determined in part (c) on the given axes. Be sure to label your axes by naming the varying quantities represented on each axes.

© 2018 Carlson, Oehrtman, and Moore

e. The value of x increases (changes) from 0 to 3.
   i. What is the corresponding value of Δy (*the change in the mark-number the water reaches in the wide cylinder*)? Illustrate these changes on your graph.

   ii. What is the value of y when $x = 3$ (*also thought of as a change of positive 3 units from an initial value of 0 units*)? How are these values illustrated on your graph?

f. As the value of x increases (changes) from 3 to 6, what is the value of Δy ? Illustrate these changes on your graph.

g. Compare and contrast what is conveyed by the three statements, $\frac{y}{x} = \frac{2}{3}$, $y = \frac{2}{3}x$, and $\Delta y = \frac{2}{3}\Delta x$.

*3. The length of a burning candle l (in inches) decreases at a constant rate of 2.2 inches per hour. When the candle has been burning for 3.5 hours it is 8.3 inches long. These co-occurring values are represented by the point (3.5, 8.3) on the graph.

a. Represent "an increase in the time spent burning of 2 hours" as a vector from the given point on the graph. What is the value of Δl (in inches) when the time spent burning increases by 2 hours from $t = 3.5$?

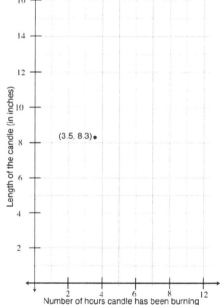

b. Represent the change in the length of the candle, Δl, that you found in part (b), as a vector from the given point on the graph.

c. Represent "a decrease in the time t spent burning of 1.8 hours" (that is, $\Delta t = -1.8$) as a vector from the given point on the graph.

d. What is the value of Δl (in inches) when the time spent burning is decreased by 1.8 hours (that is, $\Delta t = -1.8$). Represent Δl as a vector on the graph.

e. Define a formula that relates the change in the length of the candle Δl in terms of the change in the number of hours the candle has been burning, Δt ?

f. What was the original length of the candle (in inches) before it started burning? Explain how you determined this value and represent your reasoning on the graph.

g. On the axes in part (a), complete the graph that represents the *length of the candle l* (in inches) in terms of the number of hours spent burning t. Discuss in groups (or as a class) how t, l, Δt and Δl are represented on this graph.

© 2018 Carlson, Oehrtman, and Moore

4. A 19-inch candle is lit. The candle burns away at a constant rate of 2.5 inches per hour.
   a. Draw a diagram that represents a "snapshot" in the process of the burning candle. To the side of your diagram, identify every quantity that is relevant to the process and use vectors (line segments with arrows) to represent varying quantities and the direction of their variation, and fixed length line segments to represent quantities that are fixed such as the original length of the candle.

   b. Define variables to represent the values of the varying quantities that you identify in the situation. Represent the variables you defined on your diagram, being careful to indicate accurately where the measurement of each quantity begins.

   c. Write a formula to represent the **change** in the length of the candle (in inches) in terms of the **change** in the number of hours since the candle was lit.

   d. Write a formula to represent the length of the candle (in inches) in terms of the number of hours since the candle was lit.

   e. How much time will it take for the candle's length to become 0 (to burn the entire candle)? Explain your reasoning.

*5. Alan and Alissa are attempting to find each other in a crowded mall. They finally spot each other near the food court, at which point they are 140 feet apart. They begin walking towards each other. Alan travels at a constant rate of 5 feet per second and Alissa travels at a constant rate of 4 feet per second.

   a. What quantities are varying in this context? What quantities are constant? Be sure to include units for each quantity. Draw a diagram of the situation if useful.

   b. Complete this table of values.

number of seconds since Alan and Alissa spotted each other	distance (in feet) Alan has traveled	distance (in feet) Alissa has traveled	distance (in feet) between Alan and Alissa
0	0	0	140
1			
2			
4			
8			
10			

   c. For each second that passes since Alan and Alissa spotted each other, how many feet closer are Alan and Alissa? What about the situation helps to explain this?

   d. Define formulas to relate each of the following quantities. Be sure to clearly define any variables you use.
     i. Alan's distance traveled (in feet) in terms of the number of elapsed seconds since spotting Alissa.

     ii. Alissa's distance traveled (in feet) in terms of the number of elapsed seconds since spotting Alan.

     iii. The distance between Alan and Alissa (in feet) in terms of the number of elapsed seconds since they spotted each other.

   e. Use your formula(s) created in part (d) to determine how many seconds it will take for Alan and Alissa to reach one another.

6. A tortoise and hare are competing in a 1600-meter race. The arrogant hare decides to let the tortoise have a 950-meter head start. When the starting gun is fired, the hare begins running at a constant speed of 9.5 meters per second and the tortoise begins crawling at constant speed of 4 meters per second.

    a. Illustrate the situation with a diagram, and then define a formula to determine the varying distance between the tortoise and the hare in terms of the number of seconds since the start gun was fired. Be sure to define your variables before trying to write the formula.

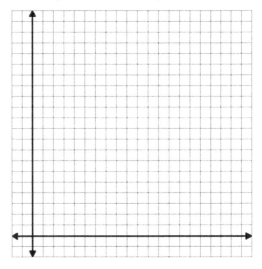

    b. Construct a graph to represent the varying distance between the tortoise and hare in terms of the number of seconds since the start gun was fired.

    c. Who finishes the race first, the tortoise or the hare? How long does it take each animal to complete the race? Make sure you can justify your answers.

*7. A 17-inch candle is lit and burns at a constant rate of 1.8 inches per hour. Let t represent the number of hours since the candle started burning.

    a. What does the expression $1.8t$ represent in this context?

    b. What does 17 represent in this context?

    c. What does the expression $17 - 1.8t$ represent in this context?

    d. What does 1.8 represent?

    e. In the formula $L = 17 - 1.8t$, what does L represent?

*1. A car is driving away from a crosswalk. The distance d (in feet) of the car from the crosswalk t seconds since the car started moving is given by the formula $d = t^2 + 3.5$.

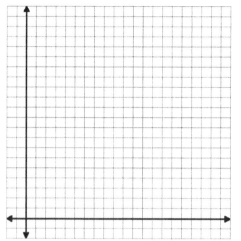

a. As the number of seconds since the car started moving increases from 1 second to 3 seconds, what is the change in the car's distance from the crosswalk?

b. Graph f, then illustrate how to represent each of the following.
   i. The increase in t from 1 to 3 seconds.
   ii. The corresponding change in the car's distance from the crosswalk as the value of t increased from 1 to 3 seconds.

c. True or False: The car travels at a constant speed as the value of t increases from 1 to 3 seconds.

   Discuss and explain. (*Hint: It may help to think about how far the car travels in the 1ˢᵗ second as compared to how far it travels in the 2ⁿᵈ second.*).

d. Since the car is not traveling at a constant speed it can be challenging to estimate its speed during the interval. It is a common practice to <u>estimate</u> the speed of the car during the interval by pretending its speed was constant and asking, "What constant speed would have resulted in the car traveling the same distance (as the distance that the car actually traveled) over this time interval from $t = 1$ to $t = 3$ seconds?"
   i. Plot the points (1, 4.5) and (2, 7.5) on the graph and draw the line passing through them.
   ii. Determine the constant rate of change of the linear relationship (slope of the line) represented by the linear graph you just drew.

   iii. <u>If</u> a car was traveling at the speed you found in part (ii), how far would it travel as t changes from $t = 1$ to $t = 3$?

e. True or False: The linear graph represents the actual distance (in feet) of the car from the crosswalk as t increases from 1 to 3 seconds. Explain.

g. Using the formula $d = t^2 + 3.5$, determine the value of d when $t = 0, 1, 1.25, 2, 2.6, 3, 4$.

t	0	1	1.25	2	2.6	3	4
d							

h. Complete the following on the graph in part (b).
  i. Using a vector, illustrate t increasing from 3 to 4 seconds.
  ii. Using a vector, illustrate the corresponding change in the car's distance (in feet) from the crosswalk as the value of t increases from 3 to 4 seconds.
  iii. Connect the two points with a straight line and describe what the slope of this line represents.

i. Graph $d = t^2 + 3.5$ on your calculator. How many seconds have elapsed when the car reaches a distance of 25 feet from the crosswalk?

*2. The distance d (in feet) of a car north of an intersection t seconds after it started moving is given by the formula $d = 2t^2 - 3$.
  a. Determine the value of d_1 when $t_1 = 2$.

  b. Determine the value of d_2 when $t_2 = 3.5$.

  c. Explain what $\frac{d_2 - d_1}{t_2 - t_1}$ represents in the context of this situation (*Hint: What constant rate of change is this?*)

  d. Construct a graph of $d = 2t^2 - 3$ and then illustrate the constant speed a car would have needed to travel in order to cover the same distance (as the car actually traveled) over the time interval from $t_1 = 2$ to $t_2 = 3.5$.

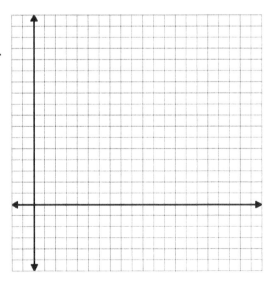

Average Rate of Change (over some interval)

The *average rate of change* of a function over some interval of the domain is the constant rate of change over that interval that produces the same net change in the function's output value.

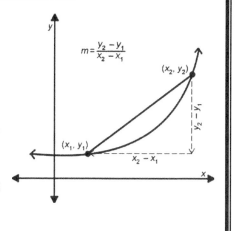

Visually, it's the slope of the line passing through the points at the beginning and end of the interval, so it makes sense that the average rate of change is calculated using the slope formula $m = \frac{y_2 - y_1}{x_2 - x_1}$.

The average rate of change is a common tool for describing the general behavior of a function over some interval when the rate of change is not constant.

---

3. When running a road race you heard the timer call out 8 minutes as you passed the first mile-marker in the race.
   a. What quantities will you measure to determine your speed as you travel? Define variables to represent the quantities' values and state the units you will use to measure the value of each of these quantities.

   b. As you passed mile-marker 6 you heard the timer call out 52 minutes. *If you had* held a constant speed (rate of change) as you ran from mile marker 1 to mile marker 6, determine the constant speed (in miles per minute) you *would have* run as you traveled from mile marker 1 to mile marker 5.

   c. After mile-marker 6 you slowed down and ran at a constant speed of 10 minutes per mile between mile-marker 6 and mile-marker 10. How many minutes did it take you to travel from mile marker 6 to 9?

---

*4. Marcos traveled in his car from Phoenix to Flagstaff, a distance of 144 miles.

   a. Determine the amount of time required for Marcos to travel from Phoenix to Flagstaff if he drove at a constant speed of 64 miles per hour.

   b. Construct a graph to represent Marcos's distance from Phoenix in terms of the time (in hours) since he left Phoenix.

   c. Joni left Phoenix at exactly the same time as Marcos and arrived in Flagstaff at exactly the same time as Marcos, **but did not drive at a constant speed.**
      i. True or False: Joni covered the same distance in the same amount of time as Marcos. Explain.

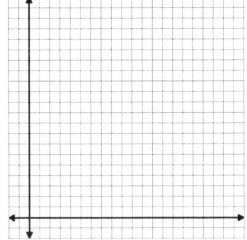

      ii. Construct a possible graph (on the same axes in part (b) that you used to construct Marcos's distance-time graph) to represent Joni's distance traveled in miles in terms of the number of hours since she left Phoenix. Discuss the thinking you used to construct your graph.

   d. **T or F:** Marcos' constant speed represents Joni's average speed as she traveled from Phoenix to Flagstaff.

*5. The distance d (in feet) of a car north of an intersection, t seconds since the car started to move, is given by the formula $d = 1.5t^2 + t + 3$.

   a. As the time t since the car started to move increases from $t = 3$ seconds to $t = 7$ seconds, what constant speed would a truck need to travel to cover the same distance over this 4-second time interval as the car?

   b. The constant speed needed to travel some distance over some interval of time is often called the average speed (or *average rate of change*). What is the meaning of average rate of change in the context of this problem?

6. Suppose that it took your car 18 minutes to travel from Kansas City to mile marker 363 and 30 minutes to travel from Kansas City to mile marker 373.
   a. Illustrate this situation with a drawing.

   b. We have seen that determining the constant speed of an object over an interval of time is determined by examining the amount of distance traveled during that interval of time. At what constant speed (in miles per minute) did your car travel as it moved from mile marker 363 to mile marker 373? Illustrate how you computed your answer and describe the rationale for your approach.

   c. Construct a possible distance-time graph to display how your car's distance (in miles) from mile marker 363 to 373 varied with the number of minutes elapsed after passing mile marker 363. Label your axis and label the points on your graph that represent the car's starting and ending positions.

   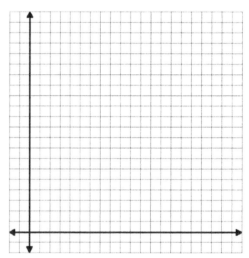

   d. A truck passed your car at mile marker 363. At mile marker 373, your car passed the truck. On the same axes on which you just graphed the distance-time relationship of your car as it traveled from mile marker 363 to mile marker 373, construct a possible distance-time graph of the truck's distance from mile marker 363 at it traveled to mile marker 373.

   e. What do the points where the two graphs intersect convey about the relative distance traveled by the car and truck, at specific times since the car left Kansas City?

   f. Using the graphs that you created, estimate the distance between your car and the truck 6 minutes after the vehicles passed mile marker 363.

   g. Was the truck's speed between mile markers 363 and 373 ever exactly the same as your car's speed? Explain.

   h. If the truck continues traveling in the same direction, now at the same constant speed as the car, how many minutes will it take the truck to drive 45 miles from mile marker 373?

You have likely observed that determining an average speed of some moving object on a time interval from t_1 to t_2 involves determining the constant speed needed to travel the same distance that the object actually traveled over the specified time interval (from t_1 to t_2).

*7. Given that a car's distance from a stop sign t seconds since it started moving is represented by $d = t^2 - 2t$, determine the car's average speed over each interval of elapsed time.
   a. $t_1 = 2$ to $t_2 = 6$
   b. $t_1 = 6$ to $t_2 = 10$
   c. $t_1 = 10$ to $t_2 = 11$

   d. What observations can you make about how the car's speed is changing on the interval from $t_1 = 2$ to $t_2 = 11$?

8. Given that a car's distance from a stop sign t seconds since it started moving is represented by $d = (t-4)(t+2)$, determine the car's average speed over each interval of elapsed time.
   a. $t_1 = 1$ to $t_2 = 5$
   b. $t_1 = 3$ to $t_2 = 5$
   c. $t_1 = 4.5$ to $t_2 = 5$

   d. What observations can you make about how the car's speed is changing on the interval from $t_1 = 1$ to $t_2 = 5$?

9. Given that a car's distance from a stop sign t seconds since it started moving is represented by $d = (t)(t-5)$, determine the car's average speed over each interval of elapsed time.
   a. $t_1 = 1$ to $t_2 = 2$
   b. $t_1 = 2$ to $t_2 = 5$
   c. $t_1 = 5$ to $t_2 = 9$

   d. What observations can you make about how the car's speed is changing on the interval from $t_1 = 1$ to $t_2 = 9$?

I. QUANTITIES AND CO-VARIATION OF QUANTITIES (Text: S1)

1. Consider a cup of coffee.
   a. Identify five attributes of the cup of coffee that can be measured. Which of these attributes are fixed and which are varying?
   b. Identify five attributes of the cup of coffee that cannot be measured.

2. A group of students are taking an exam. You walk into the room and identify some elements and aspects of the situation. Determine if the following statements define a quantity. If not, rewrite the statement so that the statement properly defines a quantity.
   a. the number of people taking the exam
   b. the people sitting around a table
   c. the exam
   d. the questions on the exam
   e. the teacher

3. For the following situations identify one constant quantity and two varying quantities. Define variables to represent the values of the varying quantities.
   a. A mountain climber hikes with two friends for 5 hours.
   b. The computer charges for 1.25 hours each night.
   c. The student studies for 8 hours each weekend.
   d. Jessica bikes 30 miles around a 5-mile course.

4. For the following situations identify the quantities whose values vary and the quantities whose values are constant. State possible units for measuring each of these quantities. Then define variables to represent the values of each varying quantity.
   a. A 10-inch candle burns for 2 hours.
      i. Identify at least one constant quantity and state the units of measurement.
      ii. Identify at least two varying quantities and state the units of measurement.
      iii. Define variables to represent the values of the varying quantities you defined in part (ii).
   b. A girl runs around a ¼-mile track.
      i. Identify at least one constant quantity and state the units of measurement.
      ii. Identify at least two varying quantities and state the units of measurement.
      iii. Define variables to represent the values of the varying quantities you defined in part (ii).
   c. A scuba diver descends from the surface of the water to a depth of 60 feet.
      i. Identify at least one constant quantity and state the units of measurement.
      ii. Identify at least two varying quantities and state the units of measurement.
      iii. Define variables to represent the values of the varying quantities you defined in part (ii).

5. The number of questions on an exam varies with the number of minutes to take the exam. For each question there are 5 minutes allotted. Write a formula that relates the number of minutes to take the exam to the number of questions on the exam. (*Be sure to define variables to represent the values of the varying quantities.*)

6. There are twelve times as many football players on a football team as there are coaches. Write a formula that relates the number of coaches to the number of players on the team. (*Be sure to define variables to represent the values of these varying quantities*).

7. This graph relates the total value of world exports (internationally traded goods) in billions of dollars to the number of years since 1950.
   a. Define variables to represent the values of the varying quantities in this situation.
   b. Interpret the meaning of the point (17.5, 1000).
   c. As the number of years since 1950 increases from 10 to 20 years what is the change in the number of years since 1950? Represent this change on the graph.
   d. As the number of years since 1950 increases from 10 to 20 years what is the corresponding change in the total value of world exports (in billions of dollars)? Explain how you determined this value and represent this change on the graph.

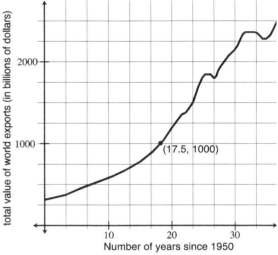

8. A ball is dropped off of the roof of a building. This graph relates the height of the ball above the ground (in feet) to the number of seconds that have elapsed since the ball was dropped.
   a. Define variables to represent the values of the varying quantities in this situation.
   b. Interpret the meaning of the point (0, 367).
   c. As the number of seconds since the ball was dropped increases from 10 to 30 seconds, how does the height of the ball above the ground change?

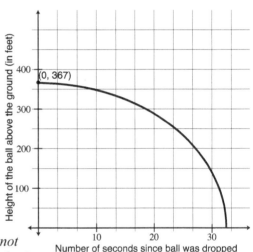

9. Write an equation for each of the relationships that are described below. Then solve the equation for the unknown. (*Do not forget to start by defining a variable to represent the unknown value.*)
   a. 17.5 is equal to 2 times some number. What is the number?
   b. The sum of 3 times some number and 12 is 42. What is the number?
   c. ¼ of some number is 4.3. What is the number?
   d. Some number is 4 times as large as 9.8. What is the number?
   e. Some number is equal to 1/3 of the sum of 88.2, 93.5, and 64. What is the number?
   f. The change from some number to 12.5 is –5. What is the number?
   g. Measuring some number in units of 12 is 3.5. What is the number?

10. Write an equation for each of the relationships that are described below. Then solve the equation for the unknown. (*Do not forget to start by defining a variable to represent the unknown value.*)
    a. 45 is some multiple of 15. Determine the value of the multiple.
    b. $1,200 is 1.5 times as large as some amount of money. What is the amount of money?
    c. 200% of some number is 38.2. What is the number?
    d. 5 is the result of 12 more than ¾ of some number. What is the number?
    e. Suppose 10 is the number that is 5 times as large as the value that is 4 less than the value of *x*. What is the value of *x*?
    f. The ratio of the change from 2 to 8 and the change from 5 to 7. What is the ratio?
    g. 7 is 3.5 times as large as some number. What is the number?

11. Evaluate the following expressions:
    a. $-2 + 5 - 12$
    b. $6 - (-4) + 1$
    c. $2(-3)(-1) - (-6)$
    d. $\dfrac{-5 + (9 - 5(4)) + 3}{5(-2) - 1}$

12. Let $y = 3.5x - 7$.
    a. Find the value of y when x is zero.
    b. What value(s) of x give a y value of 11?
    c. What value(s) of y correspond to an x value of 3?

13. Solve each of the equations for the specified variable.
    a. Given $y = 17x - 6$, solve for x when $y = 45$.
    b. Given $y = \frac{6x+5}{3}$, solve for x when $y = 2$.
    c. Given $z = \frac{12x-4}{3}$, solve for x when $z = 10$.
    d. Given $y = \frac{3.2x(6-0.5x)}{x}$, solve for x when $y = 1$.
    e. Given $y = \frac{-6a+7-2a}{2} - 3 + a$ solve for a when $y = 2$.

14. Simplify the following
    a. $\dfrac{3x^3 + 6x}{x}$
    b. $\sqrt{52x^8 y^3}$
    c. $\dfrac{2x^2 + x - 6}{x + 2}$

15. Simplify the following
    a. $\dfrac{4(x+3) + 6x - 12}{x}$
    b. $\sqrt{70x^9 y^{153}}$
    c. $\dfrac{6x^2 - 5x - 21}{(2x+3)(3x-7)}$

II. CHANGES IN QUANTITIES AND CONSTANT RATE OF CHANGE (Text: S1, 3)

16. Matthew started a regular exercise routine and his weight changed from 175 pounds to 153 pounds. What was the change in Matthew's weight?

17. After driving from Tucson to Phoenix the number of miles on your car's odometer went from 312 to 428. What was the change in the number of miles on your car's odometer?

18. After spending an hour processing emails the number of unread emails in your inbox went from 23 to 5. What is the change in the number of unread emails?

19. Let x and z represent the values of two different quantities.
    a. If the value of x decreases from $x = 2$ to $x = -5$, what is the change in the value of x?
    b. If the value of x decreases from $x = 212$ to $x = 32$, what is the change in the value of x?
    c. If the value of z decreases from $z = 2.145$ to $z = 1.234$, what is the change in the value of z?

20. Let a and b represent the values of two different quantities.
    a. If the value of a decreases from $a = 3$ to $a = -4$, what is the change in the value of a?
    b. If the value of a increases from $a = -31$ to $a = 12.2$, what is the change in the value of a?
    c. If the value of b decreases from $b = -1.15$ to $b = -4.21$, what is the change in the value of b?

21. Fill in the following tables showing the appropriate changes in the value of the variable.

s	Δs
-12.43	
0.73	
-7.3	

y	Δy
2.85	
14.3	
-1.05	

p	Δp
3.834	
-2.3	
0	

22. This morning Tom went for a run. Let d represent the number of miles that Tom has run. What is the difference in meaning between $d = 11$ and $\Delta d = 11$?

23. Use the graph to answer the following questions;
    a. Determine Δx and Δy from the point on the left to the point on the right. Illustrate the values of Δx and Δy on the graph.
    b. Determine Δx and Δy from the point on the right to the point on the left. Illustrate the values of Δx and Δy on the graph.

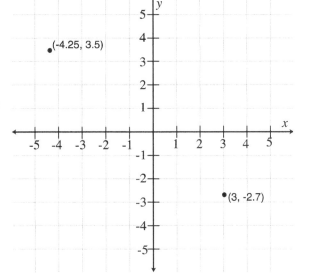

24. The number of calories Monica burns while running increases by 105 calories for every mile that Monica runs up to 15 miles. Let n represent the number of miles that Monica has run.
    a. Suppose the value of n increases $n = 3$ to $n = 7.5$.
        i. What is the change in the value of n?
        ii. What does this change represent in the context of this situation?
        iii. What is the corresponding change in the number of calories Monica burns while running?
    b. How many calories will Monica burn for *any* 4.5-mile change in the number of miles Monica has run during a 15 mile run?
    c. For the following changes in the number of miles that Monica has run determine the corresponding change in the number of calories that Monica has burn.
        i. $\Delta n = 3.5$
        ii. $\Delta n = 0.41$
        iii. $\Delta n = 13.7$
        iv. $\Delta n = k$ for some constant $k \leq 15$ miles

25. A bucket full of water has a leak. The bucket loses 71 mL of water every 5 minutes. Let t represent the number of minutes since the bucket started leaking
    a. As the number of minutes since the bucket started leaking increases from 13 minutes to 29 minutes, what is the corresponding change in the volume of water in the bucket?
    b. By how much will the volume of water in the bucket change when the number of minutes since the bucket started leaking changes by 1 minute? Explain how you determined your answer.
    c. As the volume of water in the bucket decreases from 60 mL to 23 mL, what is the corresponding change in the number of minutes since the bucket started leaking?
    d. By how much will the number of minutes since the bucket started leaking change when the volume of water in the bucket decreases by 1 mL?

26. A group of Kansas University students were traveling from Lawrence, KS to Denver, CO for a weekend ski trip. On the way they stopped for a late dinner, then continued on to Denver driving through the night. They left the restaurant, located 112 miles from Lawrence, at 10:00pm and arrived at Denver, 565 miles from Lawrence, at 5:45 am. For the purpose of this problem, assume the car maintained a constant speed from the time they left the restaurant to the time they arrived in Denver.
    a. Explain what it means to say the car maintained a constant speed from the time it left the restaurant to the time it arrived in Denver. *Make sure to explain the relationship it implies – do not say the car's speed does not change.*
    b. At what constant speed did the car travel between the restaurant and Denver?
    c. The driver was listening to music to keep awake. Between 2:03 am and 2:55 am the driver listened to his favorite album.
        i. What was the change in the time elapsed while he listened to the album in minutes? In hours?
        ii. How far did the car travel while the driver listened to this album?
    d. As the Kansas University students traveled between two towns they noticed that their trip odometer reading changed from 234.6 miles from Lawrence to 302.4 miles from Lawrence.
        i. What was the change in distance from Lawrence between these two towns?
        ii. How much time elapsed while the car traveled between these two towns?
    e. Sketch a graph of the relationship between the students' distance from Lawrence (in miles) and the number of hours since the students left the restaurant. What does the slope of the graph convey about this situation?

III. CONSTANT RATE OF CHANGE AND LINEAR FUNCTIONS (Text: S2, 3)

27. You are driving on the interstate with your cruise control on at a constant speed of 64 miles per hour. Use the number lines below to determine how long it will take to drive to the next rest sop that is 16 miles away (see textbook, page 20). Explain the thinking you used to determine your answer.

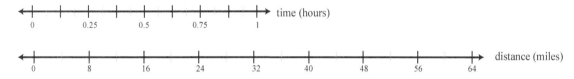

28. When an object is dropped, gravity pulls on the object and causes its speed to increase. The table below shows a certain object's speed at various moments during its fall. Does the object's speed (in feet per second) change at a constant rate with respect to the number of seconds since the object started falling? Explain your reasoning.

Number of seconds since the object started falling	The speed of the object (in feet per second)
0.15	4.83
0.4	12.88
0.52	16.744
0.98	31.556
1.26	40.572

29. The following table of values provides information about the distance of an airplane from Sky Harbor International Airport in terms of the number minutes since the plane took off. Does the distance of the airplane from Sky Harbor International Airport change at a constant rate with respect to the number of minutes since the plane took off? Explain your reasoning. If so, determine the value of the constant rate of change of the distance of the airplane from Sky Harbor International Airport in terms of the number of minutes since the plane took off.

Number of minutes since the airplane took off	Distance of the airplane from Sky Harbor International Airport (in miles)
3	16
5	32
9	64
11	92
18	170

30. Suppose that the quantities whose values are represented by x and y are related by a constant rate of change of y with respect to x.
    a. Given the information in the table determine the value of m, the constant rate of change of y with respect to x.
    b. Given the information in the graph determine the value of the constant rate of change of y with respect to x.

x	y
−3.5	7.1
−1	−0.9
2	−10.5
6	−23.3
10	−36.1

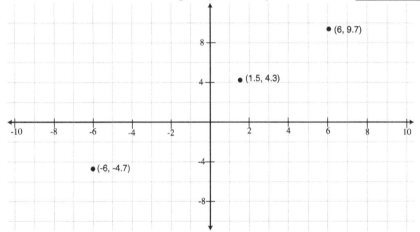

31. Given values of x and y in the tables, which table(s) contain values that could define a linear relationship between two quantities? If the two quantities whose values are represented by x and y can be related by a linear relationship, what is the constant rate of change (the value of m)?

Table 1	
x	y
−2	−14
3	1
5	7
8	16
12	28

Table 2	
x	y
1	3
2	7
4	8
5	12
9	14

Table 3	
x	y
−5	9.5
−2	5
−1	3.5
3	−2.5
10	−13

© 2018 Carlson, Oehrtman, and Moore

32. a. Between 2000 and 2005 the Burger Company's profit increased by $3,500 per year. In 2000 the Burger Company's profit was $52,000.
    i. Determine if the change in the number of years since 2000 is proportional to the change in the Burger Company's profit. Explain your reasoning.
    ii. Determine if the number of years since 2000 is proportional to the Burger Company's profit. Explain your reasoning.
  b. You are planning a trip to Las Vegas and need to rent a car. After contacting the different car companies, you choose to go with the company that charges a $25 rental fee and $0.05 per mile that the car is driven.
    i. Determine if the change in the number of miles driven is proportional to the change in the total cost of the rental car. Explain your reasoning.
    ii. Determine if the number of miles driven is proportional the total cost of the rental car. Explain your reasoning.
  c. When baking chocolate chip cookies, you need 3 cups of flour per cup of sugar.
    i. Determine if the change in the number cups of flour is proportional to the change in the number of cups of sugar. Explain your reasoning.
    ii. Determine if the number of cups of flour is proportional to the number of cups of sugar. Explain your reasoning.

33. Nick is considering joining a weight loss club that provides meals and support for people who want to lose weight. Based on an initial consultation with a weight loss advisor, Nick charted his potential weight loss based on the advisor's estimates of his expected weekly weight loss.

Number of weeks since joining	Nick's projected weight (pounds)
3	277
6	266.5
8	259.5
12	245.5
13	242

  a. Are the quantities Nick's projected weight (in pounds) and time since joining (in weeks) proportional? Justify your answer.
  b. Complete the following table showing the relative changes in the quantities change in time since joining (in weeks) and change in Nick's projected weight (in pounds).

Change in the number of weeks since joining	Number of weeks since joining	Nick's projected weight (in pounds)	Change in Nick's projected weight (pounds)
	3	277	
	6	266.5	
	8	259.5	
	12	245.5	
	13	242	

  c. Do the quantities change in Nick's projected weight (in pounds) and change in time since joining (in weeks) appear to be proportional? Justify your answer.
  d. Construct a graph showing the relationship between the quantities Nick's projected weight (in pounds) and time since joining (in weeks).
  e. What does the slope of the graph represent in this context?

34. For the tables below,
    a. Determine if the quantities are proportional.
    b. Determine if the changes in the quantities are proportional.
    c. Determine if the relationship is linear. If the table represents a linear relationship, write a formula to represent how the quantities change together

Table 1	
x	y
2	1.42
−1.2	−0.852
5.1	3.621

Table 2	
a	b
0.7	1.3
−2	5.62
5.4	−2.885

Table 3	
r	s
2.4	0.76
0.3	3.595
−1.5	6.025

IV. CONSTANT RATE OF CHANGE & LINEARITY (Text: S3)

For Exercises #35-36: Let r represent the possible values of one quantity and let p represent the possible values of another quantity.

35. Suppose r changes at a constant rate of 2 with respect to p.
    a. What does this mean for any change in p?
    b. If p changes by 6, how much does r change?
    c. If p changes by −3.1, how much does r change?

36. Suppose r changes at a constant rate of −1.3 with respect to p.
    a. What does this mean for any change in p?
    b. If p changes by 2, how much does r change?
    c. If p changes by −6.2, how much does r change?

37. Suppose the constant rate of change of y with respect to x is 0.17 and we know $y = 12.25$ when $x = 7.35$.
    a. What is the value of y when $x = 11.1$?
    b. What is the value of y when $x = −5.6$?
    c. What is the value of x when $y = 2.5$?
    d. What is the change in the value of y when the change in the value of x is 4.75?

38. Suppose the constant rate of change of y with respect to x is −11.1 and we know $y = −2.6$ when $x = −0.85$.
    a. What is the value of y when $x = 3.4$?
    b. What is the value of y when $x = −12.7$?
    c. What is the value of x when $y = 4.5$?
    d. What is the change in the value of y when the change in the value of x is −6.7?

39. Rope is wound around a large spool. The more rope wound around the spool, the greater the combined weight of the spool and rope. The graph shows that when 5 feet of rope is wound around the spool, the total weight of the spool and rope is 3.95 pounds. Note that the rope weighs 0.27 pounds per foot.
    a. If the number of feet of rope on the spool increases from the given point to 8.4 feet, what is the change in the number of feet of rope on the spool? Represent this change on the graph.
    b. By how much does the weight of the spool and rope change for the change in the amount of rope on the spool you found in part (a)? Represent this change on the graph.
    c. What is the total weight of the spool and rope when there are 8.4 feet of rope on the spool? Explain how you determined this.
    d. What is the weight of the spool without any rope? Explain how you determined this value and represent your reasoning on the graph.

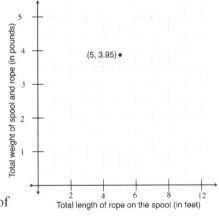

40. When a bathtub made of cast iron and porcelain contains 60 gallons of water the total weight of the tub and water is approximately 875.7 pounds. You pull the plug and the water begins to drain. (*Note that water weighs 8.345 pounds per gallon*).
    a. Describe the quantities in this situation. Which of these quantities are constant and which are changing?
    b. Suppose that some water has drained from the tub and 47 gallons of water remain in the tub.
        i. What was the change in the number of gallons of water (recall the situation begins with 60 gallons of water in the tub)?
        ii. What is the corresponding change in the total weight of the tub and water?
        iii. What is the weight of the tub and water when there are 47 gallons of water in the tub?
    c. Complete the following table of values.

Number of gallons of water remaining in the tub	Total weight of the tub and water (in pounds)
59	
40	
30	
20	
10	
8.5	

    d. Suppose you and a friend can each lift about 150 pounds. Once empty, could you and your friend pick up and carry the bathtub out of the bathroom? Explain your reasoning.

41. John inserts a partially used battery into a portable electric fan. The percent of the battery's total charge changes at a constant rate of –3.1% per minute since the fan was totally charged.
    a. Represent "an increase of 10 minutes in the amount of time the fan is used" from the given reference point on the graph.
    b. By how much will the percent of the total possible battery charge change when the fan is used for 10 minutes? Represent this on the graph.
    c. What is the percent of the battery's total possible charge when the fan has been used for 17 minutes? Explain how you determined this value.
    d. What is the vertical intercept of the graph of the function? Explain how you determined this value and represent your approach on the graph above. What does the vertical intercept represents in the context of this situation.

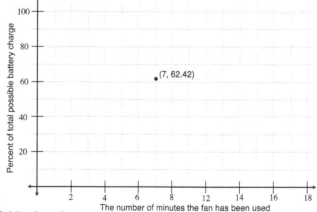

© 2018 Carlson, Oehrtman, and Moore

42. Consider the graph and assume that the values of x and y
    change together at a constant rate of change.
    a. Determine the constant rate of change of y with respect to
       x.
    b. Using the point $(-5.2, 1.30)$ as a reference point, what is
       the change in x from this point from to
       $x = 2$. Represent this change using the given axes.
    c. What is the change in y that corresponds with the change in
       x found in part (b)?
    d. What is the value of y when $x = 2$?
    e. What is the vertical intercept of the function? Explain how
       you can find this value using the meaning of constant rate
       of change and the reference point $(-5.2, 1.30)$.

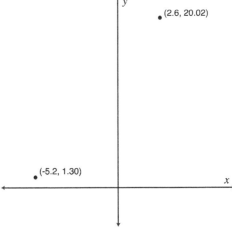

43. Consider the graph and assume that the values of x and y
    change together at a constant rate of change.
    a. Determine the constant rate of change of y with respect to x.
    b. Using the point $(1.8, 4.74)$ as a reference point, what is the
       change in x from this point from to
       $x = 3.6$. Represent this change using the given axes.
    c. What is the change in y that corresponds with the change in
       x found in part (b)?
    d. What is the value of y when $x = 3.6$?
    e. What is the vertical intercept of the function? Explain how
       you can find this value using the meaning of constant rate
       of change and the reference point $(1.8, 4.74)$

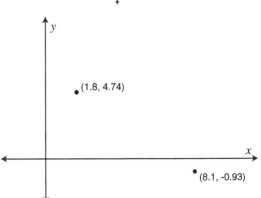

44. Two quantities (A and B) co-vary such that Quantity A changes at a constant rate with respect to
    Quantity B. Suppose the change in the value of Quantity A is always –0.82 times as large as the
    change in the value of Quantity B. Suppose also that the value of Quantity A is –1.4 when the value
    of Quantity B is –2.5.
    a. What is the value of Quantity A when the value of Quantity B is 3?
    b. What is the value of Quantity A when the value of Quantity B is –7.7?
    c. What is the value of Quantity B when the value of Quantity A is –6?

45. Given the values of x and y in the tables that follow, which table(s) contain values that could define a
    linear relationship between the two quantities? Explain your reasoning. For the table(s) that could
    represent a linear relationship, write a formula to define how the quantities change together.

Table 1	
x	y
1.25	3
3	6.5
5.5	11.5

Table 2	
x	y
3.25	10
3	9
5	4

Table 3	
x	y
3	10
6	20
7	70/3

46. Given the values of x and y in the tables that follow, which table(s) contain values that could define a linear relationship between the two quantities? Explain your reasoning. For the table(s) that could represent a linear relationship, write a formula to define how the quantities change together.

Table 1	
x	y
2	10.4
5	30.65
10	64.5

Table 2	
x	y
1.3	12.015
−4	14.4
9.7	8.235

Table 3	
x	y
−2	13.6
1	2.2
4.3	−10.34

47. Find a formula for each of the linear functions whose graphs are described below.
    a. The graph of the function that passes through the point $(2, -18.4)$ and the change in y is always -1.34 times as large as the change in x.
    b. The graph of the function with a constant rate of change of y with respect to x is $\frac{7}{9}$ and passes through the point $\left(\frac{-3}{5}, \frac{2}{11}\right)$.
    c. The graph of the function passing through the points $(-2, 14)$ and $(-12, -7.6)$.
    d. The graph of the function passing through the points $\left(\frac{11}{9}, \frac{15}{7}\right)$ and $\left(\frac{-12}{4}, \frac{15}{7}\right)$.

48. The graph of a certain linear function passes through the points $(2,9)$ and $(7, -11)$.
    a. What is the constant rate of change of y with respect to x (slope) for the function?
    b. From the point $(2, 9)$ how much must x change to reach a value of $x = 0$?
    c. What is the corresponding change in the value of y for the change in x you found in part (b)?
    d. What is the value of y when $x = 0$?
    e. Write a formula to calculate the value of y for any value of x.

49. The graph of a certain linear function passes through the points $(-7, -15)$ and $(5, -7)$.
    a. What is the constant rate of change of y with respect to x (slope) for the function?
    b. From the point $(-7, -15)$ how much must x change to reach a value of $x = 0$?
    c. What is the corresponding change in the value of y for the change in x you found in part (b)?
    d. What is the value of y when $x = 0$?
    e. Write a formula to calculate the value of y for any value of x.

50. Consider the formula $y = -12.13x + 7.14$. Suppose we want to find the value of y when $x = -1.15$. Explain how the formula determines the value of y using the meaning of constant rate of change. (You may sketch a graph or diagram if it helps you explain.)

51. The formula $a = 10 - 1.5t$ defines the remaining height (in inches) of a burning candle, a, in terms of the number of hours that the candle has been burning, t.
    a. What does 10 represent in the context of this situation?
    b. What does -1.5 represent in the context of this situation?
    c. What does $-1.5t$ represent in the context of this situation?
    d. Explain what the point $(t, a) = (2, 7)$ conveys in the context of this situation.
    e. What is the value of a when $t = 4.2$. Explain what this value represents in the context of this situation.

52. Determine a formula that defines the linear functions whose graphs are described below.
    a. The graph of the function conveys that the constant rate of change of y with respect to x is $\frac{2}{3}$ and the vertical intercept is 5.
    b. The graph of the function conveys that the constant rate of change of y with respect to x is 5 and the graph crosses the vertical axis at $(0, -2)$
    c. The graph of the function conveys that the constant rate of change of y with respect to x is $-\frac{6}{7}$ and the vertical intercept of $-\frac{1}{10}$.

53. Write the formula that defines the linear relationship given in each of the following graphs.
    a.

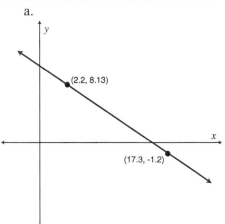

    b.

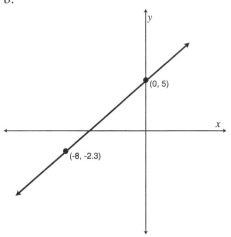

54. Use the graph to answer the following questions.
    a. The graph conveys that the constant rate of change of y with respect to x is -4.1. What is the value of y when $x = 5.15$? Explain how to find this value using the meaning of constant rate of change. Draw a diagram to help represent your reasoning.
    b. What is the value of y when $x = -3.81$? Explain how to find use the idea of constant rate of change to find the value of y.

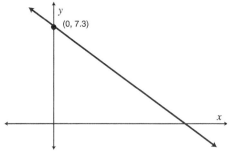

55. A tortoise and hare are competing in a race around a 1600-meter track. The arrogant hare decides to let the tortoise have a 630-meter head start. When the start gun is fired, the hare begins running at a constant speed of 8.5 meters per second and the tortoise begins crawling at constant speed of 6 meters per second.
    a. What quantities are changing in this situation? What quantities are not changing? (Be sure to include the units of each quantity.)
    b. Define a formula to determine the distance of the tortoise from the starting line in terms of the amount of time since the start gun was fired.
    c. Define a formula to determine the distance of the hare from the starting line in terms of the amount of time since the start gun was fired.
    d. The tortoise traveled 170 meters as he moved from his starting position to a curve on the track. If possible, find the following:
        i.   The amount of time that it took the tortoise to travel the 170-meter distance.
        ii. The amount of time that it took the tortoise to travel the next 80 meters on the track.

(Exercise continues on the next page.)

   e. Now consider how the distance between the tortoise and the hare changes throughout the race.
      i. Explain how the distance between the tortoise and hare changes as the number of seconds since the start gun was fired increases.
      ii. Define a formula that relates the distance between the tortoise and the hare with the number of seconds since the start gun was fired.
     iii. Is the relationship you defined in part (ii) linear? Explain.
     iv. Who finishes the race first, the tortoise or the hare? Explain.

56. Lisa and Sarah decided to meet at a park bench near both of their homes. Lisa lives 1850 feet due west of the park bench and Sarah lives 1430 feet due east of the park bench. Sarah left her house at 7:00 pm and traveled at a constant speed of 315 feet per minute towards the bench. Lisa left her house at the same time traveling a constant speed of 325 feet per minute towards the bench.
   a. Illustrate this situation with a drawing, labeling the constant and varying quantities.
   b. Define a formula to relate Lisa's distance (in feet) from the park bench in terms of the number of minutes that have passed since 7:00 pm. (Define relevant variables.)
   c. Define a formula to relate Sarah's distance (in feet) from the park bench in terms of the number of minutes that have passed since 7:00 pm. (Define relevant variables.)
   d. Who will reach the park bench first? Explain your reasoning.
   e. Now we will consider how the distance between Lisa and Sarah changes as the number of minutes since 7:00 pm increases.
      i. Explain how the distance (in feet) between Lisa and Sarah changes as the amount of minutes since 7:00pm increases.
      ii. Define a formula that relates the distance between Lisa and Sarah in terms of the number of minutes since 7:00pm.

57. John and Susan leave a neighborhood restaurant after having dinner. They each walk to their respective homes. John's home is 3120 feet due north of the restaurant and Susan's home is 2018 feet due south of the restaurant. John leaves at 7:28 pm traveling at a constant speed of 334 feet per minute and Susan leaves at 7:30 pm traveling at a constant speed of 219 feet per minute.
   a. Illustrate this situation with a drawing and define relevant variables.
   b. Define a formula to relate John's distance from the restaurant in terms of the number of minutes that have elapsed since 7:30 pm.
   c. Define a formula to relate Susan's distance from the restaurant in terms of the number of minutes that have passed since 7:30 pm.
   d. Will John or Susan arrive home first? Explain your reasoning.
   e. Now we will consider how the distance between John and Susan changes as the number of minutes that have passed since 7:30 pm increases.
      i. Explain how the distance (in feet) between John and Susan changes as the number of minutes that have passed since 7:30 pm increases.
      ii. Define a formula that relates the distance (in feet) between John and Susan in terms of the number of minutes that have passed since 7:30pm.

58. Lucia rented a car for $211 per week (with unlimited driving miles) to use during her spring break vacation. She must also pay for gasoline which costs $3.65 per gallon. The gas mileage of the car is 30 miles per gallon (mpg) on average.
   a. What quantities are changing in this situation? What quantities are not changing?
   b. i. If Lucia traveled 100 miles, how many gallons of gasoline did she use?
      ii. If Lucia traveled 200 miles, how many gallons of gasoline did she use?
     iii. If Lucia traveled 500 miles, how many gallons of gasoline did she use?

(Exercise continues on the next page.)

   c. Define a formula to determine the number of gallons of gasoline *n* used in terms of the number of miles driven *x*.

   d. Define a formula to determine the cost of gasoline *c* in terms of the number of gallons of gasoline used.

   e. Define a formula to determine the total cost *T* of driving the rental car *x* miles, including the one-week rental cost of $211.

   f. How much does the total rental cost increase for each 100 miles the car is driven during the rental period. Explain your reasoning.

   g. How much does the total rental cost increase for each mile driven? Explain the thinking you used to arrive at your answer.

59. Sketch a graph of the following relationships.
   a. $3.25 = y$
   b. $6 = x$
   c. $y = 2x + 4.3$
   d. $y = -\frac{1}{2}x + 3$

60. On the same axes sketch a graph of $y = -4x - 2$ and $y = \frac{1}{4}x + 3$. What do you notice about the graphs of two linear relationships?

61. Simplify the following expressions.
   a. $2x + 7 - 3x - 2$
   b. $\frac{3}{7}x - (-1 + \frac{2}{3}x)$
   c. $3x - (-7x) + 4 - 2.2$
   d. $2(x - 4) + 3x - \left(\frac{9}{8}x - 7\right)$

V. Exploring Average Speed (Test: S4)

62. This graph represents the distance-time relationship for Kevin and Carrie as they cycled on a road from mile marker 225 to mile marker 230.

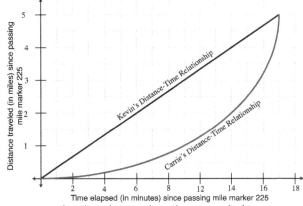

   a. How does the distance traveled and time elapsed compare for Carrie and Kevin as they traveled from mile marker 225 to mile marker 230?

   b. How do Carrie's and Kevin's speeds compare as they travel from mile marker 225 to mile marker 230?

   c. How do Carrie's and Kevin's average speeds compare over the time interval as they traveled from mile marker 225 to mile marker 230?

   d. Do Carrie and Kevin collide on the course 17 minutes after the passed mile marker 225?

63. When running a marathon you heard the timer call out 12 minutes as you passed mile-marker 2.
   a. What quantities could you measure to determine your speed as you ran the race? Define variables to represent the quantities' values and state the units you will use to measure the value of each of these quantities.

   b. As you passed mile-marker 5 you heard the timer call out 33 minutes. What was your average speed from mile 2 to mile 5?

   c. Assume that you continued running at the same constant speed as computed in (b) above. How much distance did you cover as your time spent running increased from 35 minutes after the start of the race to 40 minutes after the start of the race?

   d. If you passed mile marker 5 at 33 minutes, what average speed do you need to run for the remainder of the race to meet your goal to complete the 26.2-mile marathon in 175 minutes?

   e. What is the meaning of average speed in this context?

64. When running a road race you heard the timer call out 8 minutes as you passed the first mile-marker in the race.
    a. What quantities will you measure to determine your speed as you travel? Define variables to represent the quantities' values and state the units you will use to measure the value of each of these quantities.
    b. As you passed mile-marker 6 you heard the timer call out 52 minutes. What was your average speed from mile-marker 1 to 6?
    c. After mile-marker 6 you slowed down and ran at a constant rate of 10 minutes per mile between mile-marker 6 and mile-marker 10, how many minutes did it take you to travel from mile marker 6 to 9?

65. Marcos traveled in his car from Phoenix to Flagstaff, a distance of 155 miles.
    a. Determine the amount of time required for Marcos to travel from Phoenix to Flagstaff if his average speed for the trip was 68 miles per hour.
    b. Construct a possible distance-time graph of Marcos's trip from Phoenix to Flagstaff. Be sure to label your axes.
    c. On the same axes, construct a graph that represents the distance-time graph that represents another car traveling at a constant speed for the entire trip.

66. On a trip from Tucson to Phoenix via Interstate 10, you used your cruise control to travel at a constant speed for the entire trip. Since your speedometer was broken, you decided to use your watch and the mile markers to determine your speed. At mile marker 219 you noticed that the time on your digital watch just advanced to 9:22 am. At mile marker 197 your digital watch advanced to 9:46 am.
    a. Compute the constant speed at which you traveled over the time period from 9:22 am to 9:46 am.
    b. As you were passing mile marker 219 you also passed a truck. The same truck sped by you exactly at mile marker 197.
        i. Construct a distance-time graph of your car. On the same graph, construct one possible distance-time graph for the truck. Be sure to label the axes.
        ii. Compare the speed of the truck to the speed of the car between 9:22 am and 9:45 am.
        iii. Compare the distance that your car traveled over this part of the trip with the distance that the truck traveled over this same part of the trip. Compare the time that it took the truck to travel this distance with the time that it took your car to travel this distance. What do you notice?
        iv. Why are the average speed of the car and the average speed of the truck the same?
        v. Phoenix is another 53 miles past mile marker 197. Assuming you continued at the constant speed, at what time should you arrive in Phoenix?

67. The distance d (measured in a number of feet) between Silvia and her house is modeled by the formula , $d = t^2 + 3t + 1$ where t represents the number of seconds since Silvia started walking.
    a. Find Silvia's average speed for the time period from $t = 2$ to $t = 7$ seconds.
    b. What was Silvia's change in distance as the time since Silvia started walking increased from 2 to 7 seconds?
    c. i. Construct a graph that gives Silvia's distance from her house (in feet) in terms of the number of seconds since she started walking. Be sure to label your axes.
        ii. Illustrate (with a line segment on the graph you constructed in part (i)) Silvia's change in distance during the time period from $t = 4$ and $t = 5$ seconds since she started walking.
        iii. Illustrate (with a line segment on the graph you constructed in part (i)) Silvia's change in distance during the time period from $t = 5$ and $t = 6$ seconds since she started walking.

© 2018 Carlson, Oehrtman, and Moore

68. Bob's distance, d, north of Mrs. Bess's restaurant (in feet) is given by the formula $d = 2t^2 - 7$ where t represents the number of seconds since Bob began driving.
    a. Determine the value of d when $t = 1$. What does a negative value for d represent in the context of this problem?
    b. Find the average speed of Bob's car for the time period from $t = 3$ to $t = 5$.
    c. As the number of seconds since Bob began driving increased from 1.5 to 2 seconds, by how much did Bob's distance north of Mrs. Bess's restaurant change?
    d. As the number of seconds since Bob began driving increased from 2 to 2.5 seconds, by how much did Bob's distance north of Mrs. Bess's restaurant change?
    e. i.   How much time did it take Bob to travel from 20 to 30 feet north of the restaurant?
        ii. How much time did it take Bob to travel from 30 to 40 feet north of the restaurant?
        iii. How much time did it take Bob to travel from 40 to 50 feet north of the restaurant?

69. The graph represents the speeds of two cars (car A and car B) in terms of the elapsed time in seconds since being at a rest stop. Car A is traveling at a constant speed of 65 miles per hour. As car A passes the rest stop car B pulls out beside car A and they both continue traveling down the highway.
    a. Which graph represents car A's speed and which graph represents car B's speed? Explain.
    b. Which car is further down the road 20 seconds after being at the rest stop? Explain.
    c. Explain the meaning of the intersection point.
    d. What is the relationship between the positions of car A and car B 25 seconds after being at the rest stop?

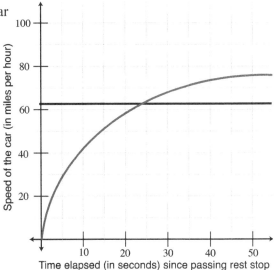

For Exercises #70-79, let d be the distance of a car (in feet) from mile marker 420 on a country road and let t be the time elapsed (in seconds) since the car passed mile marker 420. The formulas below represent various ways these quantities might be related. For each of the following:
    i. Determine the average speed of the car using the given formula and the specified time interval.
    ii. Explain the meaning of average speed for the given situation.

70. $d = t^2$ from $t = 5$ to $t = 30$.

71. $d = -3(-19t - 1)$ from $t = 3$ to $t = 9$.

72. $d = 5(12t + 1) + 3t$ from $t = 0.5$ to $t = 3.75$.

73. $d = \frac{10t(t+5)-14}{2}$ from $t = 0$ to $t = 5$.

74. $d = \frac{1}{3}\left(9t^2 + 155t - (11t - 6)\right)$ from $t = 2$ to $t = 4$.

75. $d = (2t + 7)(3t - 2)$ from $t = 2$ to $t = 2.75$.

76. $d = \left(\frac{1}{3}t + 60\right)\left(t + \frac{1}{2}\right)$ from $t = 1$ to $t = 4$.
    from $t = 30$ to $t = 35$.

77. $d = (t + 6)(t + 3) + 7t - 20 + 11t - \frac{7}{8}t^2$
    from $t = 30$ to $t = 35$.

78. $d = \frac{1}{8}t\left(3t^2 + 1.5t\right) + 16t - 3$ from $t = 2$ to $t = 4$.

79. $d = \dfrac{t\left(\frac{1}{2}t^2 + 15\right) + 3t\left(\frac{1}{10}t^2 + \frac{4}{3t}\right)}{5}$
    from $t = 5$ to $t = 9$.

This investigation contains review and practice with important skills and procedures you may need in this module and future modules. Your instructor may assign this investigation as an introduction to the module or may ask you to complete select exercises "just in time" to help you when needed. Alternatively, you can complete these exercises on your own to help review important skills.

Evaluating and Simplifying Expressions and Solving Equations
Use this section prior to the module or with/after Investigation 1.

Given that $a = 4$, $b = 11$, $c = 5$, and $d = -4$, evaluate each of the expressions in Exercises #1-6.

1. $\dfrac{\sqrt{c-a}+b}{2}$

2. $\dfrac{(a+1)-a}{b^2-b}$

3. $\dfrac{c}{8}+2c^2-6d$

4. $\dfrac{2\sqrt{b+14}}{8-a}+5$

5. $\dfrac{d\sqrt{d+6}}{d+6}$

6. $\frac{4}{9}\sqrt{2c^2+4a}-5$

In Exercises #7-10, use the given information to write an equation and then solve it.

7. solve $y = 2x - 19$ for x if $y = 5$

8. solve $y = \sqrt[3]{x}$ for x if $y = -2$

9. solve $n = -\frac{1}{3}(p-11)+19$ for p if $n = 7$

10. solve $\dfrac{w+2}{w+6} = q$ for w if $q = -1$

In Exercises #11-14, solve each equation.

11. $\frac{2}{3}x+\frac{1}{2}=\frac{17}{2}$

12. $4 = \frac{1}{5}(3n-7)$

13. $x+3 = \dfrac{x-3}{4}$

14. $\dfrac{3}{4}x+\dfrac{5}{6}=5x-\dfrac{125}{3}$

In Exercises #15-24, write an equation based on each description and then solve the equation. *Be sure to define a variable to represent the value of the unknown number before writing each equation.*

15. 17.5 is equal to 2 times some number. What is the number?

16. The sum of 3 times some number and 12 is 42. What is the number?

17. one-fourth of some number is 4.3. What is the number?

18. The difference between some number and 14.3 is 2.1. What is the number?

19. Some number is 4 times as large as 9.8. What is the number?

20. Some number is equal to one-third of the sum of 88.2, 93.5, and 64. What is the number?

21. 45 is some multiple of 15. Set up an equation and determine the value of the multiple.

22. $1,200 is 1.5 times as large as some number. What is the number?

23. 200% of some number is 38.2. What is the number?

24. Three-fourths of some number increased by 12 is equal to 5 times the number. What is the number?

Evaluating and Simplifying Expressions and Solving Equations (with Function Notation)
Use this section with/after Investigation 2.

25. Given that $f(x) = \dfrac{x}{4} + x^2$, evaluate each of the following.

    a. $f(12)$ b. $f(10)$ c. $f(-2)$ d. $2 \cdot f(3)$

26. Given that $g(x) = \dfrac{3x}{x-7} + 2$, evaluate each of the following.

    a. $g(8)$ b. $g(10)$ c. $g(-1.5)$ d. $-\dfrac{g(4)}{4}$

27. Given that $h(x) = \sqrt{2x} - x$, evaluate each of the following.

    a. $h(50)$ b. $h(14)$ c. $h(18) - h(12.5)$ d. $\dfrac{h(8) - h(2)}{8-2}$

28. Given that $f(x) = \dfrac{x}{4} + x^2$, write the expression that represents each of the following.

    a. $f(2r)$ b. $f(p+r)$ c. $f(3x)$

29. Given that $g(x) = \dfrac{3x}{x-7} + 2$, write the expression that represents each of the following.

    a. $g(n-2)$ b. $g(4x)$ c. $g(a-b)$

In Exercises #30-33, use the given information to write an equation and then solve it.

30. if $f(x) = \sqrt{x}$, find the value of x such that $f(x) = 4$

31. if $g(x) = \dfrac{2x - 6}{5}$, find the value of x such that $g(x) = 3$

32. if $h(x) = 3(7 - x) + 4$, find the value of x such that $h(x) = 31$

33. if $j(x) = \dfrac{1}{x + 2}$, find the value of x such that $j(x) = -0.5$

Modeling and Additional Content

Use this section prior to the module or with/after any of the first three investigations.

34. a. Indicate on the figure and describe the attributes of this circle that represent the following quantities.
      r = radius of the circle measured in feet
      d = diameter of the circle measured in feet
      C = circumference of the circle measured in feet
      A = area of the circle measured in square feet

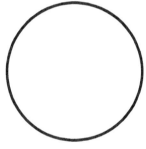

   b. Write the formula to express a circle's diameter in terms of its radius. Use the formula to determine the diameter of a circle that has a radius of 4.721 feet.

   c. Write the formula to express a circle's circumference in terms of its diameter. Use the formula to determine the circumference of a circle that has a diameter of 6.48 feet.

   d. Write the formula to express a circle's area in terms of its diameter. Use the formula to determine the area of a circle that has a diameter of 4.09 feet.

   e. Write the formula to express a circle's circumference in terms of its radius. Use the formula to determine the circumference of a circle that has a radius of 3.5 feet.

   f. Write the formula to express a circle's area in terms of its diameter. Use the formula to determine the area of a circle that has a diameter of 3.5 feet.

   g. Define a formula to express the circumference of a circle in terms of its area. Use the formula to determine the circumference of a circle that has an area of 42.7 square feet.

35. The distance between some number(s) and 0 on the number line is 4.
    a. What are the numbers?

    b. Illustrate on the number line all numbers that are 4 units away from 0.

    c. Solve the equation $|x| = 4$ for x (*what value(s) of x make this equation true*)?

    d. Describe how the solutions found in part (c) are represented on the number line.

36. a. Given that $|x| = 5$, determine the value(s) of x that makes this equation true.

    b. Given that $|x - 2| = 7$, determine the value(s) of x that makes this equation true.

    c. Given that $|x + 1| = 3$, determine the value(s) of x that makes this equation true.

37. a. This graph that represents how x and y are related, determine the value of x when $y = 8$. Describe your approach and say why it works.

    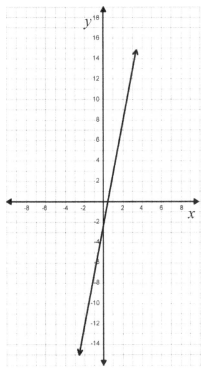

    b. Given that $y = 5x - 2$ is the equation of the graphed function, solve the equation $8 = 5x - 2$ for x algebraically. Illustrate how to use the graph to solve this equation.

    c. Use the graph to solve the equation $3 = 5x - 2$. Illustrate how you used the graph to solve this equation.

    d. Use the graph to solve the equation $0 = 5x - 2$. Illustrate how you used the graph to solve this equation.

*1. Consider what is involved in building a box (without a top) from an 8.5" by 11" sheet of paper by cutting squares from each corner and folding up the sides.

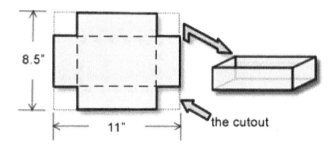

the cutout

    a.   To understand how the quantities in the situation are related it is important to first model the situation by doing the following.
        i.   Cutting four equal-sized squares from the corners of an 8.5 by 11-inch sheet of paper.
       ii.   Folding up the sides and taping them together at the edges.

    b.   Do the cutouts have to be square? Explain.

    c.   What quantities in this situation vary? What quantities in the situation are constant (do not vary)?

    d.   Describe how the configuration of the box changes as the length of the side of the square cutout varies.

    e.   Using the "Volume w/ Cubes" animation, describe how the volume of the box varies as the length of the side of the cutout varies from 0 to 4.25 inches.

    f.   Based on your response to part (e), sketch a graph of the volume of the box (in cubic inches) with respect to the length of the side of the square cutout (in inches).

    g.   Use a ruler to measure the length of the side of your square cutout (measured in inches), where the length of the base is the side that was originally 11 inches long and the width of the base is the side that was originally 8.5 inches long.

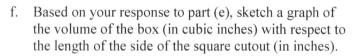

Cutout length: _____   Box's height: _____   Length of box's base: _____

Width of the box's base: _____   Volume of the box: _____

*2. Let *x* represent the varying length of the side of the square cutout in inches. Let *w* represent the varying width of the box's base in inches. Let *l* represent the varying length of the box's base in inches. Let *V* represent the varying volume of the box in cubic inches.

a. Complete the table of values.

x	w	l	V
0			
	6.5		
4.25			
5			
		15	
		2	

b. Explain how the length of the base of the box is related to the length of the side of the square cutout and how the width of the base of the box is related to the length of the side of the square cutout.

c. Define a formula to determine the width of the box in terms of the length of the side of the square cutout. *Be sure to define your variables.*

d. Define a formula to determine the length of the box in terms of the length of the side of the square cutout. *Be sure to define your variables.*

e. Define a formula to determine the volume of the box in terms of the length of the side of the square cutout.

f. Use your formula from part (e) to represent the volume of the box when *x*, the length of the side of the cutout, is 0.5 inches.

g. Use your formula from part (e) to represent the volume of the box when *x*, the length of the side of the cutout, is 3 inches.

*3. Represent the volume of the box for cutout lengths of 1.5, 2.7, 3.8, and 4.2 inches using your formula.

a. When *x* = _____ inches, *V* = _____ cubic inches.

b. When *x* = _____ inches, *V* = _____ cubic inches.

c. When *x* = _____ inches, *V* = _____ cubic inches.

d. When *x* = _____ inches, *V* = _____ cubic inches.

4. a. View the "Graphs" animation (or use your graphing calculator) to create a graph that represents the volume of the box V (measured in cubic inches) in terms of the length of the side of the square cutout x (measured in inches).

    (*When determining the window setting on your calculator, consider the possible values of x and the possible values of V.*)

    Construct the graph and label two points on the graph. State what each of these points convey about the box.

    Point 1:

    Point 2:

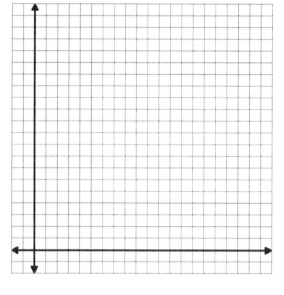

   b. Identify the point on the graph that corresponds to the dimensions of the box you created in Exercise #1.

   c. As x (the length of the side of the cutout) increases from 0.5 to 0.75 inches, how does the volume of the box change?

   d. As x (the length of the side of the cutout) increases from 2.1 to 2.7 inches, how does the volume of the box change?

   e. As x (the length of the side of the cutout) increases from 1 to 3 inches, how does the volume of the box change?

   f. Indicate on the graph i) a change of cutout length from 2 inches to 3 inches and ii) the corresponding change in the box's volume.

   g. Estimate the interval(s) of values for the length of the side of the cutout x for which the volume of the box decreases as x increases.

*5. a. Using your graphing calculator, solve for the length of the side of the square cutout if the volume of the box is 62.5 cubic inches.

   b. Using your graphing calculator, solve for the length of the side of the square cutout if the volume of the box is 23 cubic inches.

   c. Using your graphing calculator, find an approximate maximum value for the box's volume.

   d. Using your graphing calculator, solve for the length of the side of the square cutout that produces the maximum volume you found in part (c).

6. An open box is constructed by cutting four equal-sized square corners from a 12-inch by 18-inch sheet of cardboard and folding up the sides. The given graph represents the volume of a box (measured in cubic inches) in relation to the length of the side of the square cutout (measured in inches).

   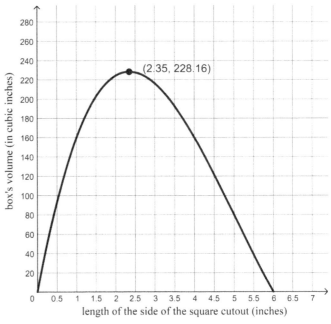

   a. Determine the box's volume for each given length of the side of the square cutout. *Use the graph to check that your answer makes sense.*
      i. 2 inches

      ii. 5 inches

      iii. 3.75 inches

   b. Write a formula to represent the box's volume V (in cubic inches) in terms of x, the length of the side of the square cutout (in inches).

   c. Use the graph to estimate the length(s) of the side of the square cutout that produces each of the following volumes.
      i. 160 cubic inches   ii. 190 cubic inches   iii. 70 cubic inches

   d. Use the graph to determine the interval(s) for the length of the side of the square cutout over which the box's volume is decreasing as the cutout length increases. Then repeat for the interval(s) over which the box's volume is increasing as the cutout length increases.

In the previous investigation we wrote formulas to describe how values of one quantity are related to values of another quantity. We say that the dependent quantity is a ***function*** of the independent quantity if every value of the independent quantity produces ***exactly one*** value of the dependent quantity.

It is also convention to say that values of the independent quantity are input to ("put into") the function rule, and a value produced from applying the function rule are output values of the function rule.

Function

A **function** consists of three parts:
1. *Domain*: The values the independent quantity may assume.
2. *Range*: The values the dependent quantity assume.
3. *Rule*: The rule assigns to each value of the independent quantity *exactly one* value of the dependent quantity.

The rule of a function can be expressed using any of: i) a worded description; ii) an algebraic expression; iii) a graph; or iv) a table of values. The rule of the function defines how a function's independent and dependent quantities are related as their values change together.

Terminology: If we want to write a function *f* to determine the perimeter of a square P (in inches) in terms of its side length s (in inches), we write $f(s) = 4s$. (It is noteworthy that $P = f(s)$ since both P and $f(s)$ represent a varying value of a quantity of the square's perimeter.)

We say that the *function f* "defines $f(s)$ in terms of *s*" meaning the value of the dependent quantity (the perimeter), represented by $f(s)$, is determined by (or depends on) the value of the independent quantity, *s*.

If we know *s* has a value of 6, we can determine the value of $f(s)$ to be 24 by inputting the value of 6 into the function rule, $4s$. Since $f(s) = 4s$ we see that the function rule conveys that $f(s)$ is always 4 times as large as *s*.

Some advantages of using function notation include:
- We can reference the function using its name, *f*. This is more concise than having to say or write out $P = 4s$.
- We can reference a function's output value that corresponds to a particular input value without having to actually compute the value. So, $f(3.2)$ represents the perimeter of a square (in inches) that has a side length of 3.2 inches.

*1. Read the definition and terminology overview above.
   a. What does $f(5.8)$ represent?

   b. Given that the square's perimeter cannot exceed 48 inches,
      i. what are the possible values that the square's side length *s* can take on?
      (*Your answer describes the **domain** of f.*)

      ii. what are the possible values that the perimeter *P* can take on? (*Your answer describes the **range** of f.*)

---

c. What is the rule that determines how *s* and $f(s)$ are related and change together?

d. T or F: In the function *f* there is exactly one value of $f(s)$ for each value of *s*. Justify your answer

2. Instead of defining a square's perimeter $f(s)$ in terms of its side length *s*, we could have chosen to define a square's side length in terms of the square's perimeter *P*.
   a. Define a function *g* to represent a square's side length $g(P)$ in terms of its perimeter, *P*.

   b. What quantity does $g(P)$ represent in this problem context?

   c. What does $g(20)$ represent? What is does $g(17.5)$ represent?

   d. What is the rule of the function? What is the name of the function?

3. Recall the box problem from Module 3, Investigation 1.
   a. Using function notation and the function name *f*, we define the box's volume *f*(*x*) in terms of the side of the square's cutout *x* as $f(x) = x(11-2x)(8.5-2x)$.

   *i. What is the independent (input) quantity?   *ii. What is the dependent (output) quantity?

   *iii. What is the rule of the function?   *iv. What is the domain of *f*?

   b. Explain the meaning of each of the following.
   *i. $f(1.5)$ ii. $f(3.62)$

   *iii. $f(2.3) = 57.408$ iv. $f(4.1) = 3.444$

   *c. What does it mean to find the value of *x* such that $f(x) = 50$?

*d. What does $f(2) - f(1)$ represent in this problem context?

Formulas with Function Notation

Let x represent the length of the side of the square cutout (in inches) and V represent the box's volume (in cubic inches). Call the relationship between these quantities f where x represents input values and V represents output values. Then:

$$f(x) = x(11 - 2x)(8.5 - 2x) \quad \text{with} \quad f(x) = V$$

Let's clarify the meaning of this notation.

$$\underbrace{\overbrace{f}^{Name} \; (\; \overbrace{x}^{Input} \;) = \overbrace{(x)(11-2x)(8.5-2x)}^{Rule}}_{Function\ Definition} \qquad \underbrace{\overbrace{f}^{Name} \; (\; \underbrace{x}_{\substack{Input\ Variable \\ Assignment}} \;) = \overbrace{V}^{\substack{Output\ Variable \\ Assignment}}}_{Relationship\ Definition}$$

When a function is defined with a formula we produce a rule that tells us how to match each value in the domain (each input value) to the corresponding value in the range (an output value).

---

*4. Billy is walking from the front door of his house to his bus stop, which is 960 feet away from his front door. As Billy walks out his front door he walks in a straight path toward his bus stop at a constant rate of 7.5 feet per second.

   a. Illustrate the situation with a diagram and define variables to represent the values of the relevant varying quantities. (Label the variables on your picture.)

   b. Define a function f to determine Billy's distance from his bus stop in terms of the number of seconds he has been walking.

   c. What is the independent quantity and what is the domain of f (the values the independent quantity can take on)?

   d. What is the dependent quantity and what is the range of f (the values the dependent quantity can take on)?

   e. What do each of the following represent: $f(0)$ and $f(60.25)$?

---

f. Use function notation to represent the following:
   i. Billy's distance from the bus stop after he has walked 23.6 seconds.

   ii. Represent using function notation the change in Billy's distance from the bus stop as the number of seconds since Billy left his front door increases from 35 seconds to 48 seconds.

g. If *t* represents the number of seconds since Billy left his front door, solve $f(t) = 150$ for *t* and say what your answer represents.

The Vertical Intercept of a Function

A function's ***vertical intercept*** is the function's output value when 0 is input to the rule of *f*.

We also say that the value of $f(0)$ is the ***vertical intercept*** of *f*.

It is noteworthy that if $g(0) = -25$, the vertical intercept of *g* is –25 and occurs at the point (0, –25) on the graph of *g*.

*5. a. Since the vertical intercept of a function *f* occurs where $x = 0$, what general method can you use to determine the vertical intercept of the graph of a function *f*?

b. If $f(x) = 5x^2 - 2x + 9$, what is the vertical intercept of *f* and what does this value represent?

c. What is the point on *f* where the vertical intercept occurs?

*6 a. If the function *h* defined by $h(x) = 39 - 6.5x$ represents the distance (in meters) between a Tortoise and Hare as they are running a 100 meter race, what is the vertical intercept of *h*?

b. Construct the graph of *h* and label the vertical intercept of *h*.

c. What does the point $(0, h(0))$ represent in this problem context?

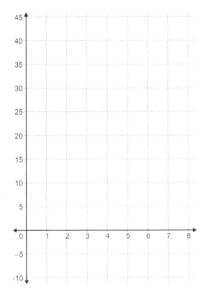

© 2018 Carlson, Oehrtman, and Moore

> ### Horizontal Intercepts (also called Zeros or Roots) of a Function
>
> A function f's **horizontal intercept(s)** are the input values where the graph of the function f crosses the horizontal axes.
>
> Since a function f crosses the horizontal-axis where $f(x) = 0$, horizontal intercepts are values of x that make $f(x) = 0$. If $f(x) = 0$ when $x = a$, we say that the constant value a is a **horizontal-intercept** of f. We can also say that $x = a$ is a **root** or **zero** of the function f.

Given a function $h(x) = x(x - 7)$, we can determine the horizontal intercepts by determining the values of x that make $h(x) = 0$. To find the horizontal intercepts, we solve the equation $0 = x(x - 7)$. Since this equation is true when either factor is 0, the solutions are $x = 0$ and $x = 7$. The values 0 and 7 are also called roots or zeros of the function h.

*7. Continuing the same context from question 6, $h(x) = 39 - 6.5x$ represents the distance (in meters) between a Tortoise and Hare as they are running a 100 meter race,

   a. Solve the equation $h(x) = 0$ for x. What does this solution represent in the problem context? Label this solution on the graph you created in Exercise #6 part (b).

   b. What is the root of h? What is the point that represents the horizontal intercept of the graph of h?

   c. T or F: The x value of the horizontal intercept of the graph of h corresponds to the root of h.

8. For each of the following functions, determine all horizontal intercepts. *Try to determine these algebraically first then verify your answers by graphing the functions on your calculator.*
   a. $h(x) = 4(x - 6) + 2$ b. $b(x) = x(11 - 2x)(8.5 - 2x)$

*9. For this graphical representation,
   a. determine if y is a function of x. Justify your answer using the definition of function—each input value of a function is assigned to exactly one output value.

   b. determine if x is a function of y. Justify your answer.

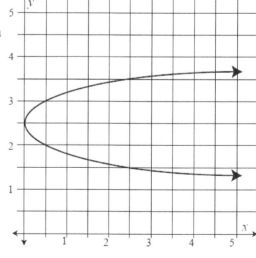

10. For this graphical representation,
    a. determine if y is a function of x.
       (Is each value of x assigned to exactly one value of y?)

       Justify your answer using the definition of function.

    b. determine if x is a function of y.
       (Is each value of y assigned to exactly one value of x?)

       Justify your answer using the definition of function.

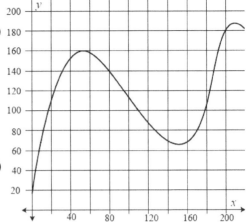

Recall that the *domain* is the set of all possible values of the independent quantity for which the function is defined. A function's domain can be restricted because:
  i)   it is not possible to determine the square root of a negative number;
  ii) the denominator of a quotient cannot be 0; or
  iii) values for the independent quantity are restricted by the context (the cutout length on the box cannot exceed 4.25, for example).

11. Without using a graphing calculator determine the domain and range of the following functions.
    a. $s(x) = \dfrac{9}{x}$

    b. $g(x) = \dfrac{1}{x^2 - 9}$

    c. $h(x) = x^2 + 2x - 5$

    d. $k(x) = \dfrac{\sqrt{x-2}}{x-9}$

*12. Without using a graphing calculator determine the domain and range of the following functions.
    a. $p(x) = \dfrac{x}{9}$

    b. $f(x) = \sqrt{x - 4}$

    c. $b(x) = \dfrac{x(x-5)}{x-5}$

    d.

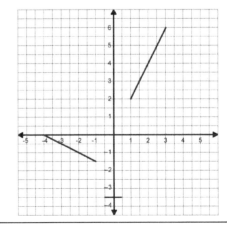

*1. If A is the area of a square measured in square inches and s is the square's side length measured in inches, then the square's side length s and its area A are related by the formula $A = s^2$. If we call this function g, recall that using function notation we can also write $g(s) = s^2$ where $A = g(s)$.

a. Use function notation to represent (NOT CALCULATE) the areas of two different squares whose side lengths are 3.5 inches and 26.92 inches..

b. Interpret the meaning of $g(4.9) = 24.01$ in this context.

c. What does it mean to solve $g(s) = 81$ for s? (*Don't solve yet and don't explain how to solve for s, instead explain what the solution would represent.*)

d. Solve for s when $g(s) = 24.01$

e. Explain what each of the following represent.

i. $g(5) + 23$ ii. $4g(3.4)$

f. If the square's side length s increases at a constant rate of 3 inches per second, where t represents the number of seconds since the square's side length started increasing, what does $3t$ represent?

g. What does $(3t)^2$ represent in this situation? Expand the expression $(3t)^2$ and explain what this new expression represents and how it compares to the expression $(3t)^2$.

2. The given table represents the retail price (in dollars) of a brand new Toyota Camry as a function of the number of years, n, after 2000.

a. What is the input quantity? What is the output quantity?

b. Evaluate each of the following and describe the meaning in this context.
i. $f(7)$ ii. $f(13)$

c. Solve for n when $f(n) = 19295$ and explain what your solution represents.

d. Evaluate each expression and describe the meaning in this context.
i. $f(6) - f(3)$ ii. $f(3) + 1250$ iii. $\frac{f(6)}{f(5)}$

# of years since 2000, n	Price of car, f(n)
0	17,520
2	18,970
3	19,045
5	19,295
6	19,545
7	19,925
10	20,835
13	21,985
18	23,495

*3. A tortoise and hare are competing in a race around a 400-meter track. The arrogant hare decides to let the tortoise have a 225-meter head start. When the start gun is fired, the hare begins running at a constant speed of 5.5 meters per second and the tortoise begins crawling at constant speed of 2.0 meters per second. Let t represent the number of seconds since the start gun was fired. We are interested in determining who won the race.

  a. Illustrate the situation with a diagram (mark off the length of the race, note the approximate position of the tortoise from the starting line and the position of the hare, illustrate varying quantities with vectors, etc.).

  b. Define a function g to represent the tortoise's distance from the finish line in terms of the number of seconds t since the start gun was fired.

  c. Define a function h to represent the hare's distance from the finish line in terms of the number of seconds t since the start gun was fired.

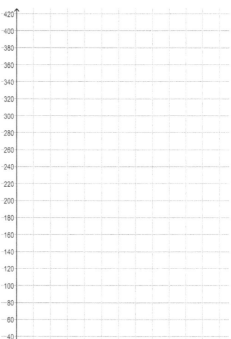

  d. Evaluate $g(40)$ and say what your answer represents.

  e. Solve $g(t) = 80$ for t and say what the solution represents.

  f. Solve $h(t) = 0$ and say what the solution represents.

  g. Construct a graph of g and h on the axes

  h. Evaluate $h(20) - g(20)$ and indicate how this quantity is represented in the graphical context in part (f). What does the quantity represent in the context of this situation.

  i. Define a new function f where $f(t) = h(t) - g(t)$, and graph this function on the axes in part (g). What does the function f represent? How does the graph of f relate to the graphs of h and g.

j. What is the slope of the graph of f? What does this value represent in the context of this situation? How does the distance between the tortoise and hare change throughout the race?

k. Solve $g(t) = h(t)$ for t and say what the solution represents.

l. Who won the race? Justify your answer using multiple methods.

4. A hose is used to fill an empty wading pool. The graph shows volume of the water in the pool (in gallons) as a function of time (in minutes) since the pool started filling.
   a. Define a function g that expresses the volume of water (in gallons) in the pool as a function of t, the elapsed time (in minutes) since the pool started filling.

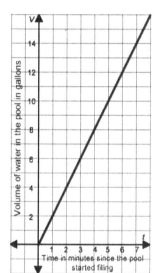

   b. Evaluate $g(4) - g(1)$ and describe what the value represents in the context of this situation. Then represent it on the graph.

   c. What could $g(4) + 100$ represent in this context?

*5. As Pat was driving across the flat plains of Kansas with his cruise control on, his gas gauge broke. At the moment the gauge broke, he had 8 gallons of gas in the car's gas tank and his gas mileage was 32 miles per gallon (assume that he maintains this gas mileage by leaving cruise control on). Pat needs to keep track of how much gas is left in his gas tank.
   a. How many gallons remain in Pat's gas tank after he has driven:
      i. 84 miles since his gas gauge broke?   ii. 150 miles since his gas gauge broke?

      iii. x miles since his gas gauge broke?

   b. If x represents the number of miles Pat has driven since his gas gauge broke, define a function f to determine the number of gallons left in Pat's gas tank $f(x)$ in terms of x.

c. What is the domain of *f* ?

What is the range of *f* ?

d. What does $f(100)$ represent in the context of this problem?

e. Construct a graph of *f* on the axes.

f. Explain what the graph of *f* conveys about how the number of miles Pat has driven since his gas gauge broke *x* and the number of gallons of gas left in Pat's tank $f(x)$ change together.

g. What is the value of $f(0)$ and what does this value represent in the context of this situation?

h. What is the value of *x* when $f(x) = 0$ and what does this value represent in the problem context? What point on the graph of *f* corresponds to where $f(x) = 0$?

i. What are the maximum and minimum values that $f(x)$ can assume in the context of this situation? Explain. (*Note: The maximum value that $f(x)$ can be is also called the maximum value of the function f.*) How do these values compare to the *f*'s range?

j. What is the horizontal intercept (zero, root) of *f* and what does this value represent in the context of this situation?

© 2018 Carlson, Oehrtman, and Moore

*1. Running is a popular form of exercise to burn calories and stay healthy. The number of calories burned while running depends on many factors but averages about 100 calories per mile. Suppose Nikki goes for a run, traveling at a constant speed of 720 feet per minute and burning 100 calories per mile she runs.

   a. What quantities are varying (changing) in this situation? What quantities are constant?

   b. Describe how you think each of the following pairs of quantities are changing together.
      i. As the time (in minutes) spent running increases, how does the distance (in feet) Nikki has traveled change?

      ii. As the distance (in feet) Nikki has traveled increases, how does the number of calories she has burned change?

      iii. As the time spent running increases, what happens to the number of calories Nikki has burned?

   c. Complete the table of values for this situation. (*Recall there are 5280 feet in one mile.*)

Time (in minutes) Nikki has been running	Distance (in feet) Nikki has traveled	Distance (in miles) Nikki has traveled
3		
14		
18.5		
22.2		
t		

   d. How many calories does Nikki burn if she runs 3 miles? 5.7 miles? m miles?

   e. Complete the table of values relating the number of minutes Nikki spends running and the number of calories she burns.

Time (in minutes) Nikki has been running	Number of calories Nikki has burned
4	
11	
15.5	
19.2	
t	

There are two key takeaways from Exercise #1.

(i) The expressions we write should be meaningful and related to our understanding of the quantities. For example, note the meaning of each of the following expressions and how new meanings develop as we modify them.

- t represents the number of minutes Nikki has been running
- $720t$ represents the distance Nikki runs (in feet) in t minutes
- $\frac{720t}{5,280}$ represents the distance Nikki runs (in miles) in t minutes
- $100\left(\frac{720t}{5,280}\right)$ represents the number of calories Nikki burns in t minutes

(ii) Using the results of one calculation or set of calculations as the basis for another calculation is one of the foundations for understanding *function composition* – the process of chaining together multiple function processes.

*2. a. Draw a diagram of a square and label the side lengths x (measured in inches). Visualize the square growing and shrinking as the value of x changes and think about how the square's perimeter length (in inches) compares to the side length.

b. Define a function g that inputs the square's perimeter P and outputs the square's side length x (both measured in inches).

c. How does the square's side length change as the perimeter changes from 6 inches to 20 inches? Calculate this value **and** represent it using function notation.

d. Define a function h that inputs the square's side length x (in inches) and outputs the square's area A (in square inches).

e. Using the functions in parts (b) and (d), determine the area of squares that have each of the following perimeters: 24 inches, 60 inches, 14 inches, and P inches.

Reflecting on Exercise #2 you should notice that we defined two functions and that the output quantity of one function matched the input quantity of the second function. Thus, when given a perimeter, we follow a two-step process.

- **Step 1:** Use *g*, which inputs the perimeter length and outputs the side length (both in inches).
- **Step 2:** Use *h*, which inputs that side length (in inches) and outputs the square's area (in in²).

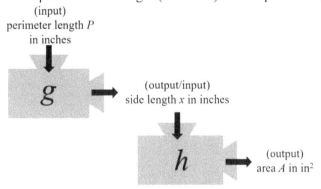

Now, suppose we want to combine these into a single function that combines the two processes together. **That is, we want to define a function *f* that inputs the perimeter length and outputs the area.**

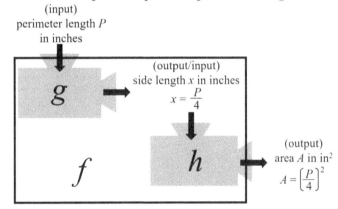

Let's write a formula defining *f*. We'll start with descriptions and move towards a symbolic representation.

$f(\text{perimeter length}) = \text{area}$

$f(\text{perimeter length}) = (\text{side length})^2$ • a square's area is product of its length and width

$f(\text{perimeter length}) = \left(\frac{\text{perimeter length}}{4}\right)^2$ • a square's side length is $\frac{1}{4}$ of its perimeter length

$$\boxed{f(P) = \left(\tfrac{P}{4}\right)^2}$$

So $f(P) = \left(\frac{P}{4}\right)^2$ with $A = f(P)$. Function *f* is a **composite function** – it is formed by uniting the process of two functions to form a single function.

Function Composition

Function composition is the process of chaining together two (or more) function processes by linking the output quantity of one function with the input quantity of another function.

The function created by doing this is called a ***composite function***.

---

3. Using the context in Exercise #2, imagine that the square's perimeter begins at 0 inches and increases at a rate of 3 inches per second.

  a. What is the square's area 8 seconds after the perimeter started increasing? 10 seconds? 40 seconds?

  b. Define a function that inputs the time elapsed (in seconds) since the perimeter started increasing and outputs the square's area (in square inches).

  c. Discuss with a group (or as a class) how the process of using a time elapsed to determine the square's area involves thinking about function composition.

*4. The following graphs show two functions, *f* and *g*. Function *g* takes as its input the high temperature in degrees Fahrenheit and outputs the expected attendance at a neighborhood carnival. Function *f* takes as its input a number of people attending the carnival and outputs the total expected revenue earned by the carnival.

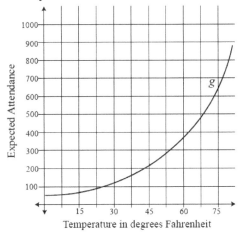
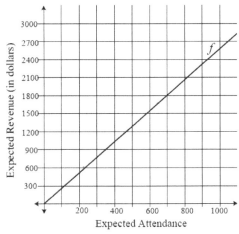

  a. If the forecast predicts clear skies and a high temperature of 45°F, what is the expected revenue from the carnival today? What if the forecast predicts a high temperature of 75°F?

  b. Function *h* inputs the high temperature in degrees Fahrenheit and outputs the expected revenue (in dollars). On the given axes plot at least 5 coordinate points representing input/output pairs for *h*.

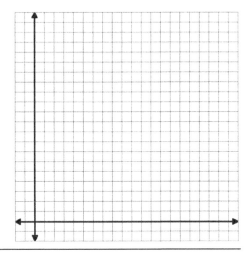

In Exercise #4 we used outputs of *g* as inputs to *f* in order to determine the expected revenue given a forecasted high temperature. The notation for representing expected revenue given the forecasted high temperature should seem very logical.

expected revenue

f(expected attendance)   • *f* inputs expected attendance and outputs expected revenue

$f\big(g(\text{high temp °F})\big)$ • *g*(temp °F) represents the expected attendance given the high temp °F

$f\big(g(x)\big)$ • Let *x* represent the high temperature in °F

So $f\big(g(x)\big)$ represents the expected revenue (in dollars) given *x*, the high temperature in degrees Fahrenheit. Evaluating an expression like $f\big(g(15)\big)$ is similar to following the order of operations. We begin with the inside function. *We used the graph to estimate each value.*

$f\big(g(15)\big)$

$f(75)$ • the expected attendance is 75 when the high temperature is 15°F

200 • the expected revenue is $200 when the expected attendance is 75 people

Note that $f\big(g(x)\big)$ represents the function's outputs, but it is not the function's *name* (just like $f(x)$ is the output of *f*, not the function name). We use the notation $f \circ g$ to name the composite function.

Function Composition Notation

If *f* and *g* are functions, then $f \circ g$ is the name of the composite function formed by chaining together the two processes where *g* is the "inside" function, meaning the process involves:
1. Inputting a value into *g* and producing an output value.
2. Using that output value as an input to *f* to get another output value. This is the output value for the composite function.

If $f \circ g$ is the name of the composite function, then $f\big(g(x)\big)$ represents the function's output values. *Note that we sometimes condense the notation by just giving this new composite function a name like h. So we could define a function h to be the composite function $f \circ g$ by saying $h(x) = f\big(g(x)\big)$.*

---

*5. a. In the context from Exercise #4 explain what $f\big(g(70)\big)$ represents.

 b. In the context from Exercise #4 explain why $g\big(f(70)\big)$ does not represent a real-world quantity.

 c. Let's define a new function *k* that is the composition of *f* and *g*, that is, $k(x) = f\big(g(x)\big)$. Explain what the equation $1800 = k(x)$ represents, then explain how you can find the value of *x* that satisfies the equation.

---

6. Use the table of values to evaluate or solve each of the following.

   *a. $g(f(-1))$ *b. $f(g(3))$

x	$f(x)$	$g(x)$
-2	0	5
-1	3	3
0	4	2
1	-1	1
2	6	-1
3	-2	0

   c. $f(f(3))$ d. $g(g(0))$

   e. If $f(g(x)) = 3$, then what must be the value of x?

7. Use the graph provided to evaluate or solve each of the following.
   Approximations are acceptable.

   *a. $f(g(2.5))$ *b. $g(f(4))$ c. $g(g(3.5))$

   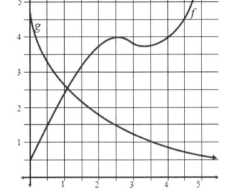

   d. Determine the value(s) of x such that $f(g(x)) = 2.5$.

8. Use the following functions to answer the questions: $f(x) = \sqrt{x+3}$, $g(x) = 2x + 9$, $h(x) = \frac{x}{4}$.

   *a. Evaluate $f(g(2))$.

   b. Evaluate $h(f(61))$.

   *c. Function m is defined as $m(x) = g(h(x))$. Write the formula for m.

   d. Function p is defined as $p(x) = g(f(x))$. Write the formula for p.

*1. A pebble is thrown into a lake and the radius length of the circular ripple increases at a constant rate of 7 cm/second. Your goal is to determine the area (in square meters) inside the ripple in terms of the number of seconds elapsed since the pebble hit the water. Before determining a function to represent this relationship, discuss the following questions in your group.

    a. Draw a picture of the situation and label the quantities. Imagine how the quantities are changing together. Discuss in your groups what processes need to be carried out to determine the area inside the ripple when the number of seconds since the pebble hit the water is known.

    b. What quantities are varying (changing) in the situation and how are they changing together?
       i. As the time since the pebble hit the water increases how does the radius of the ripple change?

       ii. As the radius of the circular ripple increases how does the area of the ripple change?

       iii. As the time since the pebble hit the water increases how does the area of the circular ripple change?

    c. Define variables to represent the values of each varying quantity in the situation.

    d. Define the following functions:
       i. f that defines the radius (in meters) of the circular ripple r as a function of the time elapsed (in seconds) t since the pebble hit the water.

       ii. g that defines the area of the circular ripple A (in meters^2) as a function of the radius length (in meters) of the circular ripple r.

e. Graph *f* and *g* and use these graphs to determine the area of the circle 4 seconds after the pebble hits the water. Make sure to reflect on the process you are using.

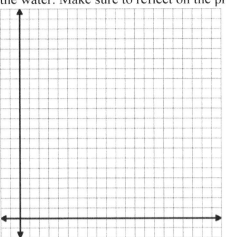 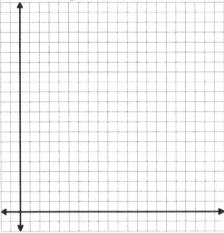

f. Use the functions defined in part (d) to define a function *h* that defines the area of the circular ripple *A* (measured in meters²) as a function of time elapsed *t* (measured in seconds).

g. Compute the value of *h*(4). How does this answer relate to the answer you obtained in part (e)?

*2. a. If a second pebble hits the water and the radius of the circular ripple increases 3 cm per second (instead of 7 cm per second), write an **expression** that represents the varying value of the circle's area.

b. A third pebble hits the water and the radius of the circular ripple increases 5 cm per second, define a function *j* that relates the amount of time *t* (in seconds) since the pebble hit the water and the area of the circle *j*(*t*).

*3. a. What is the radius of a circle with a circumference that is 15 feet?

b. What is the area of a circle with a radius of 2.387 feet?

c. What is the area of a circle when the circumference is 29.63 feet?

d. Define a function *f* that represents (or models) a circle's radius in terms of its circumference.

e. Define a function *h* that models the circle's area in terms of its circumference.

f. Use function *h* defined in part (e) to determine a circle's area when its circumference is 29.63 feet. How does your answer compare to your answer in part (c)?

4. The following graphs show two functions, *f* and *g*. Function *g* takes as its input the radius length of a sphere (in cm) and outputs the sphere's volume (in cm³). The function *f* takes as its input the radius length of a sphere (in cm) and outputs the sphere's surface area (in cm²).

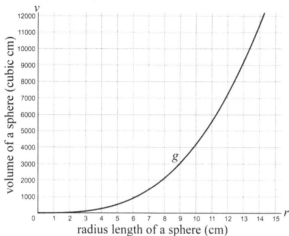 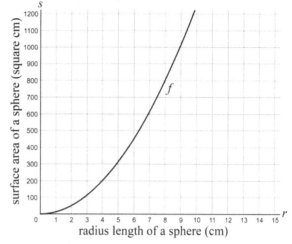

a. Does the expression $f\left(g(4)\right)$ have a real-world meaning in this context? If so, estimate its value and explain what the value represents. If not, explain your reasoning.

b. Does the expression $g\left(f(4)\right)$ have a real-world meaning in this context? If so, estimate its value and explain what the value represents. If not, explain your reasoning.

c. Is it possible, using the graphs provided, to determine the approximate volume of a sphere if its surface area is 500 cm²? If so, explain how. If not, explain your reasoning.

d. Is it possible, using the graphs provided, to determine the approximate surface area of a sphere if its volume is 3,000 cm³? If so, explain how. If not, explain your reasoning.

5. A farmer has 250 feet of fencing to create a rectangular pen.
   a. Draw a picture of the situation and label the relevant quantities.

   b. If w is of the pen's width (in feet) and l is the pen's length (in feet), then the pen's perimeter length is $2w + 2l$ feet, which must always total 250 feet (that is, $2w + 2l = 250$). Solve this equation for w.

   c. If the pen is 85 feet long, what is its width? What is its area? What if the pen is 46.5 feet long?

   d. For any value of w, what must be the corresponding value of l? The corresponding area?

   e. Define a function f that expresses the area of the rectangular pen (in square feet) as a function of w, the width of the rectangular pen (measured in feet).

6. Use the following functions to answer the questions: $f(x) = \sqrt{x + 3}$, $g(x) = 2x + 9$, $h(x) = \frac{x}{4}$.
   *a. Evaluate $f\big(g(2)\big)$.   b.   Evaluate $h\big(f(61)\big)$.

*7. Let $w = 312q - 100$ and $b = 21q^2$. Define a function h that determines w in terms of b.

*1. The formula that determines the perimeter of a square P (in inches) when the square's side length s (in inches) is known, is $P = 4s$.

    a. What thinking is involved in determining the side length, s, when the $P = 20$?

    b. When we solve the equation $20 = 4s$ for s, this is one instance of reversing the process of this formula. Use this same process to determine the side length of a square s (in inches) given the following values of a square's perimeter, P (in inches).

        i. $P = 36$ ii. $P = 22$ iii. $P = 100$

    c. What process (operations) did you use to determine a square's side length when a specific value of a square's perimeter P is known?

    d. Generalize the process you engaged in when answering part (b) by writing a formula that expresses a square's side length s in terms of its perimeter, P.

    d. How is the formula $P = 4s$ and the formula $s = \dfrac{P}{4}$ related? Do they express the same relationship between a square's side length and perimeter? Explain.

We have seen that formulas that produce a unique value of the dependent quantity for every value of the independent quantity are functions and can be represented using function notation. Recall that function notation allows us to reference a specified function relationship by name. We can also discuss a function output (dependent) value such as $f(2)$ without having to determine its value.

If $f(s) = 4s$ then a value of the square's side length (in inches) is input (or put in) to f. Applying the function rule, $4s$, determines a value for the square's perimeter, $f(s)$, in inches.

We can use the image of a "function machine" to evaluate $f(8)$. We input a particular value of 8 in for s, and apply the rule of f (we multiply 4 times 8) to obtain a value for the perimeter, $f(8) = 32$ inches.

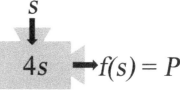

---

*2. Explain how $f(12)$ is processed by f. (*Hint: Use the image above which explains how f processes a value for the input quantity to produce the corresponding value of the output quantity.*)

If $g(P) = \dfrac{P}{4}$, then a value of a square's perimeter (in inches) is input (or put in) to g. Applying the

function rule, $\dfrac{P}{4}$, determines a value of a square's side length, $g(P)$, in inches.

If g is a function that undoes the process of the function f we
call the function g the inverse function of f. It is a convention
to represent the inverse function of some function f by writing
f^{-1}, so we can say that $g = f^{-1}$.

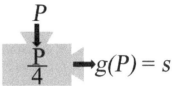

---

3.   a.   Evaluate $g(32)$ and use the above image to explain how the value of the input
quantity 32 was processed (or operated on) by g.

b.   In groups or as a class, discuss how the function $f(s) = 4s$ and $g(P) = \dfrac{P}{4}$ are related.

c.   What do you notice about how the input and output quantities for f and g are related?

d.   Use function composition to evaluate the following:
   i) $g(f(5))$ ii) $f(g(25))$ iii) $g(f(9))$ iv) $f(g(36))$

e.   T or F: For the functions f and g defined above f undoes the process of g, and g undoes the process
of f.

f.   Discuss in your groups (or as a class) how a function f and its inverse function f^{-1} are related in
terms of:
i. the process (or operations) they perform.

ii. their input quantities (and variables) and output quantities (and variables).

---

4. When traveling outside the United States it is often useful to be able to determine the temperature in Fahrenheit degrees given the temperature in Celsius degrees. The standard formula for determining the temperature in degrees Fahrenheit F when given the temperature in degrees Celsius C is, $F = \frac{9}{5}C + 32$.

   a. Determine the formula that defines degrees Celsius C in terms of degrees Fahrenheit F. What is the input quantity for this formula? What is the output quantity for this formula?

   b. Define a function g that determines the temperature in degrees Fahrenheit in terms of temperature in degrees Celsius.

   c. Define a function h that determines the temperature in degrees Celsius in terms of the temperature in degrees Fahrenheit.

   d. What does $g(C)$ represent? What does $h(F)$ represent?

   e. Determine the value of:
      i. $g(100)$ ii. $h(212)$ iii. $h\big(g(100)\big)$ iv. $g\big(h(212)\big)$

*5. The function f gives the volume V of a sphere (in cubic inches) as a function of its radius r (in inches). The function formula is $f(r) = \frac{4}{3}\pi r^3$ with $V = f(r)$.

   a. Removing the function notation produces the formula $V = \frac{4}{3}\pi r^3$. Solve this formula for r and explain what this new formula represents.

   b. Let g be the function that inputs a sphere's volume V (in cubic inches) and outputs its radius r (in inches). Use function notation to define a function g that determines a sphere's radius in terms of its volume, V.

   c. Explain what each of the following represents in this context. *You do not need to evaluate them.*
      i. $f(40)$ ii. $g(40)$

      iii. $f(7) \approx 1436.76$ iv. $g(2.14) \approx 0.8$

© 2018 Carlson, Oehrtman, and Moore

In Exercise #5 we examined and compared two functions, f and g, that represent the same relationship between two quantities (the radius and volume of a sphere). However, the input and output quantities were switched for the two functions. Thus, representing a volume of 288π (or about 904.8) in³ for a 6-inch radius is different for each function but the correspondence is the same.

*6. a. Compare and contrast the meaning of $f(6) = 288\pi$ and $g(288\pi) = 6$ given that f and g are defined in Exercise #5.

   b. Determine $g(f(6))$ and explain how functions formulas are used to determine this value.

When two functions represent the same relationship between covarying quantities, but their input and output quantities are reversed, we say they are **inverse functions**. In Exercise #3 the functions f and g are inverses.

The Inverse of a Function

A function and its inverse relation represent the same relationship between two co-varying quantities but with the independent (input) and dependent (output) quantities reversed.

If function g is the inverse of function f, then g undoes the process of f, and f undoes the process of g.

The idea of function inverse shouldn't be entirely new. When you rewrite a two-variable formula to solve for the alternative (or other) variable you are defining the inverse relationship.

7. Solve each of the following formulas for the other variable in the formula.

   *a. $y = 2x - 8$ *b. $w = \dfrac{r + 19}{4}$ c. $n = \dfrac{2x + 6}{x}$

Mathematicians developed a special function name to communicate that two functions are inverses.

Inverse Function Notation

Given a function f, its inverse (if also a function) is named f^{-1}. Since the input and output quantities are reversed in these two functions, we have that, if $y = f(x)$, then $x = f^{-1}(y)$.

The use of "−1" here is not an exponent. It's just part of the function name.

REMINDER: According to the rules of exponents, for any non-zero real number n, $n^{-1} = \frac{1}{n}$. Even though we are using similar notation here, it is **_not true_** that for any function f we have $f^{-1} = \frac{1}{f}$. You have to use context clues to understand the notation and recognize when f^{-1} is referring to the name of a function.

8. Define the inverse function for each of the following functions.

     a. $f(x) = 3x - 7$ with $y = f(x)$ *b. $j(r) = \frac{2r-5}{6}$ with $w = j(r)$

*9. Use the given table to evaluate the following.

     a. $f(0)$ b. $g^{-1}(3)$ c. $g^{-1}(0)$ d. $f^{-1}(-1)$

x	$f(x)$	$g(x)$
-2	0	5
-1	3	3
0	4	2
1	-1	1
2	6	-1
3	-2	0

Composition of Inverses

Inverse functions represent the same relationship between two quantities but with the input and output quantities reversed. We might say that inverse functions "undo" each other. If $f(a) = b$ then it must be that $f^{-1}(b) = a$ (assuming that f's inverse is a function and assuming that a is an element in f's domain and b an element of its range).

Thus,

$$f^{-1}\big(f(a)\big) = f^{-1}(b) \qquad \bullet \ \text{since } f(a) = b \qquad\qquad f\big(f^{-1}(b)\big) = f(a) \qquad \bullet \ \text{since } f^{-1}(b) = a$$
$$\phantom{f^{-1}\big(f(a)\big)} = a \qquad\quad \bullet \ \text{since } f^{-1}(b) = a \qquad\qquad\quad\ = b \qquad\quad \bullet \ \text{since } f(a) = b$$

The composition of two inverses will always produce the original input value for the "inside" function (in either order). In fact, this is one way to test if two functions are inverses.

10. Your classmate believes that each of the following pairs of functions are inverses (and thus used inverse function notation to define them). Is your classmate correct? Verify by creating the formula for $f^{-1}\big(f(x)\big)$ and simplifying.

     *a. $f(x) = 2(x+1) - 8$ and $f^{-1}(x) = \frac{x+8}{2} - 1$ b. $f(x) = \frac{3x+7}{4}$ and $f^{-1}(x) = \frac{4}{3}x - 7$

---

11. Sarah and Maria are racing. Sarah gives Maria a 30-yard head start and then she starts running. Once Maria starts running she travels at a constant rate of 4.5 yards per second while Maria travels at a constant rate of 3 yards per second.
    a. Draw a diagram of this situation.

    b. Write a formula for function f that models Maria's lead d (in yards) in terms of t, the number of seconds since Sarah began running.

    c. Write a formula for function f^{-1}.

    d. Create the composite function $f\left(f^{-1}(t)\right)$ to demonstrate that f and f^{-1} are inverses.

    f. How long does it take Sarah to catch up to Maria? Determine the value and then demonstrate how to represent this value using function notation in two different ways.

12. Use the given table to evaluate the following.
    a. $g^{-1}(3)$ b. $g^{-1}(0)$

    c. $f^{-1}\left(g(2)\right)$ d. $g^{-1}\left(f^{-1}(6)\right)$

x	$f(x)$	$g(x)$
−2	0	5
−1	3	3
0	4	2
1	−1	1
2	6	−1
3	−2	0

*13. Note that the inverse relation of a function ***might not*** be a function itself. Given the function f defined by $f(x) = x^2$ with $y = f(x)$, complete the following.

    a. Evaluate $f(2)$ and $f(-2)$.

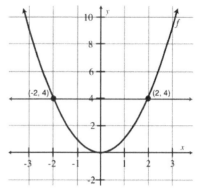

    b. Explain why f^{-1}, that is f's inverse function, is not a function. (Recall the definition of a function.)

    c. Consider $g(x) = x^2$ where the domain of g is restricted so that $x \geq 0$.
       i. Explain why g's inverse is a function.

       ii. Write the formula for g^{-1} and give its domain and range.

14. For each of the following functions f determine if its inverse will also be a function (based on the information you know). If not, then choose a restricted domain for f so that its inverse would be a function.

    a.

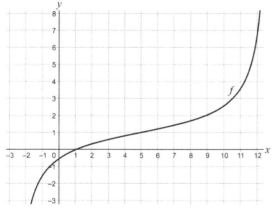

    b.

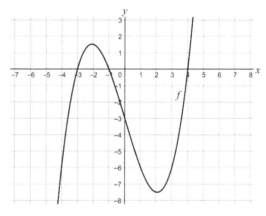

I. THE BOX PROBLEM AND MODELING RELATIONSHIPS (TEXT: S1, S2)

1. A box designer has been charged with the task of determining the volume of various boxes that can be constructed by cutting four equal-sized square corners from a 14-inch by 17-inch sheet of cardboard and folding up the sides.
   a. What quantities vary in this situation? What quantities remain constant?
   b. Create an illustration to represent the situation and label the relevant quantities.
   c. What are the dimensions of the box (length, width, and height) if the length of the side of the square cutout is 0.5 inches? 1 inch? 2 inches?
   d. Define a formula to relate the height of the box and the length of the side of the square cutout. Be sure to define your variables.
   e. Let x represent the length of the side of the square cutout; let w represent the width of the base of the box; let l represent the length of the base of the box; and let V represent the volume of the box. Complete the given table assuming each quantity is measured in a number of inches (volume measured in cubic inches).

x	w	l	V
0	14	17	0
4			
9			
		2	
	0		

   f. Define a formula to relate the length of the base of the box and the length of the side of the square cutout. Be sure to define your variables.
   g. Define a formula to relate the volume of the box to the length of the side of the square cutout.
   h. Use the formula created in part (h) to determine the change in the volume of the box as the length of the side of the square cutout increases from 0.5 inches to 1 inch and from 1 inch to 1.5 inches. Why are these values not the same?
   i. Use your graphing calculator to approximate the maximum volume of the box rounded to the nearest tenth of a cubic inch. Explain how you know that the value you obtained is the maximum value of the volume of the box rounded to the nearest tenth.

2. A box designer has been charged with the task of determining the surface area of various open boxes (no lids) that can be constructed by cutting four equal-sized surface corners from an 8-inch by 11.5-inch sheet of cardboard and folding up the sides. (*Note: The surface area is the total area of the box's sides and bottom.*)
   a. What quantities vary in this situation? What quantities remain constant?
   b. Create an illustration to represent the situation and label the relevant quantities.
   c. Complete the given table.

Cutout length (in)	Height of box (in)	Length of box (in)	Width of box (in)
0.5			
1			
2			

   d. Define a formula for the following relationships:
      i. the length of the base of the box in terms of the length of the side of the square cutout
      ii. the width of the box in terms of the length of the side of the square cutout
   e. Define a formula that relates the total surface area, s, (measured in square inches) of the open box to the size of the square cutout x (measured in inches).
   f. There are two ways to think of determining a box's surface area: by (1) adding up the area of each piece of the box; and by (2) subtracting the area of the four cutouts from the area of the initial sheet of cardboard.
      i. Which method did you use in defining your formula in part (e)?
      ii. Define a formula to compute the box's surface area by the other method. Compare the two formulas. Are they equivalent (that is, do they always produce the same result)? Show this algebraically.

3. An open box is constructed by cutting four equal-sized square corners from a 10-inch by 13-inch sheet of cardboard and folding up the sides.

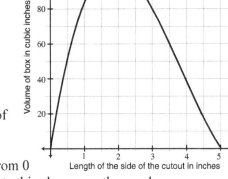

   a. Define a formula to relate the volume of the box to the length of the side of the square cutout. Be sure to define your variables.

   b. Determine the volume of the box when the length of the side of the square cutout is:
      i. 1 inch   ii. 2.5 inches   iii. 5 inches

   c. Use the graph to approximate the value(s) of the length of the side of the square cutout when the volume is:
      i.   0 in^3 ii.   100 in^3 iii.   108.4 in^3

   d. As the length of the side of the square cutout increases from 0 to 1 inch, by how much does the volume change? Illustrate this change on the graph.

   e. For what interval(s) of the cutout length is the box's volume increasing? Decreasing?

For Exercises #4-5 use the following context. *Windows, Inc. manufactures specialty windows. One of their styles is in the shape of a semicircle as shown.*

4. When a customer orders this window, they specify the length of the base of the window.

   a. Determine the total length of frame needed for a window with a base of 4 feet.

   b. Determine a formula that relates the total length of the frame to the length of the base of the window. Be sure to define your variables.

   c. If the cost of the framing material is $12 per linear foot, what is the cost of a window frame with a base-length of 4 feet?

   d. Suppose that your budget limits you to spending $500 on your window frame. What is the longest base length that you can afford?

5. Suppose that the glass pane costs $23 per square feet.

   a. What is the area of a glass pane when the base of the window is 6 feet?

   b. Write a formula that relates the area of the glass pane to the length of the base of the window. Be sure to define your variables.

   c. What is the cost of the glass pane when the base of the window is 6 feet?

   d. Suppose that your budget limits you to spending $850 on your glass pane. What is the longest base length of the window that you can afford?

   e. The total cost of the window includes both the cost of the glass pane at $23 per square foot and the cost of the window frame at $12 per linear foot. What is the total cost of a window with a base of 3 feet? (*Hint: Consider the formulas you defined in Exercises 4 and 5.*)

6. Find the value of $\dfrac{(9+x)-x^2}{2x+7}$ when $x = 3$.

7. Find the value of $\dfrac{3x^2 + x - 2(3x+5)}{2x+9}$ when $x = 8$.

8. Find the value of $\dfrac{\frac{30}{y} + \frac{49}{y+2} + \frac{100}{y^2}}{2y}$ when $y = 5$.

8. Find the value of $\dfrac{(x+4)^3 - 4y + 6xy}{-5x+6y}$ when $x = 2$ and $y = 0.5$

10. Find the value of $y\sqrt{x+4} - 3x - 7y + \frac{4x}{8}$ when $x = 12$ and $y = -4$.

11. Find the value of $\left(2(x-7)\right)^2 - \frac{y}{6}$ when $x = -2$ and $y = 54$.

II. FUNCTION RELATIONS, DOMAIN AND RANGE, AND NOTATION (TEXT: S1)

For Exercises #12-16, do the following.
   a. Determine the input quantity,
   b. Determine the output quantity,
   c. Determine if the relationship is a function. If it is, describe a possible domain and range.

12. A student's ID number with respect to the year of a student's birth.

13. The year of a student's birth in terms of the student's ID number

14. In a given apartment complex, the apartment number in terms of the number of people living in that apartment.

15. In a given apartment complex, the number of people living in that apartment in terms of the apartment number.

16. According to the information in the table, is the height of a person in terms of his/her name a function relationship? Explain your reasoning.

17. According to the information in the table, is the name of the person in terms of his/her height a function relationship? Explain your reasoning.

Person's Name	John	Mary	Sally	Michael	Dawn
Person's Height (inches)	71	63	64.5	71	68

18. For each of the given relations, determine whether y is a function of x based on the given information. Use the definition of a function to justify your answer.
   a.

x	y
1	3
2	2
1.7	4.5
2.1	9
2	1.1
5	7

   b.
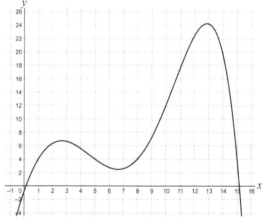

   c. $y = x(8.5 - 2x)(11 - 2x)$

   d. $y = 2^x$

   e. A manufacturing plant produces bags of plaster weighing between 0 and 90 pounds. Bags weighing up to 50 pounds are marked with a "1" (indicating that the bags can safely be carried by one person), and bags weighing more than 50 pounds are marked with a "2" (indicating that the bags are heavy and should be carried by two people). Is the number marked on the bag y a function of the weight of the bag x?

19. For each of the relations in Exercise #18, determine whether x is a function of y. Justify your answers.

20. Create two tables that represent relations between two variables that are functions. Explain why one variable is a function of the other variable.

21. Create two tables that represent relations between two variables that are NOT functions. Explain why the relationships are not functions.

Use the following functions for Exercises #22-26.

$$f(x) = 3x^2 + 5x - 7 \qquad h(x) = \frac{x}{5x - 10} \qquad k(x) = \sqrt{x + 2} \qquad n(x) = \frac{\sqrt{x - 7}}{x^2 - 4}$$

22. Evaluate each of the following expressions.
    a. $f(6)$ b. $g(-2)$ c. $k(9)$ d. $n(11)$

23. Explain the meaning of each of the following statements.
    a. $f(-3) = 5$ b. $k(17) \approx 4.36$

24. a. Explain what it means to find x such that $k(x) = 5$. (*Don't determine its value yet.*)
    b. Find the value(s) of x such that $k(x) = 5$.

25. Determine the domain of functions f and h.   26. Determine the domain of functions k and n.

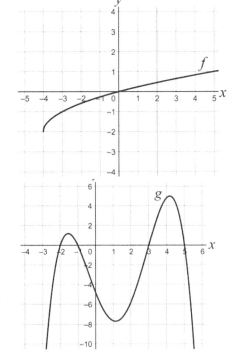

Use the graphs of f and g for Exercises #27-31.

27. Evaluate each of the following expressions. *Approximations are okay.*
    a. $f(2)$ b. $f(0)$ c. $g(0)$ d. $g(4.5)$

28. Explain the meaning of each of the following statements.
    a. $f(1) \approx 0.24$ b. $g(2.5) \approx -3$

29. a. Explain what it means to find x such that $g(x) = 4$. (Don't determine its value yet.)
    b. Find the approximate value(s) of x such that $g(x) = 4$.

30. Determine the range of f (based on the information you know from the graph).

31. Determine the range of g (based on the information you know from the graph).

32. The expression $224 - 4x^2$ calculates the surface area of a box (measured in square inches) when the box is made with a square cutout of side length x (measured in inches) from a 14" by 16" sheet of paper.
    a. Define a function g that has the length of the square cutout x as input (measured in inches) and the surface area A of the corresponding box as output (measured in square inches).
    b. Using function notation, represent the surface area of the box when the length of the side of the square cutout is 0.2 inches, 2.7 inches, and 4.1 inches. (That is, *do not* calculate the surface area. Instead *represent* the surface area determined by each length of the side of the square cutout.)
    c. What does the expression $g(1.3)$ represent?

33. The expression $\frac{4}{3}\pi r^3$ calculates the volume of a sphere (measured in cubic inches) when the radius of the sphere is r inches.
    a. Define a function h that has the radius of the sphere r as input (measured in inches) and the volume of the sphere V as output (measured in cubic inches).   *Exercise continues on the next page.*

b. Using function notation represent the volume of the sphere when the radius of the sphere is 2.4 inches, 3.1 inches, and 5.2 inches. (That is, *do not* calculate the volume. Instead *represent* the volume determined by each radius length.)

c. What does the expression $h(19.6)$ represent?

III. USING AND INTERPRETING FUNCTION NOTATION (TEXT: S3, S4)

34. The expression $224 - 4x^2$ calculates the surface area of a box (measured in square inches) when the box is made with a square cutout of side length x (measured in inches) from a 14" by 16" sheet of paper. Let g be a function that takes as its input the length of the side of the square cutout (measured in inches) and outputs the surface area of the corresponding box (measured in square inches).
    a. What does the expression $g(1.5) - g(0.5)$ <u>represent</u> in this context? What is its value?
    b. What does the expression $g(6.25) - g(2.1)$ <u>represent</u> in this context? What is its value?

35. Functions are commonly used by computer programmers to access databases. All databases that involve time have "reference times" (times they consider to be "0"). A certain database uses a function named g to access the population of Loveland, CO and uses January 1, 1990 as its reference time. So, $P = g(u)$ represents Loveland's population u years from January 1, 1990.
    a. Represent Loveland's population on 1/1/1982.
    b. Represent the change in Loveland's population from 1/1/1994 to 1/1/1997.
    c. Represent a population value 6 times as large as Loveland's population on 1/1/1972.
    d. What does $g(8) - g(-13)$ represent?
    e. What does $g(h + 3)$ represent, where h is some number of years?
    f. What does $g(h + 3) - g(3)$ represent, where h is some number of years?

36. Function h determines a dairy farmer's cost (in dollars) to produce b gallons of milk. Explain what each of the following represents in this context.
    a. $h(18)$ b. $h(b) = 25$ c. $h(15) - h(9)$ d. $h(4.3) + h(6.4)$

37. Use function notation to represent each of the following.
    a. When the input to the function q is 10, the output is 12.
    b. The output of a function h is c when the input value is 34.
    c. Function f expresses the area of a square as a function of its side length s.
        ii. The area of a square is 25m^2 when the side length is 5m.
        iii. Write an expression using the function f that represents how much larger the area of a square with side length of 6 inches is than the area of a square with side length of 2 inches.
    d. The circumference of a circle is π times as large as the circle's diameter d.
        i. Define a function g to express the circumference of the circle in terms of its diameter.
        ii. Represent the circumference of a circle with a diameter length 3 times as large as a inches.

38. The given table provides values of the circumference length C of a circle (in cm) as a function of its radius length r (in cm).
    a. What does the expression $f(1.5)$ represent? What is the numerical value of $f(1.5)$?
    b. What does the expression $f(2) - f(1.5)$ represent? What is the numerical value of $f(2) - f(1.5)$?
    c. When the radius of a circle changes from 1.5 to 2.5 cm, by how much does the circle's circumference change?
    d. Express the solution to part (c) using function notation.

radius length (cm)	circumference (cm)
r	$C = f(r)$
1	6.283
1.5	9.425
2	12.566
2.5	15.708
3	18.850

39. Given the existence of some function *b* and *k*:
    a. Use function notation to represent the change in the output value of function *k* when the input value changes from 6 to 9.
    b. Use function notation to represent the sum of the output of the function *k* at an input of –9 and the output of the function *b* at an input of 6.12

40. Use the following information to answer the questions below.
    - *C*(*t*) represents the number of cats owned by people living in the U.S. *t* years since 2000.
    - *D*(*t*) represents the number of dogs owned by people living in the U.S. *t* years since 2000.
    a. Represent the total number of cats and dogs *P*(*t*) owned by people in the U.S. *t* years since 2000.
    b. Represent, using function notation, how many *more* cats than dogs were owned by people living in the U.S. *t* years since 2000.

41. Evaluate each of the following:

    a. $f(13)$ when $f(x) = 4.5 - 6x$

    b. $f(5)$ when $f(x) = \dfrac{2x^2 + (6 - 4x)}{9 - 3x}$

    c. $g(2.6)$ when $g(x) = \dfrac{x^3 - 2.7x - 5(-2x + 4)}{-5.9 + 3.2x}$

    d. $m(-6.1)$ when $m(x) = \dfrac{(x + 4)^2 - (4.1x)^2 + 3x}{1.1 + 7x}$

42. Evaluate each of the following:

    a. $f(x + 2)$ when $f(x) = 4x^2 - 2x + 10$

    b. $h(2x)$ when $h(y) = \dfrac{y^3 - 2y^2 + 4}{2y}$

IV. Function Composition: Chaining Together Two Function Processes (Text: S5)

43. Alejandra bought a new house recently and is planning to install landscaping next week. In her initial budget, she set aside $200 to purchase ¾-inch gravel to cover part of her yard. This size gravel covers approximately 130 square feet per ton. She has four different options for this size gravel depending on the quality of the gravel. In addition to the gravel cost the company charges $59 for delivery.

¾-inch gravel type	Cost per ton (in dollars)
Grade A	$31.50
Grade B	$26.50
Grade C	$24.50
Grade D	$22.50

    a. i. How many tons of grade B gravel can Alejandra afford if she must pay the $59 delivery charge?
       ii. How many tons of grade D gravel can Alejandra afford if she must pay the $59 delivery charge?
    b. How many square feet of her yard can she cover with grade C gravel? Explain your thinking.
    c. How many square feet of her yard can she cover with grade A gravel? Grades B, C, or D?

44. Reggie, a college student, works part-time during the school year. He has to budget his expenditures so that he has enough money at the end of the month to cover his rent, car payment, and insurance. Currently, Reggie can only afford $15 per week for gas.

Price of fuel (in dollars per gallon)	Number of gallons of fuel Reggie can purchase for $15
3.199	
3.499	
3.599	
3.799	
p	

    a. As the price of gas fluctuates, the amount of gas Reggie can purchase each week varies. Complete the table of values showing the number of gallons of gas Reggie can purchase with $15 at the given fuel prices.
    b. Reggie's car gets an average of 28 miles per gallon. How many miles can he drive in a week if he purchases 3 gallons of fuel? 4.18 gallons? *g* gallons?

Exercise continues on the next page.

c. Explain how you can determine the number of miles Reggie can drive in a week if gas costs $3.899 per gallon and he has $15 to spend on gas.

d. Complete the table of values relating the price of fuel (in dollars per gallon) and the number of miles Reggie can drive on $15 worth of gas.

e. How many miles can Reggie drive on $15 worth of gas if gas costs p dollars per gallon?

Price of fuel (in dollars per gallon)	Number of miles Reggie can drive on $15 worth of gas
3.299	
3.449	
3.579	
3.839	

45. Jessie does a lot of traveling for business. When he travels he likes to go for a run in the morning to keep fit. Jessie has noticed that the elevation of the city he is visiting impacts how long he is able to spend running since there is less oxygen available at higher elevations. The graphs below provide information about Jessie's exercise routines recorded over many business trips.

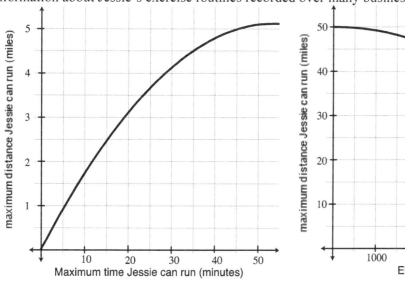 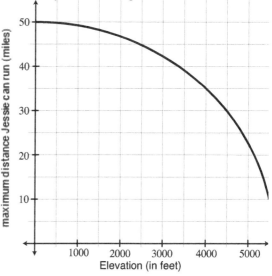

a. Describe how to determine the maximum distance Jessie can run if he is visiting a city with an elevation of 4000 feet.

b. Explain how you can determine the elevation of the city Jessie is visiting if he expects his maximum running distance to be 5 miles.

46. A ball is thrown into a lake, creating a circular ripple with a radius length that increases 7 cm per second. We want to express the circle's area in terms of the time elapsed since the ball hit the lake.

a. Draw a diagram of the situation.

b. Identify the quantities in the situation whose values vary and state what units you'll use to measure each of these quantities. Repeat for quantities whose values are fixed.

c. As the amount of time t in seconds since the ball hit the lake increases over each of the given time periods, how does the radius r of the ripple (in centimeters) change?
   i.   from $t = 0$ to 3 seconds   ii.   from $t = 4$ to 6 seconds   iii.   from $t = 6$ to 6.5 seconds

d. Define a function g that defines the radius r of the ripple in terms of the time t in seconds since the ball hit the water.

e. Define a functions f that determines the area of the ripple A in terms of the time t in seconds since the ball hit the water.

f. Define a composite function h that expresses the area of the circle as a function of the time elapsed since the ball struck the water.

g. Describe the meaning of $h(2.3)$ without performing any calculations. Then calculate and interpret the meaning of the value of this expression.

© 2018 Carlson, Oehrtman, and Moore

47. When hiring a contractor to add insulation to your attic, he provides you with information that you convert into tables specifying how input and output values are related for two functions, f and g.

Function f		Function g	
Number of bags of insulation applied, n	Depth of insulation (inches), $f(n)$	Depth of insulation (inches), d	Estimated annual heating/cooling costs (dollars), $g(d)$
11	2	15	$940
20	3.6	13	$1,000
28	5	11	$1,100
40	7.2	9	$1,250
50	9	7	$1,500
61	11	5	$1,900
70	12.6	4	$2,750
78	14	3	$3,600

  a. Describe the meaning of $g(11)$.
  b. Does the expression $f(g(11))$ have a real-world meaning in this context? If so, find the value and explain its meaning. If not, explain your reasoning.
  c. Does the expression $g(f(11))$ have a real world-meaning in this context? If so, find the value and explain its meaning. If not, explain your reasoning.
  d. Solve the equation $g(f(n)) = 1900$ for n and explain the meaning of your solution.
  e. Function T is defined as follows: $T(n) = g(f(n))$. Use the diagram to the right to describe what each of the parts (A, B, C, D, and E) of the definition represents. $\quad T(n) = g(f(n))$

48. Suppose you have a coupon for $10 off a purchase of $100 or more at Better Buys.
  a. Define a function C that determines the final cost of a purchase after applying the coupon if x is the original price (in dollars). Explain what the expression $C(215.83)$ represents.
  b. What are the domain and range of the function C?
  c. This weekend only Better Buys has a customer appreciation sale that offers 5% off all purchases. Define a function T that determines the final cost of a customer's purchase after the sale if the original purchase price is p dollars. (Do not include the coupon in this function rule.)
  d. Suppose Better Buys will allow you to use both the sale and the coupon together. If you buy a television set that is priced at $1979.99, describe what the expression $C(T(1979.99))$ represents and determine its value.

49. An oil tanker crashed into a reef off of the coast of Alaska, grounding the tanker and punching a hole in its hull. The tanker's oil radiated out from the tanker in a circular pattern. You are an engineer for the oil company and your task is to monitor the spill.
  a. Draw a diagram of the situation.
  b. What are the varying quantities in this situation? Define variables to represent the values of the varying quantities. Be sure to include the units of measure when defining the variables.
  c. If the oil tanker was 105 feet from the spill's outer edge exactly 24 hours after the spill, how much area (in square miles) did the spill cover at that time.
  d. News reporters want to know how much oil has spilled at any given time. The only information available to you is satellite photos that include the spill's radius (in feet). You also know that 7.5 gallons of oil creates 4 square feet of spill.
      i. Define a function g that expresses the number of gallons of oil spilled, x, in terms of the area of the oil spill, A, (in square feet).
      ii. Define a function, f, that expresses the number of gallons of oil spilled in terms of the spill's radius (in miles).
  e. Use your function from part (c(ii)) to represent the increase in the number of gallons spilled as the radius of the oil spill increases from 121 feet to 152 feet.

50. Given $f(x) = 2x + 1$ and $g(x) = x^2 + 2x + 1$, complete the following.
    a. Fill in the first two tables and use these two tables to complete the third table.

x	$f(x)$
0	
1	
1.5	
2	
5	

x	$g(x)$

x	$g(f(x))$
0	
1	
1.5	
2	
5	

    b. Describe how you used the first two tables to determine the values of the third table.

51. Use the given tables to answer the following questions
    a. Evaluate the following expressions:

        i. $g(f(-2))$ ii. $f(g(0))$

        iii. $g(g(4))$ iv. $f(g(2))$

        v. $g(f(-1))$ vi. $f(f(0))$

    b. Solve the equation $g(f(x)) = -10$ for x.

    c. Solve the equation $f(g(x)) = 16$ for x.

x	$f(x)$
−4	16
−3	13
−2	6
−1	0
0	−4
1	−7
2	−9
3	−10

x	$g(x)$
−8	−20
−6	−17
−4	−10
−2	−4
0	−1
2	2
4	6
6	11

52. Use the words *input* and *output* to express the meaning of the following expressions. Assume that g and h are functions.
    a. $h(g(2))$ b. $g(g(3))$ c. $g(h(x+1))$

53. The functions f, g, and h (given below) are used to define the functions s, r, and v. Re-write the definitions of s, r, and v so that their definitions do not involve function composition.

$$f(x) = \frac{2x+1}{x-3} \qquad g(x) = x^2 - 7 \qquad h(x) = -3x + 2$$

    a. $s(x) = f(g(x))$ b. $r(x) = h(h(x))$ c. $v(x) = g(h(x))$

54. The functions g, h, and k are defined below. Use these functions to answer the questions that follow.

$$g(x) = x + 5$$

x	$h(x)$
−1	−13.4
0	−7.3
2	−4.4
4	3
5	6.8
6	15
8	22

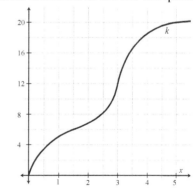

    a. $k(g(0))$ b. $h(k(1.5))$ c. $g(h(2))$ d. $k(h(4))$

    e. Solve the equation $h(g(x)) = 22$ for x.

    f. Solve the equation $g(k(x)) = 17$ for x.

55. Use the graphs below to answer the questions that follow

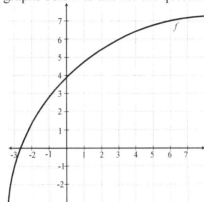 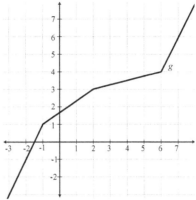

    a. Approximate the value of each of the following expressions.
        i. $f(f(3))$ ii. $g(f(6))$ iii. $g(g(-2))$ iv. $g(f(-3))$
    b. Find the value of x that satisfies each of the following equations.
        i. $f(g(x)) = 6$ ii. $g(f(x)) = 4$

56. Functions g and r are defined by their graphs to the right.
    a. Determine the values of each of the following expressions:
        i. $r(g(2))$ ii. $g(r(1))$ iii. $r(r(6))$ iv. $g(r(-2))$
    b. How does the output $g(r(x))$ vary as x varies from 1 to 3?

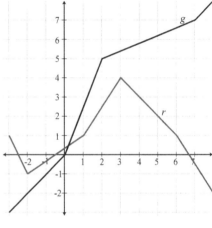

57. For each of the functions defined below, redefine that function in terms of two new functions, f and g, using function composition and function arithmetic. *For example, $f(x) = (2x)^3$ can be defined as $f(x) = h(g(x))$ if $g(x) = 2x$ and $h(x) = x^3$.*
    a. $h(x) = 3(x-1) + 5$ b. $m(x) = (x+4)^2$
    c. $k(x) = (x+2)^2 + 3(x+2) + 1$ d. $j(x) = \sqrt{x-1}$
                                                e. $p(x) = \frac{500}{100 - x^2}$

V: Extra Practice with Function Composition (TEXT: S5)

58. The standard formula for determining temperature in degrees Fahrenheit when given the temperature in degrees Celsius is $F = \frac{9}{5}C + 32$. We can write this formula using function notation by letting $F = g(C)$ and writing $g(C) = \frac{9}{5}C + 32$. The function g defines a process for converting a temperature measure in degrees Celsius to degrees Fahrenheit.
    a. State the meaning of $g(100)$ and evaluate $g(100)$.
    b. Solve the equation $g(C) = 212$ and explain how you arrived at your answer.
    c. Define a function h that converts temperature measures in degrees Fahrenheit to the corresponding measure in degrees Celsius. (*Hint: Generalize the steps you described in part (b) that reversed the process of g. You can also solve $F = \frac{9}{5}C + 32$ for C.*)
    d. State the meaning of $h(212)$ and evaluate $h(212)$.
    e. Determine the values of $g(h(212))$ and $h(g(100))$ <u>without performing any calculations</u>. What do you notice about the relationship between g and h?   *Exercise continues on the next page.*

f. Represent the value of $g(h(n))$. Represent the value of $h(g(k))$. What do you notice about the relationship between g and h?

g. Use function notation to represent the relationship between functions g and h based on your answers to (e) and (f).

59. A spherical bubble inflates so that its volume increases by a constant rate of 120 cm³ per second.
    a. Define a function f that expresses the radius of the bubble, r, (in centimeters) as a function of the bubble's volume, V, (in cubic centimeters). (*Note: The volume of a sphere is $V = \frac{4}{3}\pi r^3$*).
    b. Define a function g that expresses the bubble's volume, V, (in cubic centimeters) as a function of the number of seconds, t, since the bubble began to inflate.
    c. Use your functions from (a) and (b) to define a function h that expresses the bubble's radius, r (in centimeters) as a function of the number of seconds, t, since the bubble began to inflate.
    d. Use function notation to represent the change in the bubble's radius as the number of seconds since the ball began to inflate increases from 5 to 5.3 seconds.

60. A farmer decides to build a fence to enclose a rectangular field in which he will plant a crop. He has 1000 feet of fence to use and his goal is to maximize the area of his field.
    a. Draw a diagram that shows the quantities in this situation. Label the changing quantities with variables, and then explain what each variable represents in terms of the situation. (e.g., define each quantity and its unit of measure).
    b. What are the dimensions of the enclosed field if one side must be 200 feet? What are the dimensions of the enclosed field if one side must be 352.41 feet?
    c. Determine a formula that defines the length of the field l in terms of the field's width w given that the total amount of fence is 1000 feet. width   length
    d. Describe how the length of the field changes as the width of the field increases.
    e. Determine a formula that relates the length and width of the field to the total area of the enclosed field.
    f. Using parts (c) and (e), define a function f that expresses the area of the field (measured in square feet) as a function of the length of the side of the field l (measured in feet).
    g. Create a graph that represents the area of the enclosed field in terms of the length of the side of the field. Describe how the area of the enclosed field changes as the length of the side of the field increases.
    h. Based on your graph, what is the maximum area of the enclosed field? What are the dimensions of the enclosed field that create this maximum area?

61. Janet works 36 hours a week between two part-time jobs during the semester: residence hall front desk assistant ($7.50 per hour) and supermarket cashier ($9.25 per hour).
    a. Let r represent the number of hours Janet works in a given week as a residence hall front desk assistant. Write a formula to calculate the value of s, the number of hours Janet works as a supermarket cashier the same week.
    b. Define a function f that calculates the amount of money Janet makes for working r hours as a resident hall front desk assistant and then define a function g that calculates the amount of money Janet makes as a supermarket cashier working r *hours as a residence hall front desk assistant.*
    c. Define a function T that calculates the total amount of money Janet makes in a given week if she is working both jobs and works r hours at the residence hall front desk.
    d. The supermarket requires Janet to work between 15 and 30 hours each week. What is the domain of function T? What is the range of function T?

62. You are planning a trip to Japan where the currency is the yen. On your way to Japan you will stop in Italy where the currency is the euro. You know that you will need to convert your US dollars to euros before your trip and know that the number of euros is 0.78 times as large the number of dollars. You also know the number of yen is 103 times as large as number of dollars.
    a. Write a formula that expresses the number of yen, y, you will have if you begin with d dollars.
    b. Write a formula that expresses the number of euro, e, you will have if you begin with d dollars
    c. You know that you will not be converting from dollars to yen because you will first stop in Italy. So it would be more helpful to know the conversion rate between euros and yen. Write a function g that expresses the number of yen you will have, y, in terms of the number of euros you convert.

63. The length of a steel bar changes as the temperature changes. Consider a 10-meter steel bar that is placed outside in the morning when the temperature is 20 degrees Celsius. Let l represent the length of a steel bar in meters. Let t be the temperature of the steel bar in degrees Celsius. And let n be the number of minutes since you placed the bar outside. You are given the following relationships: $l = 0.00013(t - 20) + 10$ and $n = 12t - 240$. Write a function f that gives the length of the bar, l, (in meters) in terms of the number of minutes elapsed, n, since the bar was placed outside.

64. Let $n = 240s + 123$ and let $t = 0.14s^2$. Write a function h that gives n in terms of t.

65. Let $160 = 2t + 4m$ and let $p = \frac{1}{4}tm^2$. Write a function k that gives p in terms of t.

VI. INVERSE FUNCTIONS: REVERSING THE PROCESS (TEXT: S6)

In Exercises #66-68, do the following.
    a. Describe the function process (for example, "the input is increased by 2 and then tripled").
    b. Describe the process that undoes the function (for example, if f is a process that increases its input by 7, the process that undoes f will decrease its input by 7).
    c. Algebraically define a process that undoes the process of the given function – that is, define the inverse function for each of the given functions.

66. $f(x) = \frac{7}{5}x$ 67. $g(x) = 10 + x$ 68. $h(x) = \frac{x}{12}$

69. a. Define algebraically a process f that multiplies its input by 3, and then decreases this result by 1.
    b. Describe the process that undoes the process of f described in part (a).
    c. Algebraically define the process f^{-1} that undoes the process of f that is described in part (a).

70. Given the function f defined by $f(x) = 3x + 2$,
    a. Define f^{-1}, the function that undoes the process of f.
    b. Show that $f\left(f^{-1}(x)\right) = x$ for the function f that is given above.
    c. Show that $f^{-1}\left(f(x)\right) = x$ for the function f that is given above.
    d. What do you conclude about the relationship between f and f^{-1}

71. Given $g(x) = 14x - 9$, what are the value(s) of the input x when $g(x) = 109$?

72. Given $h(x) = \frac{1}{6}x^2 + 7$, what are the value(s) of the input x when $h(x) = 31$?

73. Given that $h(x) = 4x$ determines the perimeter of a square given a square's side length x
   a. Algebraically define h^{-1} and describe its input quantity, output quantity, and process.
   b. Describe the input quantity, function process, and output quantity for $h\left(h^{-1}(x)\right)$.

74. Assume that g and z are functions that have inverse functions. Use the words *input* and *output* to express the meaning of the following expressions.
   a. $g^{-1}(21)$
   b. $z^{-1}(32) = 43$

In Exercises #75-78, find the inverse of each given function. Then, determine if the inverse that you found is a function. Justify your answer.

75. $g(x) = 2x + 4$ 76. $h(x) = 2x^3 - 6$ 77. $k(x) = \frac{1}{2}x^2 + 12$ 78. $m(x) = \frac{2}{x+3}$

79. After Julia had driven for half an hour, she was 155 miles from Denver. After driving 2 hours, she was 260 miles from Denver. Assume that Julia drove at a constant speed. Let f be a function that gives Julia's distance in miles from Denver after having driven for t hours.
   a. Determine a rule for the function f.
   b. Interpret the meaning of $f^{-1}(500)$ and then find its value.
   c. Determine a rule for f^{-1}.
   d. Construct a graph for $f^{-1}(d)$.

80. The functions f and g are defined in the given table. Based on this table, complete the following.

x	-3	-2	-1	0	1	2	3
$f(x)$	9	2	6	-4	-5	-8	-9
$g(x)$	3	0	3	2	-3	-1	-5

   a. Is f^{-1} a function? Explain why or why not.
   b. Is g^{-1} a function? Explain why or why not.
   c. Evaluate the following expressions:
      i. $f^{-1}(-9)$ ii. $g(3)$ iii. $f(g(2))$ iv. $f^{-1}(2)$ v. $f^{-1}(g(3))$ vi. $g(f^{-1}(-4))$

79. The graphical representation of the functions g and h are given. Use this information to complete the following.
   a. As x increases from 0 to 5, how does $g(x)$ change? Be specific.
   b. As x increases from 0 to 4.5, how does $h(x)$ change?
   c. Use the graphs above to evaluate the following:
      i. $g^{-1}(2)$ ii. $g^{-1}(h(2))$ iii. $g(h^{-1}(4))$
   d. Is the inverse to h a function?

80. Given the functions $f(y) = \frac{3}{2}y + 21$ and $g(x) = 2x + 1$, answer the following questions.
   a. Determine f^{-1} and explain how f^{-1} relates to f in terms of the input values and output values of each function.
   b. Find $g^{-1}(g(2))$. Find $g^{-1}(g(3.5))$.
   c. What pattern do you observe about $g^{-1}(g(x))$? Explain.   *Exercise continues on the next page.*

© 2018 Carlson, Oehrtman, and Moore

d. Determine the composite function $f(g(x))$ and explain, using input-output language, the meaning of the function $f(g(x))$ relative to the functions f and g.

e. Considering the description of the function $f(g(x))$ given in part (d), describe the inverse of this function. Justify whether $f^{-1}(g^{-1}(x))$ or $g^{-1}(f^{-1}(x))$ is the proper notation for representing this function's inverse, and then determine the rule of the chosen function.

f. What are the domain and range of the function f?

81. Apply the ideas of function inverse and function composition to answer each of the following.
    a. Define the area of a square A in terms of its perimeter p.
    b. Define the diameter of a circle d in terms of its circumference C.

82. Apply the ideas of function inverse and/or function composition to answer each of the following.
    a. Define the perimeter of a square p in terms of its area A.
    b. If the radius of a circle is growing at 8 cm per second, define the area of a circle A in terms of the amount of time t since the radius was 0 cm and started growing.
    c. Define the diameter of a circle d in terms of its area A.

This investigation contains review and practice with important skills and procedures you may need in this module and future modules. Your instructor may assign this investigation as an introduction to the module or may ask you to complete select exercises "just in time" to help you when needed. Alternatively, you can complete these exercises on your own to help review important skills.

Meaning of Exponents
Use this section prior to the module or with/after Investigation 1.

Exponents are used to represent the number of identical factors in a product. For example, in the product $5 \cdot 5 \cdot 7 \cdot 7 \cdot 7$, the factor 5 appears twice and the factor 7 appears three times. Thus:

$$5 \cdot 5 \cdot 7 \cdot 7 \cdot 7 \text{ is equivalent to } 5^2 \cdot 7^3$$

Here are a few more examples. Note that each column represents the same value in three different forms (product notation, exponential notation, and decimal notation).

product notation	$4 \cdot 4 \cdot 4 \cdot 4 \cdot 4$	$2 \cdot 2 \cdot 2 \cdot 2 \cdot 5 \cdot 5 \cdot 5$	$7 \cdot 6 \cdot 4 \cdot 6 \cdot 7$
exponential notation	4^5	$2^4 \cdot 5^3$	$4 \cdot 6^2 \cdot 7^2$
decimal notation	1,024	2,000	7,056

In Exercises #1-3, rewrite each product in exponential and decimal notation.

1. $2 \cdot 6 \cdot 7 \cdot 7 \cdot 6 \cdot 6$
2. $4 \cdot 5 \cdot 5 \cdot 4 \cdot 4 \cdot 4 \cdot 4$
3. $5 \cdot 5 \cdot 5 \cdot 5 \cdot 5 \cdot 3 \cdot 7$

It's important to realize that exponents do <u>not</u> have to be whole numbers. It is possible to evaluate a^b where b is not a whole number. Use a calculator to evaluate each of the expressions in Exercises #4-6. Round your answers to three decimal places.

4. $8^{4.3}$
5. $256^{0.5}$
6. $80^{1.715}$

Even if you don't have a calculator, you should be able to estimate the value of exponential expressions with non-whole number exponents. For example, $2^{4.7}$ must be between 16 and 32 because $2^4 = 16$ and $2^5 = 32$. In Exercises #7-10 estimate the value of each exponential expression by giving two whole number values between which the value must fall.

7. $3^{3.4}$
8. $10^{2.5}$
9. $7^{0.8}$
10. $4^{-1.9}$

The same number can be represented in terms of ANY base we choose. For example, consider the number 64. Each of the following exponential expressions represents a value of 64. *Take a moment to verify this.*

$$2^6 \quad 4^3 \quad 8^2 \quad 64^1 \quad 4{,}096^{1/2} \quad 16{,}777{,}216^{1/4}$$

However, the following expressions ALSO represent a value of 64 (up to a small rounding error). *Take a moment to verify this.*

$$3^{3.78558} \quad 5^{2.58406} \quad 10^{1.80618} \quad 15^{1.53575} \quad 28^{1.24809} \quad 100^{0.90309}$$

11. Which of the following exponential expressions also represent a value of 64 (up to a small rounding error)? Select all that apply.
    a. $3^{3.4}$
    b. $10^{2.5}$
    c. $7^{0.8}$
    d. $4^{-1.9}$

12. Group the following exponential expressions based on their values (up to a small rounding error).
    a. $3^{3.72683}$
    b. $12^{1.50415}$
    c. $46^{1.02178}$
    d. $15^{1.44459}$

    e. $10^{1.77815}$
    f. $50^{0.95543}$
    g. $80^{0.89274}$
    h. $215^{0.76236}$

Properties of Exponents
Use this section prior to the module or with/after Investigation 2.

The following box shows the most common exponent properties we use to rewrite expressions.

Exponent Properties

For any real numbers a, b, m, and n, the following properties hold.

Product Rule: $a^m \cdot a^n = a^{m+n}$ **Quotient Rule:** $\dfrac{a^m}{a^n} = a^{m-n}$ (if $a \neq 0$)

Power Rule: $(a^m)^n = a^{m \cdot n}$ **Distributive Property:** $(ab)^m = a^m \cdot b^m$

Zero Exponent Rule: $a^0 = 1$ (if $a \neq 0$)   **Negative Exponent Rule:** $a^{-m} = \dfrac{1}{a^m}$ (if $a \neq 0$)

---

13. Write out each of the following in expanded form to demonstrate why the product rule $a^m \cdot a^n = a^{m+n}$ is true. *For example, $3^2 \cdot 3^4$ would be written as $3 \cdot 3 \cdot 3 \cdot 3 \cdot 3 \cdot 3$ in expanded form.*

14. Write out each of the following in expanded form to demonstrate why the product rule $(a^m)^n = a^{m \cdot n}$ is true.

15. Write out each of the following in expanded form to demonstrate why the product rule $(a^m)^n = a^{m \cdot n}$ is true.

16. Use the quotient rule as well as the expanded form of the following expressions to demonstrate why it makes sense that $a^0 = 1$.

In Exercises #17-28, use the exponent properties to rewrite each of the following using only positive exponents.

17. $\left(x^7\right)^3$

18. $(xy)^4\left(xy^2\right)$

19. $\left(r^2t\right)^3$

20. $\left(2h^3\right)\left(6h^2\right)$

21. $\left(x^3y^{-4}\right)\left(x^5y^2\right)$

22. $\left(p^2z^{-4}\right)^3$

23. $\left(a^4y\right)^2\left(a^5\right)^0$

24. $\left(4d^{-2}\right)\left(3n\right)^6$

25. $\dfrac{21x^{12}y}{x^7y}$

26. $\dfrac{14a^5p^2}{7ap^2}$

27. $\dfrac{x^4y^{10}z^3}{x^2y^5z^6}$

28. $\dfrac{9x^3y^4z^5}{12x^7y^3z^{11}}$

Solving Equations Involving Integer Exponents

Use this section prior to the module or with/after Investigation 4.

Consider an equation like $4x^3 + 9 = 35$. The solution is the value of x such that $f(x) = 4x^3 + 9$ outputs a value of 35.

$$4x^3 + 9 = 35$$
$$4x^3 = 26 \qquad \bullet \text{ subtract } 9$$
$$x^3 = 6.5 \qquad \bullet \text{ divide by } 4$$
$$x = \sqrt[3]{6.5}$$

The solution is $x = \sqrt[3]{6.5}$, or $x \approx 1.86626$.

In Exercises #29-32, solve each equation.

29. $2x^3 - 110 = 140$

30. $2(x^3 + 13) = -28$

31. $\frac{1}{2}x^5 - 20 = -1$

32. $3(x^5 - 8) + 10 = -182$

In Exercises #29-32 all of the exponents were odd integers. This is convenient because it created no doubt about the solution. If $x^3 = 64$, then $x = 4$ since $(4)^3 = 64$. If $x^3 = -64$, then $x = -4$ since $(-4)^3 = -64$. If the exponent is even this is not the case. For example, if $x^2 = 25$, then the solutions are $x = 5$ and $x = -5$ because $(5)^2 = 25$ AND $(-5)^2 = 25$. Therefore, if the exponent is even we have to consider that there are two possible solutions to the equation. For example, let's solve the equation $3x^4 - 10 = 7$.

$$3x^4 - 10 = 7$$
$$3x^4 = 17 \qquad \bullet \text{ add } 10$$
$$x^4 = \tfrac{17}{3} \qquad \bullet \text{ divide by } 3$$
$$x = \pm\sqrt[4]{\tfrac{17}{3}}$$

The solutions are both $x = \sqrt[4]{\tfrac{17}{3}}$ AND $x = -\sqrt[4]{\tfrac{17}{3}}$. Note that mathematicians often combine these two solutions into one statement by writing $x = \pm\sqrt[4]{\tfrac{17}{3}}$. It's important to recognize that "$\pm$" is indicating two different values for x.

In Exercises #33-36, solve each equation.

33. $\tfrac{1}{2}(x^2 + 5) = 82$
34. $3x^2 - 13 = 41$
35. $2x^4 + 25 = 187$
36. $\tfrac{1}{4}x^6 - 5 = 5$

Solving Equations Involving Variable Exponents (without Logarithms)
Use this section prior to the module or with/after Investigation 5.

The previous two sections were based on solving equations involving power expressions (monomials). But sometimes we have equations where the exponent is unknown. For example, consider the equation $2 \cdot 3^x - 52 = 110$. Its solution is the value of x such that $2(3)^x - 52$ has a value of 110.

We start the solution process as shown.

$$2 \cdot 3^x - 52 = 110$$
$$2 \cdot 3^x = 162 \qquad \bullet \text{ add } 52$$
$$3^x = 81 \qquad \bullet \text{ divide by } 2$$

At this point we have no algebraic method for solving the equation. However, if you know your powers of 3, then you know (or can easily verify) that $3^4 = 81$. So the solution is $x = 4$.

If we instead ended up with something like $5^x = 112$, then for now we can estimate that the solution would be between $x = 2$ and $x = 3$ because $5^2 = 25$ and $5^3 = 125$.

In Exercises #41-44, solve each equation. If the solution is not an integer, then provide the two consecutive integers between which the answer must fall.

41. $3(2^x - 14) = 54$
42. $\tfrac{1}{2}(3^x) + 17 = 52$
43. $16(4^x) + 10 = 11$
44.

$6(3^x) - 2 = 28$

> ### Percentage
> A *percentage* refers to a type of measurement where the measurement unit is a specific value of some quantity. To be exact, **1% is $\frac{1}{100}$ of the value of the reference quantity**.

*1. On one day during a recent trip you drove 340 miles. If we use 340 miles as our reference, then "1% of the distance you drove on that day" corresponds to $\frac{1}{100}$ of 340 miles.

$$\underline{\hspace{3cm}\text{340 miles}\hspace{6cm}}$$

⊢
1% of 340 miles, or
$\frac{1}{100}$ times as large as 340 miles

   a. What distance corresponds to 1% of the distance you drove on that day?

   b. To find the distance in miles in part (a), we can multiply 340 miles by what number?

   c. If you had driven 1% of the 340 miles, what percent of the total distance do you still have left to drive? What is this distance in miles?

   d. To find the distance in miles in part (c), we can multiply 340 miles by what number?

*2. a. What distance corresponds to 36% of the distance you drove on that day?

   b. To find the distance in miles in part (a), we can multiply 340 miles by what number?

   c. If you had driven 36% of the 340 miles, what percent of the total distance do you still have left to drive? What is this distance in miles?

   d. To find the distance in miles in part (c), we can multiply 340 miles by what number?

*3. In order to make room for next year's models, a car dealership reduced the price of all new cars on their lot. One car that used to cost $24,995 now costs $22,355.

new price: $22,355
_____

old price: $24,995
_____

Suppose we use the old price as a "measuring stick" to measure the new price as shown.
   a. How many times as large is the new price as the old price?

   b. *Fill in the blank*: "The new price is _____% of the old price."

*4. Siblings Sydney, Michael and Alexis each want to set up their own lemonade stand in their front yard. Sydney, the oldest, decides to charge 50 cents per cup. Michael decides to copy his older sister's price and also charge 50 cents per cup. Alexis, the youngest, decides to charge $1.50 per cup.

Sydney: 50 cents = 0.5 dollars   _____

Michael: 50 cents = 0.5 dollars   _____

Alexis: 150 cents = 1.5 dollars   _____

  a. Compare the prices charged by Sydney and Michael.
     i.   How many times as large is Sydney's price as Michael's price?

     ii.   *Fill in the blank*: "Sydney's price is _____% of Michael's price."

  b. Compare the prices charged by Alexis and Sydney.
     i.   How many times as large is Alexis's price as Sydney's price?

     ii.   *Fill in the blank*: "Alexis's price is _____% of Sydney's price."

  c. Compare the prices charged by Sydney and Alexis.
     i.   How many times as large is Sydney's price as Alexis's price?

     ii.   *Fill in the blank*: "Sydney's price is _____% of Alexis's price."

When working with percentages, it's important to recognize that a constant percent does NOT represent a constant amount if the quantity being considered varies.

For example, if there is a sale for "30% off" the retail price of any item, the actual discount amount (in dollars) is different for different prices even though the discount is <u>always</u> 30%.

retail price is $75
_____

discount is $22.50
_____

retail price is $49   retail price is $26
_____   _____

discount is $14.70   discount is $7.80
____   ___

the discount is 30% in each case

5. For each price and discount given, find the value of the discount in dollars.
  a. price was $114, discount is 20%   b. price was $28, discount is 45%

*6. For each price and price increase given, find the value of the increase in dollars.
  a. price was $52, increase is 35%   b. price was $199, increase is 215%

Percent Change

Percent change refers to the *difference* between two values of a quantity, measured as a percentage of the "starting" value.

For example, if the price of an item was $50 and increased to $59, then we can say the following.
- The change in price is $9.
- The percent change from the old price to the new price is $\frac{9}{50}$, or $\frac{18}{100}$, or 18% of the old price.
- The new price is $59, which is 118% of the old price of $50.

Note that it's common (and good practice) to describe a *decrease* as a negative change. For example, if the original price of an item was $80 and decreased to $62, then we can say the following.

- The change in price is –$18.

- The percent change from the original price to the new price is $-\frac{18}{80}$, or –0.225, or $-\frac{22.5}{100}$, or
  –22.5% of the original price.

- The new price is $62, which is 87.5% of the original price.

---

*7. You walk into a store that is having a sale. For each sale described, do the following.
   i) State the percent change in the price.
   ii) State the number we can multiply the original price by to find the sale price.
   iii) Find the sale price in dollars.

   a. original price: $150, sale: 40% off

   b. original price: $19, sale: 10% off

   c. original price: $915.99, sale: 15% off

   d. original price: $22.99, sale: 12.5% off

*8. A store needs to raise prices on some of its items. For each price change described, do the following.
   i) State the percent change in the price.
   ii) State the number we can multiply the original price by to find the new price.
   iii) Find the new price in dollars.

   a. original price: $52, increase: 10%

   b. original price: $13, increase: 50%

c. original price: $14.99, increase: 2.3%   d. original price: $1,499.99, increase: 100%

9. In 2010 an investment was worth $12,000. By 2015, the investment had lost 20% of its value (a
    percent change of –20%).
    a. What was the value of the investment by 2015?

    b. The investor wants the value of the investment to return to its 2010 value within the next 3 years.
        Determine the percent change necessary for her investment to return to its previous value.

*10. You bought a pair of jeans on sale for $18, which was discounted 25% from the normal
      retail price. What is the normal retail price?

*11. A new company expanded rapidly and doubled the number of its employees every month over the
      last year.
      a. *Fill in the blank*: The number of employees in one month was _____% of the number of
          employees in the previous month.

      b. What was the percent change in the number of employees from one month to the next?

*12. A motion picture company released the new trailer for an upcoming movie yesterday. Today, its
     website received 5 times as many visitors as it did yesterday.
     a. What was the percent change in the number of visitors from yesterday to today?

     b. *Fill in the blank*: The number of visitors today was _____% of the number of visitors yesterday.

When examining situations with varying quantities, we typically want to identify pairs of quantities that change together (co-vary). When we identify such a pair, our next goal is to understand *how* their values change together and, if possible, to identify patterns in the relationship. In other words, when studying co-varying relationships we want to identify what stays the same while the quantities change.

In a previous module we closely examined ***linear functions***. A linear relationship exists when two quantities' values change together with a ***constant rate of change***. In such a relationship the two quantities' values are free to vary, but they must do so in such a way that the ratio of their changes $\frac{\Delta y}{\Delta x}$ is a constant. But not all co-varying relationships exhibit a constant rate of change. In this investigation we will encounter examples of a different type of relationship and identify what remains the same as two quantities co-vary.

For Exercises #1-5, use the following information. When a piece of new technology is invented and sold, its value decreases over time because it wears down and because even newer, better technology is developed to replace it. Suppose two electronic devices have the same resale value right now and that their resale values are expected to change according to the following patterns.

- **Product #1: iTech Device** The current resale value is $300. The resale value is expected to decrease 30% per year for the next several years.
- **Product #2: Dynasystems Device** The current resale value is $300. The resale value is expected to decrease $45 per year for the next several years.

*1. a. Find the expected resale value (in dollars) for both devices 1 year from now and describe how you determined each value.

b. Without performing additional calculations, predict which device will have a greater resale value 6 years from now.

c. Complete the given table showing the expected resale value for each device over the next 6 years.

Δt	Years from now, t	Expected resale value for the iTech Device, s (dollars)	Δs		Δt	Years from now, t	Expected resale value for the Dynasystems Device, n (dollars)	Δn
	0	300				0	300	
	1					1		
	2					2		
	3					3		
	4					4		
	5					5		
	6					6		

d. Check your prediction from part (b) by using the table in part (c).

e. The table on the left demonstrates how the expected resale value for the iTech Device co-varies with elapsed time. What stays the same as these two quantities' values change together?

f. The table on the right demonstrates how the expected resale value for the Dynasystems Device co-varies with elapsed time. What stays the same as these two quantities' values change together?

*2. a. Define function formulas to model the expected resale value in dollars for each device as functions of the number of years from now, t.

iTech Device: $s = f(t)$; where $f(t) =$ _____

Dynasystems Device: $n = g(t)$; where $g(t) =$ _____

b. Explain what each part of the formulas represents relative to the context we are exploring.

3. Find and interpret the following using your functions from Exercise #2.
   a. $f(4)$ b. $g(3)$

   c. $g(6) - g(2)$ d. $f^{-1}(147)$

*4. In Exercise #1, the table on the left has a column showing values of $s = f(t)$ (the expected resale value for the iTech Device in dollars) as well as a column showing values of Δs (the change in the expected resale value for the iTech Device in dollars).

    a. What are the ratios of consecutive entries in the column for s? That is, what are the values of $\frac{f(1)}{f(0)}$, $\frac{f(2)}{f(1)}$, $\frac{f(3)}{f(2)}$, and so on?

    b. How does your answer to part (a) relate to the original problem context? In other words, what do these ratios tell us about the resale value of the iTech Device?

    c. What are the ratios of values of Δs compared to the values of s at the beginning of each interval?

    d. How does your answer to part (c) relate to the original problem context? In other words, what do these ratios tell us about the resale value of the iTech Device?

The following are graphs of functions f and g that model the expected resale values for each device over the next 6 years. On each graph we have plotted the points that correspond to the ordered pairs you should have calculated in Exercise #1.

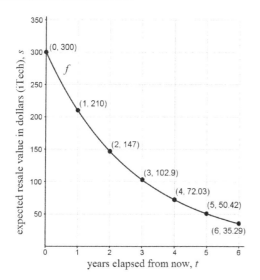
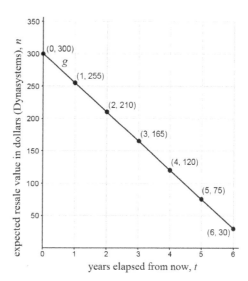

To help focus attention on the values of s and n (the expected resale values of each device in dollars) represented in our previous tables, we have drawn vertical line segments whose lengths represent values of s and n respectively.

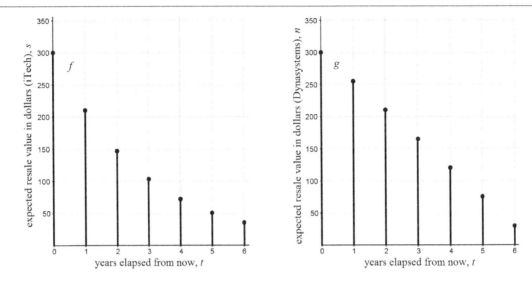

*5. a. Explain how we can "see" on the graph the fact that the expected resale value of the iTech Device at some moment is 70% of its expected resale value one year earlier.

  b. Explain how we can "see" on the graph the fact that the expected resale value of the iTech Device changes by –30% each year.

  c. Explain how we can "see" on the graphs that only one of the two devices has an expected resale value that changes at a constant rate of change with respect to the number of elapsed years.

6. Suppose another piece of technology (the iTech2 Device) has a current resale value of $400, and that this value is expected to change by −50% per year. Let function *h* model its expected resale value in dollars *t* years from now.

    a. *Without performing any calculations*, plot the approximate values for the ordered pairs $(1, h(1))$, $(2, h(2))$, $(3, h(3))$, $(4, h(4))$, $(5, h(5))$, and $(6, h(6))$.

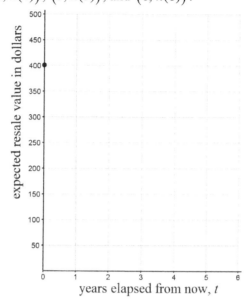

    b. Explain how you were able to estimate the values for the ordered pairs in part (a).

    c. Suppose that another device (TecTone) has a current resale value of $500 and its resale value is expected to decrease by 20% each year. Let function *j* model its expected resale value *t* years from now. Plot the point (0, 500) on the graph in part (a), then *without performing any calculations*, plot the approximate values for the ordered pairs $(0, j(0))$, $(1, j(1))$, $(2, j(2))$, $(3, j(3))$, $(4, j(4))$, $(5, j(5))$, and $(6, j(6))$.

    d. Write formulas to represent functions *h* and *j*.

Exponential Functions

When two quantities change together such that, for equal changes in one quantity's values, the second quantity's values have a ***constant percent change***, then we say that the relationship is an ***exponential function***.

---

*7. In Exercises #1-6 you explored several examples of relationships that can be modeled with an exponential function. Using your work with these examples, explain why exponential functions *do not* have a constant rate of change of one quantity with respect to the other quantity.

*8. From about 2000 to 2006, home prices in the United States increased dramatically prior to the real estate "crash" that began around 2007-2008. Suppose that from 2000 to 2006 the value of a specific house in California increased by 25% per year.

a. Complete the following table and draw a graph modeling the value of this house in dollars *n* years since the beginning of 2000.

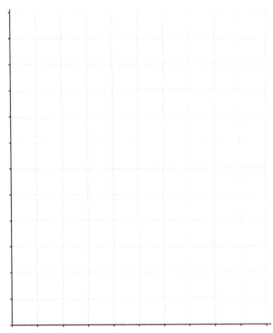

years since the beginning of 2000	home price (in dollars)
0	210,000
1	
2	
3	
4	
5	
6	

b. By what number can we multiply the value of the home at one moment in time to find its value one year later?

c. Fill in the blank: The value of the home at one moment in time is _____% of its value one year earlier.

d. Explain how we can "see" the value of the multiplier you identified in part (b) in the graph from part (a).

*1. The function $f(x) = 2^x$ is an example of an exponential function, and some people call this a *doubling function*.

    a. If we allow x to vary, and it increases by 1, what happens to the output value of the function?

    b. i.   When x increases by 1, the new output value is _____% of the previous output value.

        ii. What is the percent change in the output value when x increases by 1?

    c. If we allow x to vary, and it increases by 3, what happens to the output value of the function?

    d. If we allow x to vary, and it increases by 8, what happens to the output value of the function?

In the previous investigation we only explored exponential functions with a limited domain (such as $0 \le x \le 6$). However, without a context to restrict the value of x, the function $f(x) = 2^x$ can accept any real number as its input and produces the following graph.

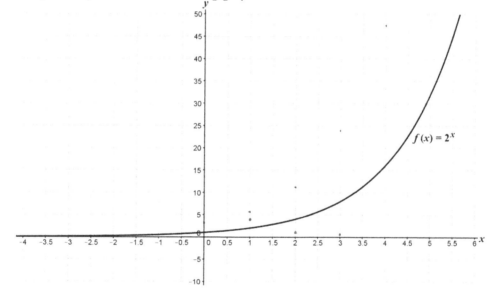

2. a. Determine the value of $f(0)$.

    b. As x increases away from $x = 0$, how do the function values change? What happens as x gets very, very large?

    c. As x decreases away from $x = 0$, how do the function values change? What happens as x gets very, very small (becomes a large magnitude negative number)?

*3. View the Module 4 Investigation 3 PowerPoint animation titled **Exercise 3 Animation**.
   a. What idea or ideas are being demonstrated in this animation?

   b. How is this image different from thinking about the function using a table of values like the one shown?

x	0	1	2	3	4	5
$f(x)$	1	2	4	8	16	32

*4. In Exercises #1-3 we looked at a specific example of a doubling function $f(x) = 2^x$. Give three more examples of exponential functions whose values double whenever x increases by 1.

5. Consider the function $g(x) = 3^x$.
   a. On the graph shown prior to Exercise #2, add the graph of g.

   b. Compare the behavior of functions f and g. How are they alike? How do they differ?

   c. i. For function g, whenever x increases by 1, the new function value is _____% of the previous function value.

      ii. What is the percent change in the output value as x increases by 1?

   d. For function g, whenever x increases by 2, what happens to the function's output value?

6. Consider the function $h(x) = 6\left(\frac{2}{3}\right)^x$.
   a. On the graph shown prior to Exercise #2, add the graph of h.

   b. As x increases away from $x = 0$, how do the function values change? What happens as x gets very, very large?

(1-Unit) Growth Factor

For an exponential function, the ratio of output values is always the same for equal-sized intervals of the domain. When x increases from x_1 to x_2, this ratio $\frac{f(x_2)}{f(x_1)}$ is called a ***growth factor***. If the interval is 1-unit wide (that is, if the change in x from x_1 to x_2 is 1), then the ratio is the ***1-unit growth factor***.

The growth factor is a useful number because it tells us how many times as large $f(x_2)$ is compared to $f(x_1)$, and thus can be used to determine $f(x_2)$ if we know $f(x_1)$.

Note that if this factor is between 0 and 1 it is often called a ***decay factor*** because a multiplier between 0 and 1 means that the function values are decreasing as x increases.

---

*7. The following table shows values for an exponential function f.

x	$f(x)$	$\Delta f(x)$
1.24	3.1000	
2.24	4.3400	
3.24	6.0760	
4.24	8.5064	

a. What are the ratios for the function's output values when x varies by 1? That is, what is the value of $\frac{f(2.24)}{f(1.24)}$, $\frac{f(3.24)}{f(2.24)}$, and $\frac{f(4.24)}{f(3.24)}$?

b. Why does the answer to part (a) tell us the function's (1-unit) growth or decay factor?

c. Complete the third column in the table showing the differences in the output values when x varies by 1.

d. What are the values of the ratios for each change in the output value compared to the value of the function at the beginning of the interval? What is the percent change in the output value when x increases by 1 (this is the 1-unit percent change)?

*8. View the Module 4 Investigation 3 PowerPoint animation titled **Exercise 8 Animation**. What idea or ideas are being demonstrated in this animation?

In Exercises #9-12, do the following.
   a. Find the ratio of output values that correspond to increases of 1 in the input value (this value is the 1-unit growth/decay factor).
   b. Determine the 1-unit percent change by comparing the change in the output values to the function value at the beginning of a 1-unit interval for *x*.
   c. Identify or determine the value of the function when *x* = 0.
   d. Use the information from parts (a) through (c) to define a function formula for the relationship.

*9.

x	0	1	2	3
$f(x)$	16	4	1	0.25

   a.

   b.

   c.

   d.

10.

x	1	2	3	8
$g(x)$	260	299	343.85	691.605

   a.

   b.

   c.

   d.

11.

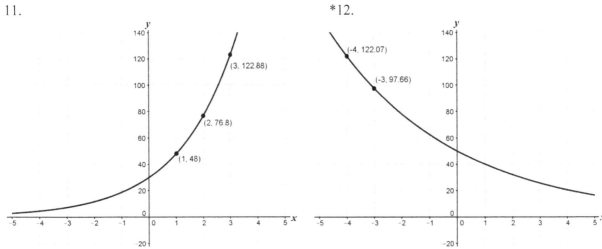

   a.

   b.

   c.

   d.

*12.

   a.

   b.

   c.

   d.

13. Let $f(x) = 34(1.19)^x$.

    a. What does the number "34" represent for this function?

    b. What does the number "1.19" represent for this function?

    c. Fill in the blank: Whenever x increases by 1, the new output value is _____% of the old output value.

    d. What is the 1-unit percent change and what does it tell us?

*14. Let $g(p) = 1.578(0.68)^p$.

    a. What does the number "1.578" represent for this function?

    b. What does the number "0.68" represent for this function?

    c. *Fill in the blank*: Whenever p increases by 1, the new output value is _____% of the old output value.

    d. What is the 1-unit percent change and what does it tell us?

*15. An investment of $3300 increases by 4.7% each month.

    a. What is the 1-month percent change in the investment value?

    b. *Fill in the blank*: When the time elapsed since the investment was made increases by 1 month, the new value of the investment is _____% of the old value of the investment.

c. What is the 1-month growth or decay factor and what does this value tell us about the situation?

d. Write a function formula to model the value of the investment (in dollars) in terms of the time elapsed since the investment was made (in months).

16. After having 1.4 million people at the start of 2010, the population of a city has been decreasing by 2.1% per year.
    a. What is the 1-year percent change in the city's population?

    b. *Fill in the blank*: When the time elapsed since the beginning of 2010 increases by 1 month, the new population is _____% of the old population.

    c. What is the 1-year growth or decay factor and what does this value tell us about the situation?

    d. Write a function formula to model the city's population (in millions) in terms of the time elapsed since the beginning of 2010 (in years).

*17. Some of your classmates made the following claim. "The functions $f(x) = x^2$ and $g(x) = x^3$ are some other examples of exponential functions."
    a. Are your classmates correct? Justify your answer using what you've learned so far in this module.

    b. If you agree with your classmates, then come up with at least two more examples of exponential functions. If you disagree with your classmates, then give a possible reason for why this might be a common mistake for students.

*1. Express your understanding of exponents by answering the following questions.

   a. i. In the term b^x what does x represent?

      ii. What does b^5 represent?

      iii. Evaluate 4^3 and say what your answer represents.

   b. Calculate the following: i. $9^{1/2}$ ii. $4^{1/2}$ iii. $121^{1/2}$

   c. What do your answers in (b) represent? In general, how do you go about determining the value of some number b raised to the ½ power?

   d. In general, how do you go about determining the value of $x^{1/3}$?

   e. Calculate $4^{3/2}$ (also represented as $4^{1.5}$). What does your answer represent?

   f. Solve the following equations for x:
      i. $x^2 = 81$ ii. $x^3 = 27$ iii. $x^{3/4} = 8$ iv. $x^{1/5} = 2$

   g. Simplify: $a^{2.5} \cdot a^4$. Describe what your answer represents.

   h. Simplify: $\dfrac{b^{7.8}}{b^2}$. Describe what your answer represents.

   i. Simplify: $(c^2)^{3.1}$. Describe what your answer represents.

*2. You are given that (4, 38) and (7,50) are two ordered pairs for an *exponential growth function*. Your classmate noticed that the difference in the outputs is 12 as the inputs change by 3, and created the table showing some additional ordered pairs.

x	y
4	38
5	42
6	46
7	50

Explain how you know that the two additional ordered pairs (bolded) cannot be accurate even though we don't have the function formula or the graph for this relationship.

3. Urban planners noticed that the population of a certain county doubled over 20 years (from 1990 to 2010), following a pattern of exponential growth. The population of the county was 756,000 people at the end of 1990.
   a. What was the population of the county at the end of 2010?

   b. If the growth pattern were to continue for another 20 years, what is the projected population at the end of 2030?

   c. Which quantities are changing in this situation? Which quantities are not changing?

   d. If we assume that this population growth will continue into the far future, complete the table.

Number of years since 1990	Population	The current population is _____ times as large as the population at the end of 1990
0		
20		
40		
60		
80		

   e. Define a function *f* that expresses the population of the county, *P*, after a number of 20-year periods, *n*, that have elapsed since the end of 1990.

4. Since 20-year changes in time are quite long, we might want to know how much the population changes over shorter periods of time.
   a. Given that the population grew exponentially, which statement [(i) or (ii)] best describes what happens every 10 years? Justify your choice.

      i. Every 10 years, the population increases by a constant amount. That is, a constant amount is added to the population at the end of 1990 to get the population at the end of 2000, and the same amount is added to get the population at the end of 2010.

      ii. Every 10 years, the population increases by a constant factor. That is, this constant factor is multiplied by the population at the end of 1990 to get the population at the end of 2000, and this constant factor is multiplied by the population at the end of 2000 to get the population at the end of 2010.

   b. Given that the population increases exponentially and doubles over 20 years,
      i. What is the 10-year growth factor?

      ii. What is the 1-year growth factor?

iii. What is the 2-year growth factor? What is the 3-year growth factor? What is the 7-year growth factor?

iv. Complete the table.

Number of years since 1990	0	1	2	3	13	16	20
Population							

c. Define a function g that expresses the population of the county, P, as a function of the number of years t since the end of 1990.

d. Define a function h that expresses the population of the county c months since the end of 1990.

*5. A farm in Canada had 218 alpacas on January 1, 2004. After 8 years the alpaca population decreased to 187. Assume the number of alpacas decays exponentially.
  a. What is the 8-year growth/decay factor?

  b. Fill in the blank: The number of alpaca on the farm on January 1, 2012 was _____% of the number of alpaca on the farm on January 1, 2004.

  c. What is the 8-year percent change?

  d. Assuming the alpaca population continues to be modeled by the same exponential model, how many alpacas can we expect to be on the farm on January 1, 2020?

  e. Since 8-year changes in time are quite long, we might want to know how the population of alpacas changes over shorter periods of time. What is the 1-year growth/decay factor?

  f. What is the 1-year percent change?

  g. Define a function f that relates the number of alpacas on the Canadian farm t years from January 1, 2004 (Assume the alpaca population continues to change by the same decay factor each year).

*6. Assume the number of alpacas continues to change by the same decay factor each year as defined in Exercise #5. Use your calculator determine the following;
  a. After how many years will there be 109 alpacas remaining on the farm, assuming the herd started with 218 alpacas?

  b. After how many total years will there be 55 alpacas?

  c. After how many years will a herd of 120 alpacas decrease to 60 alpacas?

*7. Assume the number of alpacas continues to change by the same decay factor each year as defined in Exercise #5.
   a. What is the 1-month growth/decay factor?

   b. Define a function g that relates the number of alpacas on the Canadian farm k months from January 1, 2004 (Assume the alpaca population continues to change by the same decay factor each year).

   c. What is the 2-month growth/decay factor?

8. After taking medicine, your body begins to break it down and remove it according to a pattern of exponential decay. Suppose you take 500 mg of Ibuprofen and that your body removes 85% of the Ibuprofen every 5 hours.
   a. After 5 hours, what percent of the 500 mg dose remains in your body? How much medication is this?

   b. Define a function f that expresses the amount of Ibuprofen in milligrams (mg), B, present after n 5-hour time intervals since taking the medicine.

   c. Define a function g that expresses the amount of Ibuprofen in milligrams (mg), B, present t hours after taking the medicine.

   d. How much Ibuprofen remains in your body 3 hours after taking the medicine? After 12 hours?

   e. How does the *change* in the amount of Ibuprofen remaining change as the number of hours elapsed increases?

For Exercises #1-2, determine the specified growth or decay factor, percent change, and initial value for each of the following exponential functions.

*1. $f(x) = 9.5(1.24)^x$

    a. 1/2-unit Growth Factor:

    b. 2-unit Growth Factor:

    c. 2-unit Percent Change:

    d. Initial Value:

*2. $g(x) = 0.46(0.874)^{4x}$

    a. 1/4-unit Decay Factor:

    b. 1-unit Decay Factor:

    c. 5-unit percent change:

    d. Initial Value:

In Exercises #3-4, determine the specified growth or decay factor, percent change, initial value, and function formula for each of the tables modeled by exponential functions.

3.

x	0	2	4	6
$f(x)$	16	10.24	6.554	4.194

    a. 2-unit Decay Factor:

    b. 1-unit Percent Change:

    c. 3-unit Decay Factor:

    d. ½ -unit Decay Factor:

    e. Initial Value:

    f. Formula:

*4.

x	1	4	7	10
$g(x)$	260	278.2	297.674	318.511

    a. 3-unit Growth Factor:

    b. 6-unit Percent Change:

    c. 1-unit Growth Factor:

    d. ¼-unit Growth Factor:

    e. Initial Value:

    f. Formula:

In Exercises #5-6, determine the specified growth or decay factor, percent change, initial value, average rate of change, and function formula for the exponential function with the graph.

*5. Use the graph to complete the following.

    a. 2-unit Growth/Decay Factor:

    b. 6-unit Growth/Decay Factor:

    c. 1-unit Percent Change:

    d. ½-unit Growth/Decay Factor:

    e. 3-unit Growth/Decay Factor:

    f. Initial Value:

    g. Formula:

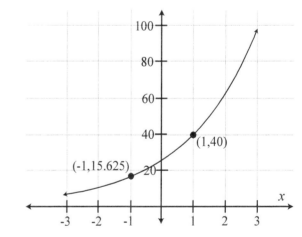

    h. The average rate of change of $r(x)$ with respect to x as the value of x increases from −1 to 1.

    i. Explain how to interpret the value you found in (h).

*6. Use the graph to complete the following.
   a.   3-unit Growth/Decay Factor:

   b.   6-unit Growth/Decay Factor:

   c.   1-unit Percent Change:

   d.   ½-unit Growth/Decay Factor:

   e.   5-unit Growth/Decay Factor:

   f.   Initial Value:

   g.   Formula:

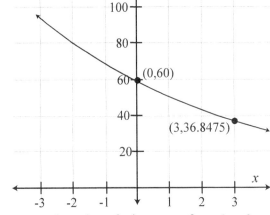

   h.   The average rate of change of $w(x)$ with respect to x as the value of x increases from 0 to 3.

   i.   Explain how to interpret the value you found in (h).

In Exercises #7-9, determine the growth or decay factor, percent change, initial value and function for each exponential situation.

7.   An investment of $6300 increases by 7.3% each year.
   a. 2-year Growth Factor: b. 1/2-year Percent Change:

   c. Initial Value: d. Function:

*8.   After having 1.97 million people in 2010, the population of a city has been decreasing by 4.2% every three years.
   a. 1-year Decay Factor: b. ¼ -year Percent Change:

   c. Initial Value: d. Function:

9. The amount of caffeine in your body decreases by 27% every 4 hours.
   a.   24-hour Decay Factor: b.   24-hour Percent Change:

   c.   1-hour Decay Factor: d.   1-hour Percent Change:

10. Consider an exponential relationship in which b represents the 1-unit growth factor, c represents the n-unit growth factor, and d represents the m-unit growth factor.
   a.   Write a formula that expresses the n-unit growth factor in terms of the 1-unit growth factor.

   b.   Write a formula that expresses the 1-unit growth factor in terms of an n-unit growth factor.

   c.   Write a formula that expresses the m-unit growth factor in terms of an n-unit growth factor.

When you deposit money in a bank they pay you interest based on the balance. The interest can be paid in many different ways such as once a year, twice a year, once a month, etc. By convention, banks calculate the interest rate per compounding period by dividing the advertised annual interest rate (often called the Annual Percentage Rate or APR) by the number of compounding periods in one year. ***Note that this is a different technique from determining partial growth factors.***

*1. Suppose you are going to invest $1000. You have three choices on how to invest your money and in all three situations the annual interest rate (APR) is 8%.
   a. The first account advertises, "8% APR compounded annually". This means that at the end of each year 8% of the current balance is added to the value of the account.
      i.   What is the interest rate per compounding period?

      ii. Complete the following table.

8% Compounded Annually	
number of years since investment was made	value of the investment (in dollars)
0	
1	
2	
t	

      iii. What is the annual growth factor for this account? Interpret the annual growth factor in the context of this problem.

   b. The second account advertises "8% APR compounded semiannually". This means that interest is added two times per year (every six months).
      i.   What is the interest rate per compounding period?

      ii. Complete the following table.

8% Compounded Semiannually	
number of years since investment was made	value of the investment (in dollars)
0	
0.5	
1	
2	
t	

      iii. What is the six-month growth factor for this account?

iv. What is the annual growth factor for this account? Interpret the annual growth factor in the context of this problem.

v. Use the annual growth factor computed in part (iv) to determine the actual percentage change of the account over a 1-year time period. This percentage is often referenced as the annual percentage yield (APY).

c. The third account advertises "8% APR compounded daily". This means that interest is added 365 times per year (every day).
   i. What is the interest rate per compounding period?

ii. Complete the following table.

8% Compounded Daily	
number of years since investment was made	value of the investment (in dollars)
0	
$\frac{1}{365}$	
$\frac{2}{365}$	
1	
2	
t	

iii. What is the daily growth factor for this account?

iv. What is the annual growth factor for this account? Interpret the annual growth factor in the context of this problem.

v. Use the annual growth factor computed in part (iv) to determine the annual percentage yield (APY).

d. Which of the three accounts would you chose for your investment? Justify your answer.

1

*2. A bank offers an annual interest rate of r compounded n times per year, where r is the APR expressed as a decimal. Let a be the initial value of the investment. Define a function g that determines the value of the investment B in terms of the number of years since the investment was made, t.

3. Bank USA is offering a 9% annual rate compounded monthly and Southwest Investment Bank is offering an annual rate of 8.5% compounded daily. Which bank would you choose for your investment?

*4. You should have noticed that the techniques in this investigation for finding growth factors related to different units of time are not the same as the techniques used in previous investigations. This is because bank policy differs from our goals in creating partial growth factors. Look at the following comparison.

Non-Financial Contexts	**Compound Interest**
The population of a certain country is 26.4 million people and is increasing by 4% per year. Annual growth factor: 1.04 Annual percent change: 4% Monthly growth factor: $\qquad (1.04)^{1/12} \approx 1.003274$ Monthly percent change: 0.3274%	*$1200 is deposited into an account with an APR of 4%.* If interest is compounded once per year, the annual growth factor is: 1.04 The annual percent change is: 4% If interest is compounded once per month, the monthly growth factor is: $1 + \frac{0.04}{12} = 1.00\overline{3}$ The monthly percent change is: $0.\overline{3}\%$
When the monthly growth factor is applied 12 times it produces the annual growth factor. $\qquad [(1.04)^{1/12}]^{12} = 1.04$	If interest is compounded once per month, and we do this for one year, the annual growth factor is different than when interest is compounded only once per year. $\qquad (1.00\overline{3})^{12} \approx 1.04074$

a. In non-financial contexts, we know the actual annual growth factor based on data and we cannot change the long-term growth pattern of the function relationship. How does this play a role in the methods we use for computing growth factors for different-sized changes in the input quantity's value?

b. Why don't banks have the same restrictions as those described in part (a) and how might this impact their techniques?

*5. A deposit of $5,000 is made into an account paying an APR of 5%. Determine the amount in the account 10 years after the investment was made if the interest is compounded:
a. Annually

b. Monthly

c. Weekly

d. Daily

*1. $1000 is invested into an account with an annual percent rate (APR) of 8%. Given the compounding period, determine the account value at the end of the fifth year. Also determine the annual percent yield (APY) for the given compounding period. (*Round to at least 3 decimal digits.*)

	APY	Difference in the value of the APY	Value of Investment after 5 years	Difference in the value of the investment
Compounded Yearly				
Compounded Quarterly				
Compounded Monthly				
Compounded Daily				
Compounded Hourly				
Compounded Every Minute				

2. How is the number of compounding periods per year related to the annual growth factor and the APY? Why do you think this is happening?

*3. a. What do you anticipate the APY will be if the APR is 8% and the investment is compounded every second, every $1/100^{th}$ of a second?

   b. What do you predict is the largest annual growth factor possible given an APR of 8%? Interpret the meaning of this value in the context of this situation.

*4. Consider investment APRs of 5%, 6%, 7%, and 8%.
   a. Complete the following table by predicting the largest annual growth factor that corresponds to those APRs. (Round to at least 6 decimal digits)

APR	5%	6%	7%	8%
Largest Annual Growth Factor, g				
$g^{1/r}$ (where r is the APR as a decimal)				

   b. What do you notice about the values in the second row of the table?

An interesting mathematical idea is that no matter what the APR is for a given investment, the largest annual growth factor for that investment is related to the number 2.71828… This irrational number is referred to as e.

*5. The value of e is equal to $g^{1/r}$ where g is the largest annual growth factor and r is the decimal value of the given APR. Undo this process to find an equation for g in terms of e and r.

*6. An investment of $1000 was made in four different banks at the given APRs. Complete the table by finding the largest annual growth factor for each APR. This value should be a decimal. Since this decimal is a rounded value (and therefore not exact), complete the second row by writing an expression that determines the exact value of the largest annual growth factor. Finally, write a formula that can be used to find the maximum value of the investment after t years (the value of the investment assuming the largest annual growth factor).

APR	5%	6%	7%	8%
Largest Annual Growth Factor (decimal form)				
Exact Representation of the Largest Annual Growth Factor				
Maximum Value of Investment After t Years				

*7. Define a function f that gives the value of an investment, B, in terms of the number of years since the initial investment was made, t. Let a represent the value of the initial investment and let r represent the decimal form of the APR.

Another way to think about the largest annual growth factor is to say that it is the growth factor that corresponds to compounding as many times as possible in a year. In other words, if the investment were to be compounded more often than daily, more often than hourly, more often than every second, etc., then we would say the investment is being ***compounded continuously***.

8. $1500 is invested into an account with an advertised APR of 7% compounded continuously.
   a. Determine the value of the investment after 6 years.

   b. Determine the amount of time required for the value of the investment to double.

   c. Determine the value of the account after 6 years had the investment been compounded quarterly instead of continuously.

Up until this point we have been unable to algebraically solve equations where the unknown is in the exponent. We utilized our graphing calculators in order to solve these equations. In this investigation we will learn how to solve these equations algebraically.

*1. a. Without a calculator approximate the solution to the following equations. (*Think about what value of x makes each equation true.*)

   i. $2^x = 10$ ii. $17^x = 10$

   b. Describe the process (thinking) you used to determine your solutions in part (a).

   c. What does each of your solutions in part (a) represent?

   d. For the equations in part (a), what information was needed to determine (or estimate) the value of the exponent.

Determining the solutions of the equations in Exercise #1 involved undoing the process of exponentiation. Instead of raising a base to a power we determined the power to which a number (the base) is raised to obtain some number.

As seen in Exercise #1, it can be difficult to determine the exact number of times a base value is a factor of some other number. The standard way of expressing the specific value of an unknown exponent, when provided the base value and the result of exponentiation, utilizes what we call ***logarithmic notation***. As an example, to represent the number of times 5 is a factor of 125, we write $\log_5(125)$. In general, we say, $\log_b(m)$ represents the number of times b is a factor of m.

   e. Using logarithmic notation, represent the exact solutions to the equations in part (a).

   f. Describe what each of the following logarithmic expressions represents.

   i. $\log_{16}(94)$ ii. $\log_{3.4}(17.2)$ iii. $\log_{19}(2.7)$

The function that undoes the process of exponentiation is called the ***logarithmic function***. The input of the logarithmic function is the output of the exponential function (the result of raising some base to a power) and the output of the logarithmic function is the input of the exponential function (the exponent or power to which the base is raised). We use "log" as an abbreviation for "logarithm" in expressions.

As an example, $\log_2(10) = x$ is read "log base 2 of 10 equals x" and is equivalent to $2^x = 10$ in exponential form. The number 10 represents the result of raising 2 to an exponent x. The value of x can be determined by considering the power that 2 is raised (or number of factors of 2) to obtain the value 10.

© 2018 Carlson, Oehrtman, and Moore

2. Rewrite each of these equations in logarithmic form (if possible). If it is not possible, say why.
   a. $4^x = 64$
   b. $5^x = \frac{1}{125}$
   c. $2^x = -32$

We can rewrite any exponential equation in logarithmic form. *Note that the input to the logarithmic function can only be non-negative real numbers.*

Logarithmic Function

For $x > 0$ and $b > 0$, with $b \neq 1$, $y = \log_b x$ is equivalent to $b^y = x$. The function $f(x) = \log_b(x)$ is the logarithmic function with base b.

Note that logarithmic functions are the inverses of exponential functions with the same base.

---

*3. Rewrite the following exponential equations in logarithmic form.
   a. $y = 4^x$
   b. $b = 1.5(5)^a$
   c. $m = 2^{4t}$
   d. $q = 3(5)^{2k}$

*4. Without using your calculator, determine/estimate the value of the variable that makes the equation true.
   a. $\log_2 4 = y$
   b. $\log_9\left(\frac{1}{81}\right) = t$
   c. $\log_3(-2) = k$
   d. $\log_5 10 = s$

*5. Logarithmic functions are the inverses of exponential functions. That is, both functions show the same relationship between two quantities, but the input and output quantities are switched.
   a. The graph of $f(x) = \log_4(x)$ is given.
      i. Plot the points $(x, f(x))$ when $x = \frac{1}{2}$, 1, 4, 16

      ii. Explain how you know that f is an increasing function.

      iii. Explain how you know that y increases less and less, for equal increases in x.

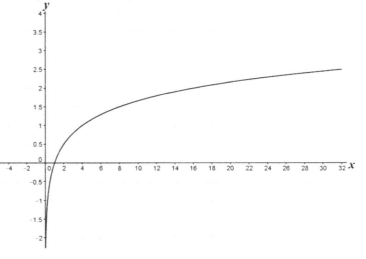

   b. Determine the average rate of change of y with respect to x as:
      i. x increases from 2 to 4
      ii. x increases from 4 to 6

c. On the axes in part (a), draw the graph of $g(x) = \log_2(x)$.

d. On the axes in part (a), draw the graph of $h(x) = \log_{0.5}(x)$.

Recall that in Module 4 Investigation 7 we defined the irrational number $e = 2.718281828\ldots$ A logarithm with base e or $\log_e c = x$ is commonly called the ***natural logarithm*** and is abbreviated "ln".

*Note: Your calculator has two logarithm buttons, log and ln. Even though we can use any base (greater than zero) in a logarithmic function, some calculators only evaluate logarithms for two bases: base 10 and base e. The log x button evaluates $f(x) = \log_{10}(x)$ and is referred to as the **common log**. The ln x button evaluates $\log_e(x)$ x and is referred to as the **natural log** of x.*

6. Convert the following to exponential form and evaluate/estimate the value of the unknown. Check your answer using your calculator.

    a. $\log\left(\frac{1}{100}\right) = x$ b. $\ln(e^2) = k$ c. $\ln(7) = t$ d. $\log(1000) = s$

Recall the Properties of Exponents:

- **Property of Exponents #1:** $b^x \cdot b^y = b^{x+y}$

- **Property of Exponents #2:** $\dfrac{b^x}{b^y} = b^{x-y}$ for $b \neq 0$.

- **Property of Exponents #3:** $\left(b^x\right)^y = b^{xy}$

*7. Use your understanding of exponents and the meaning of b^x to justify each property stated above.

Because the result from evaluating a logarithmic expression (and the output of a logarithmic function) represents an exponent, the properties of exponents also apply to logarithms, with the rules of exponents expressed using logarithms and logarithmic form.

Logarithm Properties

Property #1: $\log_b(m \cdot n) = \log_b(m) + \log_b(n)$ for any $b > 0$, $b \neq 1$, and $m, n > 0$

Property #2: $\log_b\left(\dfrac{m}{n}\right) = \log_b(m) - \log_b(n)$ for any $b > 0$, $b \neq 1$, and $m, n > 0$

Property #3: $\log_b\left(m^c\right) = c \cdot \log_b(m)$ for any $b > 0$, $b \neq 1$, and $m, n > 0$

The first property of logarithms states $\log_b(m \cdot n) = \log_b(m) + \log_b(n)$. For example, $\log_2(4) + \log_2(8)$ asks to find the power to which 2 is raised to in order to get a result of 4, and the power 2 is raised to in order to get a result of 8, and then add those two powers together ($2 + 3 = 5$). We could have instead considered $\log_2(4 \cdot 8) = \log_2(32)$ and determined directly that 5 is the power 2 must be raised to in order to get a result of 32.

---

*8. Use your understanding of logarithmic functions (knowledge of what the input and output quantities represent) to justify at least one of the logarithmic properties above.

*9. Use the properties of logarithms to simplify the following expressions.
   a. $\ln(x) + \ln(x)$
   b. $\log_3(5) + \log_3(2)$
   c. $\log_4(16) - \log_4(4)$

   d. $\log_3(2) + \log_5(3)$
   e. $\log_3(9) + \log_3(4) - \log_3(6)$
   f. $\log_7(49) - \log_7(-3)$

*10. Solve each of the following for x.
   a. $\log_5(30x^2) = 3$
   b. $\log(1.5x) = 0$
   c. $\log_3 x + \log_3(2x) = 3$

11. Let $f(x) = 10^x$ and $g(x) = \log(x)$.
   a. Complete the tables.

x	$f(x)$
-2	
-1	
0	
1	
2	

x	$g(x)$
0.01	
0.1	
1	
10	
100	

   b. Evaluate the following expressions:
   i. $g(f(-2))$
   ii. $g(f(0))$
   iii. $f(g(1))$
   iv. $f(g(10))$
   v. $f(g(x))$
   vi. $g(f(x))$

   c. What do you notice about the relationship between the functions f and g?

12. Use the fact that the word "log" is the name of a function and the statement $\log_2(x)$ represents the output values of the logarithmic function (with a base of 2) for varying values of x.
   a. What does $\log_2(x)$ represent?
   b. What does $\log_4(x)$ represent?

   c. Write an equation relating $\log_2(x)$ and $\log_4(x)$.
   d. Write an equation relating $\log_3(y)$ and $\log_{27}(y)$.

*1. Solve each of the following equations for *x*. Find the exact answer and then use your calculator to approximate the answer to the nearest thousandth (3 decimal places).

    a. $4 = 3^x$ b. $22.4 = 17.5(3.4)^x$

2. a. What does $\log_2(A)$ represent? What does $\log_2(B)$ represent? If *A* = *B*, how are $\log_2(A)$ and $\log_2(B)$ related?

    b. Why is it mathematically valid to "take the log" of both sides of an equation? (*In other words, how do you know the two sides of the equation are still equal?*)

    c. Is it mathematically valid to take the log of both sides of an equation if the expressions on each side of the equation can have a value less than or equal to zero? Explain.

*3. In 2009 the enrollment at Mainland High School was 1650 students. Administrators predict that the enrollment will increase by 2.2% each year
    a. Determine when the enrollment at Mainland High School is expected to reach 2600 students.

    b. Suppose that Mainland High School requires 5 teachers per 65 students. How many teachers are required if the student enrollment is 2600 students?

c. Define a function *f* that gives the number of years since 2009 in terms of the number of teachers employed by Mainland High School

*4. *Recall the alpaca problem from Module 4 Investigation 4*. A farm in Canada had 218 alpacas on January 1, 2004. After 8 years the alpaca population decreased to 187. Assume the number of alpacas decays exponentially.

a. Define a function *f* that expresses the number of alpacas on the farm in terms of the number of years since 2004.

b. Using the function defined in part (a) estimate the number of alpaca on the farm in 2013.

c. Use algebraic methods to determine the year when the number of alpaca on the farm was 165. Check your answer using a graph or by using the function you defined in part (a).

*5. 22 koala bears were introduced to Wallaby Island in 1928. In 1992, the population of koala bears on the island was about 2000. Assume the population of koala bears can be modeled by exponential growth.

a. Determine the annual growth factor in this situation.

b. Use algebraic methods to determine the year when the population of koala bears on the island will be 4500.

6. You deposited $2,500 in a CD to help save for your college tuition. The annual interest rate of the CD is 4.5% compounded continuously.
   a. Define a function that gives the value of the CD in terms of the number of years that have elapsed since you opened the CD.

   b. How many years will have elapsed before the CD is worth $7,000?

*7. In 1990, the population of Diamond Bar was 45,000 and the population of Chino Hills was 37,000. In 1992, the population of Diamond Bar was 51,750 and the population of Chino Hills was 44,400. Assuming both cities' populations grow at an exponential rate, how many years will it take for the population of Chino Hills to surpass the population of Diamond Bar?

*8. In 1935, Charles Richter, a seismologist at the California Institute of Technology, invented a method for comparing the magnitude of earthquakes. Since the amplitude of seismic waves of different earthquakes can be over a million times as large as the waves of small earthquakes, Richter developed a special scale (now called the Richter Scale) for measuring the magnitude of these earthquake waves. This formula or function takes as input the amplitude of the seismic waves of an earthquake and outputs what we call the magnitude of the earthquake. The magnitude is the Richter scale rating of the strength of the earthquake and is the number reported in the media.

The magnitude M of an earthquake whose seismic waves are of amplitude A is defined to be

$$M = \log_{10}\left(\frac{A}{A_0}\right),$$

where A_0 represents the amplitude of seismic waves of a "standard" earthquake (whose amplitude is 1 micron = 10^{-4} cm).

   a. i. Describe the meaning of the ratio $\dfrac{A}{A_0}$ in this context.

ii. Describe the effect of inputting $\dfrac{A}{A_0}$ into the $\log_{10}$ function and what the value of M represents.

b. Let M_1 and M_2 represent the magnitudes of two earthquakes whose seismic waves are of amplitudes A_1 and A_2, respectively. Use the formula given above and the properties of logarithms to define a simplified formula for the difference $M_2 - M_1$ in terms of A_1 and A_2.

c. On May 22, 1960, a 9.5 magnitude earthquake struck near Valdivia, Chile. On November 1, 2015, a 4.1 magnitude earthquake struck Phoenix, Arizona. How many times as large were the seismic waves of the Chile earthquake compared to the Arizona earthquake?

d. Write a formula that determines the amplitude of the seismic waves of an earthquake in terms of the magnitude of the earthquake.

*9. On May 15, 2016, Nancy paid the balance on her loans and was finally debt free! Since she had extra money she deposited $50 into a savings account that same day and then forgot about the account (so she made no additional deposits). The number of dollars $w(t)$ in this savings account t months since May 15, 2016 is given by the function w defined by, $w(t) = \log_4(t+1) + \log_2(t+1) + 50$.

a. What is the practical domain and range of the function w?

b. Evaluate $w(15)$. What does this value represent in the situation?

c. Evaluate $w(43) - w(0)$. What does this value represent in the situation?

d. What does $\dfrac{w(22)-w(0)}{22-0}$ represent in this situation?

e. Solve for t when $w(t) = 114$.

f. Define a function, p, that expresses the number of months since May 15, 2016 in terms of the amount of money a in Nancy's savings account.

I. PERCENTAGES AND PERCENT CHANGE (TEXT: S1)

1. You worked a total of 450 minutes at your job yesterday.
   a. What amount of time corresponds to 78% of the total time you spent working yesterday?
   b. If you had worked for 78% of the 450 minutes, what percent of the total time do you still have left to work? What is this time in minutes?

2. Suppose that you fill a glass with 860 milliliters of water.
   a. What volume of water corresponds to 44% of 860 mL?
   b. If you drank 44% of the water you poured into the glass, what percent of the starting 860 mL remains? How much water is this in mL?

3. A local bicycle shop placed older model bikes on sale last weekend. A customer bought a bike on sale for $299 that had a normal retail price of $495.

   sale price: $299

   retail price: $495

   a. How many times as large is the sale price compared with the retail price?
   b. *Fill in the blank*: "The sale price is ____% of the retail price."
   c. How many times as large is the retail price compared with the sale price?
   d. *Fill in the blank*: "The retail price is ____% of the sale price."

4. Your doctor recommends that you increase or decrease your daily intake of certain vitamins and minerals. For each recommendation described, do the following.
   i) State the percent change in daily intake.
   ii) State the number by which we can multiply the original daily intake to find the new daily intake.
   iii) Find the new recommended daily intake amount.
   a. original vitamin D intake: 3μg; increase: 60%
   b. original potassium intake: 1500mg; increase: 135%
   c. original zinc intake: 30mg; decrease: 45%
   d. original calcium intake: 820mg; increase: 25%

5. A store is adjusting the prices of several items. For each price change, do the following.
   i) State the percent change.
   ii) State the number by which we can multiply the old price to find the new price.
   iii) Find the new price.
   a. old price: $29; increase: 5%
   b. old price: $84; increase: 140%
   c. old price: $89.99; decrease: 34%
   d. old price: $6.49; decrease: 22%

6. A major record label has seen its annual operating profit decrease in recent years, likely because of greater accessibility of music online. In 2011, the label's operating profit was $135 million. By 2015, the label's operating profit had decreased by 43% (a percent change of –43%).
   a. What was the record label company's operating profit in 2015?
   b. The record label wants to increase its operating profit to $100 million by 2017. By what percent must the label's operating profit increase from its 2015 value to reach $100 million within the next two years?

7. During a recession, Tina had to take a 10% pay cut. Her original salary was $58,240.
   a. What was her salary after the pay cut?
   b. Once the recession was over, Tina's company wanted to increase her pay to her original salary. What percent change in her salary was required to return it to its original $58,240?

II. COMPARING LINEAR AND EXPONENTIAL BEHAVIOR (TEXT: S2)

8. Joni, a graduating biomedical engineer, was offered two positions, one with Company A, and the other with Company B. Company A offered her a starting salary of $66,000 with a 5% guaranteed raise at the end of each of the first five years. Company B offered her $75,000 as her starting salary with a guaranteed raise of $1,500 every year for the first 5 years. She likes both companies and believes she will continue with the company she selects for at least 5 years.
    a. What is the ratio of Joni's salary one year compared to her salary in the previous year for Company A? Describe how to interpret this ratio.
    b. Fill in the blank: If Joni works for Company A, her salary for any year is _____% of her salary for the previous year.
    c. Define a function f that expresses her salary at Company A in terms of the number of years n since she accepts the position.
    d. Define a function g that expresses her salary at Company B in terms of the number of years n since she accepts the position.
    e. After how many years will Joni's salary at Company A overtake her salary at Company B?
    f. Suppose that she will work for one of these companies for exactly 5 years. A classmate says she should choose Company A because by the time she leaves the company she will have a higher salary. Do you agree? Defend your reasoning.
    g. Construct a graph of the two functions and explain the meaning of the intersection point in the context of this situation (Note that the graphs of the two functions will not be continuous. Before creating your graph think about the discrete instances when her salary changes and the fact that her salary remains constant during each year.)
    h. Find and interpret the following using the functions created in parts (b) and (c).
        i. $f(8)$ ii. $g^{-1}(8200)$ iii. $g(16)$ iv. $f(20) - f(11)$

9. You are researching jobs in advertising.
    a. You are told that the salary for Job A increases exponentially. The salary for Year 1 is $29,000 while the salary for Year 2 will be $31,066.
        i. How many times as large is the salary in Year 2 compared to the salary in Year 1?
        ii. Fill in the blank: The salary in Year 2 is _____% of the salary in Year 1.
        iii. What is the percent change in salary from Year 1 to Year 2?
        iv. If the salary continues to increase by the same percent each year, what will the salary be in Year 5?
    b. You are told that the salary for Job B also increases exponentially. The salary for Year 1 is $27,500 while the salary for Year 2 will be $28,600.
        i. How many times as large is the salary in Year 2 compared to the salary in Year 1?
        ii. Fill in the blank: The salary in Year 2 is _____% of the salary in Year 1.
        iii. What is the percent change in salary from Year 1 to Year 2?
        iv. If the salary continues to increase by the same percent each year, what will the salary be in Year 5?
    c. Based on the information found in parts (a) and (b), which job would you take? Explain your reasoning.

10. A chemist monitored the mass of bacteria in a Petri dish after applying a chemical to kill the bacteria. This chemical causes the mass of bacteria of this type to decrease by 12% each hour that elapses after applying the chemical. The mass when applying the chemical was 203 micrograms.
    a. Fill in the blank. At any given time, the mass of the bacteria is _____% of the mass one hour earlier.
    b. What would the mass of bacteria be after 1 hour? After 2 hours? After 8 hours?

Exercise continues on the next page.

c. Define a function that expresses the mass of bacteria B remaining in the Petri dish as a function of the number of hours t since applying the chemical.

d. After how many hours since applying the chemical will the bacteria's mass be less than one microgram?

e. A different type of chemical was applied to another Petri dish of bacteria that caused the mass to decrease by 26% each hour. If the initial mass of bacteria in this dish was 230 micrograms, define a function which gives the mass of bacteria in this Petri dish as a function of the number of hours t that have elapsed since applying the chemical.

11. Last year, Jenny invested her birthday money in 3 different penny stocks. The following functions represent the daily value (rounded to the nearest cent) of each stock over the first 7 days after making the investment. For each investment,

    i) State the amount of the initial investment;

    ii) Describe how the value of the investment grew over the first 7 days since making the investment?

    iii) Determine the value of investment at the end of the 7th day. (Round your answers to the nearest penny.)

    a. $h(n) = 25(1.45)^n$ b. $f(n) = 120(3)^n$ c. $g(n) = 275(0.9)^n$

12. The rabbit population on a 10-acre wildlife preserve was 24 on January 1, 2011.

a. Assuming the number of rabbits doubled each year, determine a function that gives the number of rabbits R in the preserve in terms of the number of years t elapsed since January 1, 2011.

b. Using the function created in part (a), approximate the number of rabbits in the preserve on January 1, 2018.

c. What is the percent change per year if the population of rabbits doubles each year?

13. A firework stand opened on June 28th. The number of customers at the stand over the first 5 days since it was opened is defined by the function, $N(x) = 7(2)^x$. At the end of July 2, the function was updated to $N(x) = 224(3)^x$, with x continuing to represent the number of days passed since the firework stand was opened. What implications can you draw from this information?

14. When a teacher asked her beginning algebra class to provide an example of an exponential function, over half of the students offered the function $f(x) = x^2$ because "the function is growing faster and faster".

a. What is your assessment of these students' answer?

b. Compare the growth patterns of $f(x) = x^2$ and $g(x) = 2^x$. Construct a table of values and create a graph of f and g on the same axes. Then use the graphs and table values to compare and contrast their growth patterns.

c. Compare the growth patterns of $h(x) = x^3$ and $j(x) = 3^x$. Construct a table of values and create a graph of h and j on the same axes. Then use the graphs and table values to compare and contrast their growth patterns.

15. Define a function that models each town's population growth in terms of the number of years since the town was established.

a. Smallsville starts with 500 people and grows by 10 people per year.

b. Growsville starts with 500 people and grows by 10% each year.

c. Shrinktown starts with 500 people and declines by 10% each year.

d. Littletown starts with 500 people and declines by 10 people per year.

16. Each given function defines the population for a city in terms of the time t in years since the city was established. Write a sentence that describes the city's initial population and growth pattern.

    a. $f(t) = 2000(1.24)^t$ b. $g(t) = 1500 + 20t$ c. $h(t) = 4000(0.68)^t$

    d. $k(t) = 2500 - 40t$ e. $f(t) = 1500(1.4)^{t/2}$

17. The US population was about 273.6 million in 1996. Since that time the population increased by approximately 1.1% each year.

    a. Define a function f that expresses the population P of the US in millions as a function of the number of years t since 1996.

    b. What was the approximate population of the US in 2010 according to your model?

    c. Assuming the population continues to grow at 1.1% per year, in what year will the US population reach 400 million people?

18. A biologist counted 426 bees in a bee colony. His tracking of the colony revealed that the number of bees increased by 4% each month over the next year.

    a. Approximately how many bees were in the colony 3 months after the initial count?

    b. How many months passed before the number of bees reached 500?

19. A company purchases a new car for $25,000 for their employees to use. For accounting purposes, they decide to depreciate the value of the car by 14.5% each year.

    a. Using this method of depreciation, what is the value of the car after 2 years?

    b. What is the ratio of the car's value in one year compared to its value the previous year? Explain the meaning of the value of this ratio.

    c. Define a function that models the value of the car as a function of the number of years since the company purchased it.

    d. When will the value of the car be less than $1000?

III. 1-UNIT GROWTH AND DECAY FACTORS, PERCENT CHANGE, AND INITIAL VALUES (TEXT: S2)

20. Determine the growth or decay factor, percent change, and initial value for each of the following exponential functions.

    a. $f(x) = 2^x$

    Initial Value:
    1-unit Growth Factor:
    1-unit Percent Change:

    b. $f(x) = (0.98)^x$

    Initial Value:
    1-unit Decay Factor:
    1-unit Percent Change:

    c. $f(x) = 0.56 \cdot (0.25)^x$

    Initial Value:
    1-unit Decay Factor:
    1-unit Percent Change:

    d. $f(x) = 3 \cdot (1.6)^x$

    Initial Value:
    1-unit Growth Factor:
    1-unit Percent Change:

21. The given tables represent patterns of exponential growth. Determine the initial value, 1-unit growth/decay factor, 1-unit percent change, and define a formula to model the data in each table.

    a.

x	0	1	2	3
$f(x)$	512	384	288	216

    Initial Value: 1-unit Decay Factor:
    1-unit Percent Change: Formula:

    b.

x	1	2	3
$g(x)$	11.2	15.68	21.952

    Initial Value: 1-unit Growth Factor:
    1-unit Percent Change: Formula:

22. Determine the growth or decay factor, percent change, initial value, and formula for each of the following graphs modeled by exponential functions.

a.

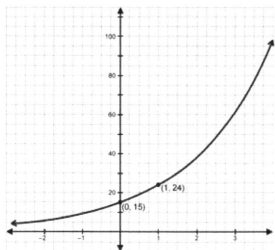

b.

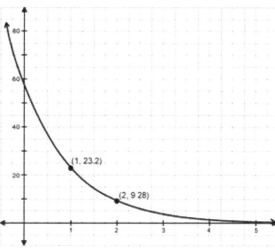

Growth Factor:
Percent Change:
Formula:

Decay Factor:
Percent Change:
Formula:

23. An investment of $9000 decreased by 2.4% each month.
    a. Determine the initial value of the investment, the 1-month decay factor, and the 1-month percent change of the investment.
    b. Define a function f that determines the value of the investment in terms of the number of months since the initial investment was made.
    c. Determine the value of the investment 12 months after the money was invested.

24. The population of Canada in 1990 was 27,512,000 and in 2000 it was 30,689,000. Assume that Canada's population increased exponentially over this time.
    a. Determine the initial value, the 10-year growth factor, and the 10-year percent change of Canada's population.
    b. Define a function f that defines the population of Canada in terms of the number of *decades* (10-year periods) since 1990.
    c. Assuming Canada's growth rate remains consistent, predict the approximate population of Canada in 2030.

25. One year after an investment was made, the amount of money in the account was $1844.50. Two years after the investment was made, the amount of money in the account was $2001.28.
    a. Determine the initial value of the investment, the investment's 1-month growth factor, and the investment's 1-month percent change.
    b. Define a function f that defines the value of the investment in terms of the number of months since the investment was made.
    c. Determine when the value of the investment will reach $4000.

26. The mass of bacteria in a Petri dish was initially measured to be 14 micrograms and increased by 12% each hour over a period of 15 hours.
    a. Determine the 1-hour growth factor of the bacteria.
    b. By what total percent did the bacteria increase during the 15-hour time period?
    c. Determine how long it will take for the mass of bacteria to double.

IV. PARTIAL AND *N*-UNIT GROWTH FACTORS (TEXT: S3)

27. A certain strain of bacteria that is growing on your kitchen counter doubles in number every 5 minutes. Assume that you start with only one bacterium.
    a. What quantities are changing in this situation? What quantities are not changing?
    b. Define a function that gives the number of bacteria present after *n* 5-minute intervals.
    c. Represent the number of bacteria present after 30 minutes. How many bacteria are there at that time?
    d. How many bacteria are present after 1 minute? 2 minutes? 5 minutes?
    e. Determine the 1-minute growth factor. By what percent does the bacteria change every *minute*?
    f. Determine the 2-minute growth factor and 2-minute percent change.
    g. Define a function that gives the number of bacteria present after *t* minutes.
    h. Define a function that gives the number of bacteria present after *h* hours.

28. The number of deer in a park reserve was counted to be 27 on January 1, 2000. Six months later, the number of deer was counted to be 38.
    a. Determine the 6-month growth factor and 6-month percent change for the situation.
    b. Determine the 1-month growth factor and 1-month percent change for the situation.
    c. Define a function that relates the number deer in the park reserve since January 1, 2000 in terms of the number of months that have elapsed since January 1, 2000. (*Assuming the number of deer continues to increase by the same percent each month.*)
    d. Define a function that relates the number deer in the park reserve since January , 2000 in terms of the number of *6-month intervals* that have elapsed since January 1, 2000. (*Assuming the number of deer continues to increase by the same percent each month.*)
    e. Use one of your functions to determine when the number of deer will reach approximately 125.

29. The population of Egypt in 2002 was 73,312,600, and was 78,887,000 in 2006. Assume the population of Egypt grew exponentially over this period.
    a. Determine the 4-year growth factor and percent change.
    b. Determine the 1-year growth factor and percent change.
    c. Define a function that gives the population of Egypt in terms of the number of years that have elapsed since 2002.
    d. Re-write your function from part (c) so that it gives the population of Egypt in terms of the number of *decades* that have elapsed since 2002.
    e. Assuming Egypt's population continued to grow according to this model, how long will it take for population of Egypt to double?

30. An animal reserve in Arizona had 93 wild coyotes. Due to drought, there were only 61 coyotes after 3 months. Assume that the number of coyotes decreases (or decays) exponentially.
    a. Find the 3-month decay factor and percent change.
    b. Find the 1-month decay factor and percent change.
    c. Define a function that represents the number of coyotes in terms of the number of elapsed months.
    d. Re-write your function from part (c) so that it gives the number of coyotes in terms of the number of *years* that have elapsed.
    e. How long will it take for the number of coyotes to be one-half of the original number?

31. Sales of music albums decreased by 6% each year over a period of 8 years.
    a. Determine the decay factor for 1 year.
    b. By what total percent did album sales change during the 8-year time period?
    c. How long will it take for the album sales to be half of what they were at the beginning of this period? A*ssume the trend continues in the future.*

32. The population of a town increased or decreased by the following percentages. For each situation, find the population's *annual percent change*.
    a. increases by 60% every 12 years
    b. decreases by 35% every 7 years
    c. doubles in size every 6 years
    d. increases by 4.2% every 2 months
    e. decreases by 7% every week

33. The number of asthma sufferers in the world was about 84 million in 1990 and 130 million in 2001. Let N represent the number of asthma sufferers (in millions) worldwide t years after 1990.
    a. Define a function that expresses N as a linear function of t. Describe the meaning of the slope and vertical intercept in the context of the problem.
    b. Define a function that expresses N as an exponential function of t. Describe the meaning of the growth factor and the vertical intercept in the context of the problem.
    c. The world's population grew by an annual percent change of 3.7% over those 11 years. Did the percent of the world's population who suffer from asthma increase or decrease?
    d. What is the long-term implication of choosing a linear vs. exponential model to make future predictions about the number of asthma sufferers in the world?

34. In the second half of the 20th century, the city of Phoenix, Arizona exploded in size. Between 1960 and 2000, the population of Phoenix increased by 2.76% each year. In the year 2000, the population of Phoenix was determined to be 1.32 million people.
    a. Define an exponential function f that gives the population P in Phoenix (in millions of people) where the input values t represent the number of years after the year 2000.
    b. Sketch a graph of this function.
    c. What input to your function will give the population of Phoenix in 1972? 1983? 1994? According to your model, approximately how many people lived in Phoenix in 1972? 1983? 1994?
    d. In what year did the population reach 1,000,000 people?
    e. The change in the population of Phoenix is increasing for equal changes in time. Illustrate this on the graph of f for at least 3 different equal intervals of time.
    f. Now, define an exponential function, g, modeling the population of Phoenix in millions of people n years after 1960. Sketch a graph of this function.
    h. How does the function you created in part (f) compare to the original function created in part (a)? How are the graphs of the two functions similar and different? Explain your reasoning.

V. *n*-UNIT GROWTH AND DECAY FACTORS ($n \neq 1$) (TEXT: S3)

35. For each function given below, find the initial value, specified factors, and specified percent changes.
    a. $f(x) = 2^{x/3}$
       i) Initial Value:
       ii) 1-unit Growth Factor:
       iii) 1-unit Percent Change:
       iv) 4-unit Growth Factor:
       v) 1/5-unit Growth Factor:

    b. $f(x) = 5 \cdot (0.98)^{x/4}$
       i) Initial Value:
       ii) 1-unit Decay Factor:
       iii) 1-unit Percent Change:
       iv) 3-unit Decay Factor:
       v) 1/2-unit Decay Factor:

    c. $f(x) = (0.25)^{2x}$
       i) Initial Value:
       ii) 1-unit Decay Factor:
       iii) 1-unit Percent Change:
       iv) 5-unit Decay Factor:
       v) 1/3-unit Decay Factor:

    d. $f(x) = 3 \cdot (1.6)^{5x}$
       i) Initial Value:
       ii) 1-unit Growth Factor:
       iii) 1-unit Percent Change:
       iv) 3-unit Growth Factor:
       v) 1/4-unit Growth Factor:

36. For each exponential relationship, determine the specified growth factors. Write your answers in exponential and decimal form (rounded to the nearest thousandth). In addition, determine the initial value and define the exponential function formula that models the data.

a.

x	1	3	5	7
$f(x)$	512	384	288	216

   i) Initial Value:
   ii) 1-unit Decay Factor:
   iii) 1-unit Percent Change:
   iv) 3-unit Decay Factor:
   v) 1/3-unit Decay Factor:
   vi) Function Formula:

b.

x	2	5	8	11
$g(x)$	8	11.2	15.68	21.952

   i) Initial Value:
   ii) 1-unit Growth Factor:
   iii) 1-unit Percent Change:
   iv) 2-unit Growth Factor:
   v) 1/4-unit Growth Factor:
   vi) Function Formula:

37. Determine the specified decay factors. Write your answers in exponential and decimal form (round to the nearest thousandth). Then determine the function formula that models the data.
   a. 3-unit Decay Factor:
   b. 5-unit Decay Factor:
   c. 1-unit Decay Factor:
   d. 0.6-unit Decay Factor:
   e. Initial Value:
   f. Function Formula:

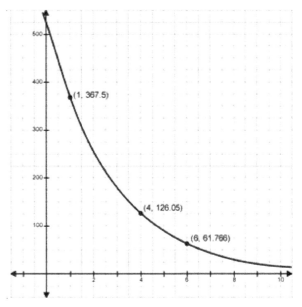

38. Determine the specified decay factors. Write your answers in exponential and decimal form (round to the nearest thousandth). Then determine the function formula that models the data.
   a. 2-unit Growth Factor:
   b. ½-unit Growth Factor:
   c. 1-unit Growth Factor:
   d. 2.5-unit Growth Factor:
   e. 5-unit Growth Factor:
   f. Initial Value:
   g. Function Formula:

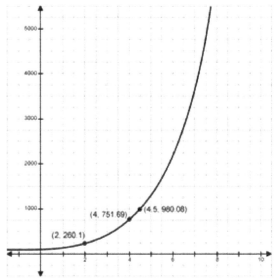

39. *Determine the specified growth factors for the following relationship. Write your answers in exponential and decimal form (round to the nearest thousandth).* The mass of bacteria in an experiment at time t days after its start is given by $f(t) = 95(4)^{t/5}$.
    a. 5-day growth factor: b. 1-day growth factor:
    c. Circle the statement(s) below that describes the behavior of the function above and give reasoning for why the statement(s) are true:
        i.   An initial mass of 95 μg of bacteria quadruples every 1/5-day.
        ii. An initial mass of 95 μg of bacteria quadruples every 5-days.
        iii. An initial mass of 95 μg of bacteria increases by 50% every 1-day.

40. *Determine the specified growth factors for the following relationship. Write your answers in exponential and decimal form (round to the nearest thousandth).* The number of buffalo in a wildlife preserve at time t months after its initial measure is given by $f(t) = 49(0.97)^{2t}$.
    a. 1-month decay factor: b. ½-month decay factor:
    c. Circle the statement(s) below that describe(s) the behavior of the function above:
        i.   An initial number of 49 buffalo decreases by 3% every ½-day.
        ii. An initial number of 49 buffalo decreases by 3% every 2-days.
        iii. An initial number of 49 buffalo decreases by 5.91% every 1-month.

41. *Determine the specified growth factors for each relationship. Write your answers in exponential and decimal form (round to the nearest thousandth).*
    a. The population of Jackson has 57,421 people and is growing by 4.78% every 4 years.
        i)   8-year growth factor:
        ii) What is the percent change (increase) over 8-year period?
        iii) 1-year growth factor:
        iv) What is the percent change (increase) over 1-year period?
    b. The amount of drug B in your body decreases by 18% every 3 hours.
        i)   24-hour decay factor:
        ii) What is the percent change (decrease) over a 24-hour period?
        iii) 1-hour decay factor:
        iv) What is the percent change (decrease) over a 1-hour period?

42. For each relationship, do the following.
    a. Determine whether the relationship could be linear or exponential.
    b. Fill in the blanks of the tables based on your answer to (a).
    c. Define a function formula that models the data in each table.

Table i	
Input	Output
−2.0	−10.0
−1.5	
−1.0	−7.5
−0.5	
0.0	−5.0
0.5	
1.0	−2.5
1.5	
2.0	0

Table ii	
Input	Output
−4.0	0.1111
−3.0	
−2.0	0.3333
−1.0	
0.0	1.0
1.0	
2.0	3.0
3.0	
4.0	9.0

Table iii	
Input	Output
0.0	132.0
0.5	
1.0	29.04
1.5	
2.0	6.3888
2.5	
3.0	1.4055
3.5	
4.0	0.309
4.5	

VI. COMPOUNDING PERIODS & COMPOUND INTEREST FORMULA (TEXT: S4)

43. The given table illustrates the value of an investment from the end of the 7th compounding period to the end of the 10th compounding period.

Number of compounding periods p	Investment value
7	$7,105.57
8	$7,209.31
9	$7,314.57
10	$7,421.36

   a. Verify that the data in the table represents exponential growth.
   b. How does the investment value change from the end of the 7th to the end of the 9th compounding period? From the end of the 8th to the end of the 10th compounding period?
   c. What is the value of the investment after 3 compounding periods? After 20 compounding periods?
   d. Define a function f that expresses the investment as a function of the number of compounding periods p. *Note: p is defined to be the values* $\{0,1,2,3,...\}$. Explain the meaning of each of the values in your function.
   e. Construct a graph of the function defined in part (d). Label the axes appropriately, then pick one coordinate point from the graph and explain what it represents.
   f. Determine the number of compounding periods until the investment reaches $400,000.

44. For each of the following accounts, determine the percent change per compounding period. Give your answer in both decimal and percentage form.
   a. 5% APR compounded monthly
   b. 6.7% APR compounded quarterly
   c. 3.2% APR compounded daily
   d. 8% APR compounded each hour

45. For each of the accounts in Exercise #44, give the growth factor per compounding period, then give the annual growth factor and the annual percent change (APY).

46. If you invest $1,200 in a CD with an APR of 3.5% compounded monthly, the following expression will calculate the value of the CD in 6 years: $1200\left(1+\frac{0.035}{12}\right)^{12(6)}$

   Explain what each part of the expression represents in this calculation.
   a. $\frac{0.035}{12}$
   b. $1+\frac{0.035}{12}$
   c. $12(6)$
   d. $\left(1+\frac{0.035}{12}\right)^{12}$
   e. $\left(1+\frac{0.035}{12}\right)^{12(6)}$

47. Write an expression that would calculate the value of the following account after 14 years: $8100 is invested at an APR of 4.8% compounded semiannually (twice per year).

48. Write an expression that would calculate the value of the following account after 30 years: $16,000 is invested at an APR of 3.5% compounded daily.

49. An investment of $10,000 with Barnes Bank earns a 2.42% APR compounded *monthly*.
   a. Define a function that gives the investment's value as a function of the number of years since it began.
   b. Determine the investment's value after 20 years.
   c. Determine the annual growth factor and annual percent change (APY).
   d. Determine how long will it take the investment value to double.
   e. Another bank says they will pay you the same interest (2.42% APR), but compounded daily. What would be the value of a $10,000 investment with this bank, leaving it there for 20 years? Compare this answer to your account with Barnes Bank.

50. You just won $1000 in the lottery and you decide to invest this money for 10 years.
    a. Which of the three different accounts would you choose to invest your $1000? Provide calculations for each account and justify your reasoning.
        - Account #1 pays 14% interest each year, compounded annually (once per year).
        - Account #2 pays 13.5% interest per year, compounded monthly.
        - Account #3 pays 13% interest per year, compounded weekly.
    b. Describe how your money increases as time increases for each account. Be sure to incorporate the annual growth factor and annual percent change into your description!

51. Karen received an inheritance from her grandparents and wants to invest the money. She is offered the following options of accounts to invest into:
        - 4.5% APR, compounded semi-annually
        - 4.3% APR, compounded daily
    a. Which option should she choose? Explain your reasoning using the accounts' APY.
    b. If Karen decides on the first option, by what *percent* will her investment have *increased* after 10 years?

52. John decides to start saving money for a new car. He knows he can invest money into an account which will earn a 6.5% APR, compounded weekly, and would like to have saved $10,000 after 5 years.
    a. How much money will he need to invest into the account now so that he has $10,000 after 5 years?
    b. Determine the APY (Annual Percent Yield) for the account.
    c. Determine the 5-year percent change for the account.

VII.   INVESTMENT ACTIVITY: FOCUS ON FORMULAS AND MOTIVATING *e* (TEXT: S4)

53. $4500 is initially invested into an account with an APR of 7%.
    a. Determine the value of the account at the end of the given years and the APY for each type of compounding per year.
    b. Compare the short-term vs. the long-term impact of increasing the number of times interest is compounded each year.

Year	Compounded Monthly	Compounded Daily	Compounded Continuously
1			
2			
4			
10			
30			
APY			

54. Determine the value of each of the following accounts after 14 years.
    a. Initial investment is $4000 with a 7.1% APR compounded continuously.
    b. Initial investment is $750 with a 3.3% APR compounded continuously.
    c. Initial investment is $2000 with a 5% APY compounded continuously.

55. $2000 is initially invested in an account with an APR of 3.4% compounded continuously.
    a. Determine the value of the account at the end of 5 years.
    b. Write a function that models the value of the account at the end of *t* years.
    c. What is the annual percent change (APY) of the account? What does this value represent?
    d. What is the percent change over 10 years for this account?

56. $18,000 is initially invested in an account with an APR of 5.1%.
    a. Does it make a bigger impact going from compounding interest annually to monthly or going from compounding interest daily to continuously?
    b. What is the annual percent change (APY) for each of the four compounding methods listed in (a)?
    c. If interest is compounded continuously, how much interest does the account earn over the first 10 years?

57. An initial population of 32 million people increases at a continuous percent rate of 1.9% per year since the year 2000.
    a. Determine the function that gives the population in terms of the number of years since 2000.
    b. Determine the population in the year 2019.
    c. What is the annual growth factor for this context? Explain two ways we can determine this value.
    d. What does your answer to part (c) represent in this context?

58. Carbon-14 is used to estimate the age of organic compounds. Over time, carbon-14 decays at a continuous percent rate of 11.4% per thousand years from the moment the organism containing it dies. Carbon-14 is typically measured in micrograms.
    a. What quantities are changing in this situation? What quantities are not changing?
    b. Define a function that gives the amount, at any moment, of Carbon-14 remaining in a piece of wood that starts out with 150 micrograms of Carbon-14. (*Remember that Carbon-14's decay rate is per thousand years.*)
    c. Construct a graph of this function. Be sure to label your axes!
    d. What is the percent change every 1000 years?
    e. What is the percent change every 5000 years? Explain your reasoning.

VIII.   THE INVERSE OF AN EXPONENTIAL FUNCTION (TEXT: S5)

Log Property #1: $\log_b(m \cdot n) = \log_b(m) + \log_b(n)$ for any $b > 0$, $b \neq 1$ and $m, n > 0$

Log Property #2: $\log_b\left(\frac{m}{n}\right) = \log_b(m) - \log_b(n)$ for any $b > 0$, $b \neq 1$ and $m, n > 0$

Log Property #3: $\log_b\left(m^c\right) = c \cdot \log_b m$ for any $b > 0$, $b \neq 1$ and $m, n > 0$

59. Estimate the value of each logarithmic expression. Explain why your estimate makes sense:
    a. $\log_4(60)$ b. $\log_3(143)$ c. $\log_8\left(\frac{1}{64}\right)$ d. $\log_9(27)$

60. Find the unknown in each of the following equations. *Estimate if necessary. For parts (g) and (h), assume z is a positive number.*
    a. $\log_3(20) = y$ b. $2\left(\log_5(625)\right) = y$ c. $\log_5(1) = y$ d. $\log_2(30) = y$
    e. $\log_2(x) = 4.2$ f. $\log_7(x) = -2$ g. $\log_z(343) = 3$ h. $\log_z(1) = 0$

61. For each of the following:
    • Write the expression as a single logarithm.
    • Evaluate to a single number or estimate the value of the expression.
    a. $\log_5(6.25) + \log_5(100) + \log_5(25)$ b. $\log_4\left(\frac{1}{32}\right) + \log_4\left(\frac{1}{8}\right)$ c. $2 \cdot \log_6(12) + \log_6(4)$
    d. $\ln(6) + \ln(3) - \ln(2)$ e. $\log_5(6) - \log_5(100)$ f. $\frac{1}{2}\left(\log_5(8) + \log_5(3)\right)$

62. Solve each of the following for *x*. (*Hint: Use the properties discussed in class or your understanding of logarithms.*)

    a. $\log(0.01x) = 0$ b. $\log_5(25x^2) = 6$ c. $\ln\left(\frac{x}{10}\right) = 4$

63. Solve each of the following for *x*.

    a. $\log_2(2+x) + \log_2(7) = 3$ b. $\ln(3x^2) - \ln(5x) = \ln(x+9)$

64. Rewrite each of the following as sums and differences of a logarithm of some number.

    a. $\log_7\left(\frac{4}{y}\right)$ b. $\log_2\left(x^4 \cdot 12\right)$ c. $\log_5\left(\frac{10x^3}{y^5}\right)$

65. Rewrite each of the following exponential equations in logarithmic form.

    a. $y = 11^x$ b. $y = 1.7(3.2)^t$ c. $y = 200(1.0027)^{12t}$

66. Graph each of the following functions.

    a. $f(x) = \log_3(x)$ b. $g(x) = \log_5(x)$

67. a. Sketch the following two functions on the same set of axes: $f(x) = \log(x)$ and $g(x) = \log_5(x)$

    b. Consider the rates of change of each of the functions. Explain why $g(x)$ has a greater rate of change than $f(x)$ for all values of $x > 1$.

    c. For what values of *x* is $\log(x) > \log_5(x)$? Explain your reasoning.

IX. SOLVING EXPONENTIAL AND LOGARITHMIC EQUATIONS (TEXT: S5)

68. The amount of an investment is represented by $f(t) = 4186.58(1.025)^t$. Algebraically, determine when (in compounding periods, *t*) the investment will reach $1,000,000.

69. An initial amount of 120 mg of caffeine is metabolized in the body and decreases at a continuous percent rate of 21% per hour.

    a. Define an exponential function that gives the amount of caffeine remaining in the body after *t* hours.

    b. How many hours will it take for the amount of caffeine to reach half of the initial amount? (*Solve this both graphically and symbolically to verify your answers.*)

70. An initial investment of $6000 is made to an account with an APR of 4.7%.

    a. If interest is compounded monthly, how many years will it take for the account balance to be $10,290.32? Solve algebraically and check your answer.

    b. If interest is compounded continuously, how many years will it take for the account balance to be $9,510.15?

71. The amount of medicine in a patient's bloodstream for reducing high blood pressure decreases at a continuous percent rate of 27% per hour. This medicine is effective until the amount in the bloodstream drops below 1.2 mg. A doctor prescribes a dose of 85 mg.

    a. Define the function *A* that models the amount of medicine remaining in the bloodstream after *t* hours.

    b. About how long until 45 mg of medicine remains in the patient's bloodstream? 1.2 mg?

72. The rate at which a wound heals can be modeled by the exponential function $f(n) = Ie^{-0.1316n}$ where I represents the initial size of the wound in square millimeters and $f(n)$ represents the size of the wound after n days. This function assumes no infection is present and no antibiotic ointment is used to speed healing.
    a. Suppose you scrape your knee and get a wound 300 square millimeters in size. Define a function to model the size of the wound with respect to time.
    b. How large will the wound be after one week?
    c. How long will it take for the wound to be 20% of its original size?
    d. You want to know how long it will take to reduce the size of the wound to 20% of the size you determined in part (c). How will the amount of time it takes to do this compare to the amount of time it took to reduce the wound to 20% of its original size? Explain your reasoning.

73. Given the function $f(t) = 10(0.71)^t$, where t is in years, complete the following.
    a. What is the annual percent change?
    b. Convert the function $f(t) = 10(0.71)^t$ into the equivalent form $f(t) = ae^{kt}$
    c. What is the continuous annual percent rate?

74. The town of Gilbertville increased from a population of 3,562 people in 1970 to a population of 9,765 in 2000.
    a. Define an exponential function that models the town's population as a function of the number of years since 1970.
    b. What is the annual percent change?
    c. Use your function to predict the town's population in 2019.
    d. According to your function, when will the town's population reach 40,000 people? (*Answer this question both graphically and symbolically.*)
    e. After how many years from *any* reference year will the population triple?

This investigation contains review and practice with important skills and procedures you may need in this module and future modules. Your instructor may assign this investigation as an introduction to the module or may ask you to complete select exercises "just in time" to help you when needed. Alternatively, you can complete these exercises on your own to help review important skills.

Factoring Variable Expressions
Use this section prior to the module or with/after Investigation 1.

Factoring is the process of rewriting a number as a product of factors. For example, we can rewrite 10 as $5 \cdot 2$. The value is still the same but we've written the number as a product.

What if the number is the value of a varying quantity? For example, the variable x could be used to represent all the values of some varying quantity. Then, for ALL possible values of x, the expression $(\frac{1}{2}x)(2)$ has the same value but is written as a product.

If $x = 8$, then $\frac{1}{2}x = 4$, and so $(\frac{1}{2}x)(2)$ is $(4)(2)$, which is 8 written as a product of two numbers.

1. Repeat this for each of the following values of x (use the expression $(\frac{1}{2}x)(2)$ to write that value of x as a product of two numbers).
   a. $x = 12$ b. $x = 17$ c. $x = -28$ d. $x = 1.3$

2. a. Can you create a variable expression different from $(\frac{1}{2}x)(2)$ that will always represent the value of x written as a product of two other numbers? Give an example.

   b. Choose two different values for x and show how your answer to part (a) "works".

3. $2x^2 + 3x$ is a variable expression that can be written in factored form as $x(2x + 3)$.
   a. Pick two values for x and evaluate $2x^2 + 3x$.

   b. Use the same values for x to show that $x(2x + 3)$ represents the same value as $2x^2 + 3x$ but written as a product of two numbers. `

In Exercises #4-6, do the following.
- (i) Rewrite the expression in factored form.
- (ii) Pick a value for x and use it to evaluate the original expression and your factored form to demonstrate that your answer to part (a) represents the same value as the original expression written as a product of two numbers.

4. $5x + 35$ 　　　　　　　5. $6x^2 - 13x$ 　　　　　　　6. $3x^2 + 12x$

In Exercises #7-9 you are given a variable expression written in factored form. Use the distributive property to rewrite each expression in expanded form.

7. $6x(x + 7)$ 　　　　　　　8. $6y(3y - 2x)$ 　　　　　　　9. $a(ab^2 + a^3c)$

Expanding Binomial Products
Use this section prior to the module or with/after Investigation 3.

When a product involves two variable expressions with two or more terms, writing the expanded form can sometimes be tricky. One very useful way to think about the product is to use an area model. To demonstrate the idea, let's think about the number 21, which could be written as a product $(7)(3)$, and even broken down further and written as a product of two sums like $(3 + 4)(2 + 1)$. Let's visualize this product as representing a rectangular area of 21 square units. *See diagram to the right.*

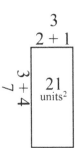

If we break down this area into sub-rectangles, we can see that the entire area is made up of four sub-areas measuring $(3)(2)$ square units, $(3)(1)$ square units, $(4)(2)$ square units, and $(4)(1)$ square units. *See diagram to the left.*

Thus, $(3 + 4)(2 + 1)$ is equivalent to $(3)(2) + (3)(1) + (4)(2) + (4)(1)$.

We can use the same basic idea to product of $(x + 2)(x + 3)$. *See diagram to*

	x	$+$	2
x	$(x)(x)$ or x^2 units²		$(x)(2)$ or $2x$ units²
$+$			
3	$(3)(x)$ or $3x$ units²		$(3)(2)$ or 6 units²

visualize the the right.

Using this diagram it should be clear that $(x + 2)(x + 3)$ is $x^2 + 3x + 2x + (2)(3)$. This expression can be simplified to x^2 the expanded (and simplified) form.

equivalent to $+ 5x + 6$. This is

In Exercises #10-12, rewrite each product in expanded form by first drawing an area diagram.

10. $(x + 6)(x + 2)$ 11. $(x + 3)(x + 5)$ 12. $(x + 1)(x + 4)$

In Exercises #13-18, rewrite each product in expanded form. *You do not need to draw an area diagram but you can if it helps you. Remember that something like $(x + 3)^2$ is shorthand for $(x + 3)(x + 3)$.*

13. $(x + 8)(x + 3)$ 14. $(x + 1)(2x + 5)$ 15. $(2x + 3)(3x + 7)$

16. $(x + 5)^2$ 17. $(x + 8)^2$ 18. $(2 + x)^2$

In Exercises #19-24, rewrite each product in expanded form. *We recommend rewriting subtraction as addition with a negative to avoid sign errors. For example, rewrite $x - 5$ as $x + (-5)$. You do not need to draw an area diagram but you can if it helps you. Remember that something like $(x - 3)^2$ is shorthand for $(x - 3)(x - 3)$.*

19. $(x - 3)(x + 5)$ 20. $(x + 2)(3x - 1)$ 21. $(3x - 2)(3x - 4)$

22. $(x - 1)^2$ 23. $(x - 6)^2$ 24. $(2x - 3)^2$

25. a. Your friend said that $(a + b)^2$ can be written as $a^2 + b^2$. Is he right? Justify your answer using an area diagram.

    b. Use an area diagram to help you write the general expanded form for any product $(a - b)^2$.

Factoring Polynomial Expressions

Use this section prior to the module or with/after Investigation 3.

If we want to write a polynomial expression like $x^2 + 7x + 10$ in factored form we can use an area diagram to help us organize our thinking. From our work above it should be clear that the top left rectangle in our area diagram will have an area of x^2 square units (with side lengths of x and x units) and the bottom right rectangle must have an area of 10 square units.

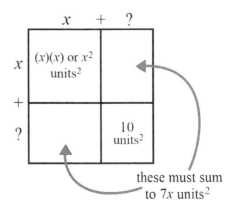

What we need to figure out are the dimensions of the bottom right rectangle that will 1) make its area 10 square units and 2) the areas of the other two rectangles sum to $7x$ square units.

Our options include any pair of numbers with a product of 10 (which includes $10 \cdot 1$ and $5 \cdot 2$). These options are shown below.

$$(x+10)(x+1) \qquad \text{or} \qquad (x+5)(x+2)$$

26. a. Which of the options is "correct"? What does that tell us about the factored form of $x^2 + 7x + 10$?

   b. Choose a value for x and evaluate the expression $x^2 + 7x + 10$. Then use the same value to evaluate the factored form to show that it represents the same value of $x^2 + 7x + 10$ but written as a product of two numbers.

   c. Repeat part (b) with a different value for x.

In Exercises #27-32, rewrite each expression in factored form. For example, $x^2 + 9x + 14$ would be rewritten as $(x+7)(x+2)$. *Draw an area diagram if it helps you complete the process.*

27. $x^2 + 8x + 12$
          28. $x^2 + 9x + 8$
          29. $x^2 + 2x - 15$

30. $x^2 - x - 42$
          31. $x^2 - 7x + 12$
          32. $x^2 + 3x - 40$

In Exercises #33-35, rewrite each expression in factored form by first factoring x out of the expression. For example, $x^3 - 3x^2 - 10x$ can be written as $x(x^2 - 3x - 10)$, and then can be written as $x(x+2)(x-5)$.

33. $x^3 + 10x^2 + 24x$
          34. $x^3 - 6x^2 - 16x$
          35. $x^3 - 6x^2 + 9x$

Solving Polynomial Equations
Use this section prior to the module or with/after Investigation 4.

Consider the polynomial equation $x^2 + 8x + 7 = 0$. The solutions are the values of x such that the expression $x^2 + 8x + 7$ has a value of 0. There are several ways to solve these equations. Let's start by factoring the expression.

$$x^2 + 8x + 7 = 0$$
$$(x + 7)(x + 1) = 0$$

We now have a product of two numbers (the number $x + 7$ and the number $x + 1$) that evaluates to 0. What does that tell us? Well, the only way a product of two numbers can be 0 is if one of the two numbers in the product is 0. In other words, if $ab = 0$, then either $a = 0$ or $b = 0$. This is known as the ***zero-product property***.

What that means in this context is that either $(x + 7) = 0$ or $(x + 1) = 0$.

$$x^2 + 8x + 7 = 0$$
$$(x + 7)(x + 1) = 0$$
$$x + 7 = 0 \quad \text{or} \quad x + 1 = 0$$
$$x = -7 \quad \text{or} \quad x = -1$$

So either $x = -7$ or $x = -1$. These are the only values that could make $x^2 + 8x + 7$ have a value of 0.

36. Substitute $x = -7$ and $x = -1$ into the expression $x^2 + 8x + 7$ to show that each produces a value of 0.

In Exercises #37-39 solve each equation by factoring and using the zero-product property. Check your answer by graphing. *To do this, graph a function f whose outputs are defined by the polynomial expression and demonstrate that the function value is 0 for each x-value solution.*

37. $x^2 - 13x + 30 = 0$ 38. $x^2 + 7x - 18 = 0$ 39. $2x^2 + 5x + 3 = 0$

Sometimes the equation is not set equal to 0, meaning we can't use the zero-product property. However, we can rewrite the equation so that the zero-product property applies. See the following example.

$$x^2 + 9x + 13 = 4x + 7 \qquad \text{(subtract } 4x \text{ and 7 from both sides)}$$
$$x^2 + 5x + 6 = 0$$
$$(x + 3)(x + 2) = 0$$
$$x + 3 = 0 \quad \text{or} \quad x + 2 = 0$$
$$x = -3 \quad \text{or} \quad x = -2$$

In Exercises #40-42, solve each equation by first rewriting it so that the equation is equal to 0.

40. $x^2 + 5x + 2 = 3x + 10$ 41. $x^2 - 12x + 24 = -2x + 3$ 42. $x^2 + 1 = 2x + 16$

If the equation is quadratic (and written in the form $ax^2 + bx + c = 0$), then the x-values that make the expression evaluate to 0 (the solutions to the equation) can be represented by $x = -\frac{b}{2a} \pm \frac{\sqrt{b^2 - 4ac}}{2a}$. This is called the **quadratic formula** and represents the solutions to equations of the form $ax^2 + bx + c = 0$.

Note that "$\pm$" indicates that the quadratic formula can produce two solutions.

$$2x^2 - 5x + 1 = 0 \quad (\text{so } a = 2, b = -5, c = 1)$$

$$x = -\frac{b}{2a} \pm \frac{\sqrt{b^2 - 4ac}}{2a}$$

$$x = -\frac{-5}{2(2)} \pm \frac{\sqrt{(-5)^2 - 4(2)(1)}}{2(2)}$$

$$x = -\frac{-5}{4} \pm \frac{\sqrt{25 - 8}}{4}$$

$$x = \frac{5}{4} \pm \frac{\sqrt{17}}{4}$$

The solutions are $x = \frac{5}{4} + \frac{\sqrt{17}}{4}$ and $x = \frac{5}{4} - \frac{\sqrt{17}}{4}$.

In Exercises #43-48, solve each equation using the quadratic formula $x = -\frac{b}{2a} \pm \frac{\sqrt{b^2 - 4ac}}{2a}$. *Be very careful and pay attention to the signs.*

43. $2x^2 + 6x + 3 = 0$ 44. $x^2 + 4x - 1 = 0$ 45. $x^2 - 3x - 5 = 0$

46. $3x^2 + 8x + 3 = 0$ 47. $5x^2 - 2x - 1 = 0$ 48. $2x^2 + 11x - 7 = 0$

*1. Examine the bottle given below and imagine the bottle filling with water.
   a. Sketch a graph of the height of water in the bottle as a function of the volume of the water in the bottle. (*It may be helpful to imagine adding equal volumes of water and then consider how the height of the water in the bottle will change.*)

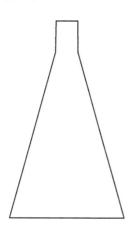
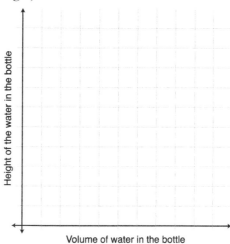

   b. Based on your graph, describe how the height of the water in the bottle changes as the volume of water in the bottle increases throughout the domain. *You may use centimeters and cups as units of measurement to help your description. If you do, add these units to the axes.*

*2. a. Use the bottle animation to determine (and record in the table) the height of the water in the bottle for 6 different volumes of water.

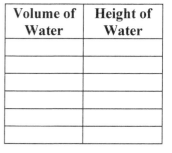

Volume of Water	Height of Water

   b. Use the values in your table to create a revised sketch of the graph of the height of the water in the bottle in terms of the volume of water in the bottle.

   c. Revise your description from Exercise #1 part (b) based on your new graph (if necessary).

   d. Choose an interval of change for the volume of water (please choose an interval of change other than 1 cup). Determine the average rate of change of the height of water in the cup with respect to the volume of water in the bottle. Then explain how to interpret your result.

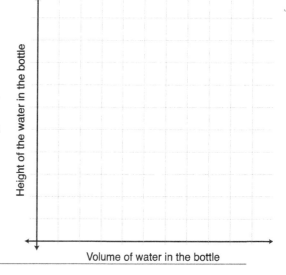

*3. a. Use the graph of the function *f* that represents the *height of water in the bottle* in terms of the *volume of water in the bottle* to complete the following table.

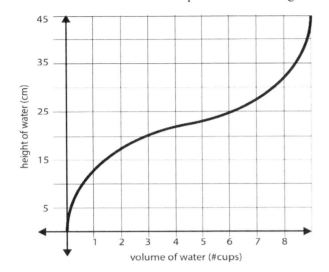

Volume of Water (cups)	Height of Water (cm)	Change in the Water's Height (cm)
0		
1		
2		
3		
4		
5		
6		
7		
8		
9		

b. Use the graph of *f* and table of values to answer the following questions.
  i. How does the water's height change as the volume changes from 0 to 4 cups?

  ii. How does the *change in the water's height* change as the volume changes from 0 to 4 cups?

  iii. Repeat parts (i) and (ii) as the volume changes from 4 cups to 9 cups.

  iv. Find the function's average rate of change over the interval from 0 cups to 3 cups.

  v. Find the function's average rate of change over the interval from 5 cups to 9 cups.

c. Draw a picture of a bottle that would produce the volume-height relationship conveyed in the table and graph of *f*. Label any landmarks on your bottle, and on the graph in part (a), where the function's behavior changes in important ways.

The given graph (from Investigation 1, Exercise #3) represents the relationship between the height (in cm) and volume of water (in cups) in a bottle. Call this function relationship f.

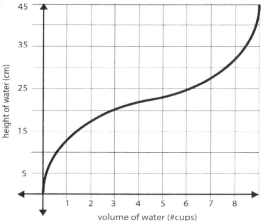

*1. a. On the graph, plot the points $(0, f(0))$ and $(5, f(5))$.

   b. Draw a line that passes through these points.

   c. Determine the constant rate of change for the line you drew. *You can use your estimated values for the water height from Investigation 1.*

It's clear that as the volume of water in the bottle changes from 0 cups to 5 cups the water height does NOT change at a constant rate. However, as we have mentioned before in this course, it's often useful to imagine what the constant rate of change would be to have the same net change in the output for the same change in the input. We call this the ***function's average rate of change over that interval.***

*2. a. Explain how to interpret the meaning of the answer to part (c) in Exercise #1.

   b. Find the average rate of change of the water height in terms of the water volume for each of the following intervals. Make sure to explain how to interpret the meaning of your answer.
     i. As the volume changes from 2 cups to 8 cups.

     ii. As the volume changes from 1 cup to 9 cups.

3. For each of the given functions find the average rate of change over the indicated interval and then discuss with a partner or as a class how to interpret the meaning of your answer.

a. $f(x) = x^3 - 6x^2 + 9x + 10$
as x changes from $x = -1$ to $x = 3$

b. $g(x) = -3 \cdot \sqrt{x+4} + 6$
as x changes from $x = -4$ to $x = 5$

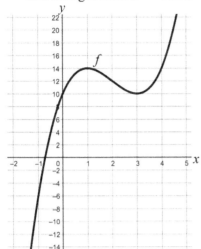 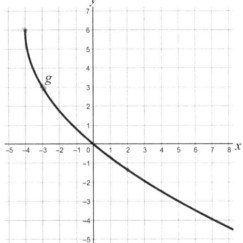

*4. a. Illustrate a change in x from -6.3 to -3.9 on the number line below.

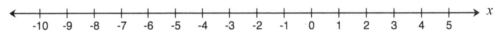

b. T or F: The value of x is decreasing as x changes from -6.3 to -3.9. Justify your response.

c. Function h is defined by $h(x) = -x^2$.

   i. As x increases from -4 to -2.5, $h(x)$ changes from _____ to _____.

   ii. As x increases from -2.5 to -1, $h(x)$ changes from _____ to _____.

   iii. Determine the average rate of change of h on the interval from $x = -4$ to -2.5 and explain how to interpret the meaning of your answer.

   iv. Determine the average rate of change of h on the interval from $x = -2.5$ to -1 and explain how to interpret the meaning of your answer.

   v. **T or F:** The average rate of change of h on the interval from -4 to -2.5 is greater than the average rate of change of h on the interval from -2.5 to -1.

Rates of change (and average rates of change) are measurements of how a function's output quantity changes in tandem with changes in the input quantity. ***Concavity*** is a measurement of how a function's rate of change itself changes in tandem with changes in a function's input quantity.

Concavity

For any function f, imagine looking at an interval of the domain from $x = a$ to $x = b$ and dividing it into any number of equal-sized subintervals.

- f is said to have ***positive concavity*** on the interval (a, b) if the function's average rate over successive intervals always increases.
- f is said to have ***negative concavity*** on the interval (a, b) if the function's average rate over successive intervals always decreases.

---

*5. Return to Exercise #1. Over what interval(s) of the domain does the function have positive concavity? Over what interval(s) of the domain does the function have negative concavity? Make sure you can justify your answer.

In Exercise #1 the function changed from having negative concavity when the volume was less than 4 cups to having positive concavity when the volume was greater than 4 cups. The point (5, 23) is thus an ***inflection point*** for the function.

Inflection Point

A function f has an inflection at $(a, f(a))$ if the function has a different concavity when $x < a$ compared to when $x > a$.

---

6. For each of the given functions, do the following.
   i. State any interval(s) of the domain over which it appears the function has positive concavity.
   ii. State any interval(s) of the domain over which it appears the function has negative concavity.
   iii. Estimate any inflection points for the function.

   a. $f(x) = x^3 - 6x^2 + 9x + 10$

   b. $g(x) = -3 \cdot \sqrt{x+4} + 6$

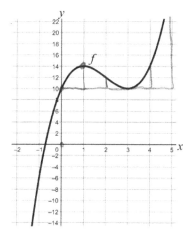

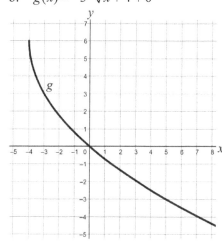

You will sometimes hear people use the phrases *concave up* and *concave down* instead of *positive concavity* and *negative concavity*, especially when discussing graphs. Graphs of functions over intervals with positive concavity will tend to "curve up" as *x* increases. Graphs of functions over intervals with negative concavity will tend to "curve down" as *x* increases. Examples are shown below, along with line segments whose slopes represent the functions' average rates of change over consecutive intervals.

Example I: positive concavity
("concave up") on the entire domain

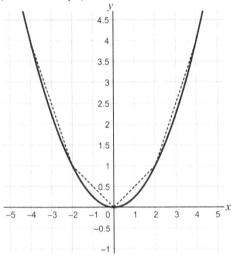

Example II: positive concavity
("concave up") on the entire domain

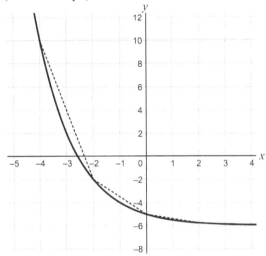

Example III: negative concavity
("concave down") on the entire domain

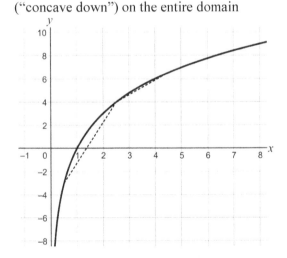

Example IV: negative concavity
("concave down") on the entire domain

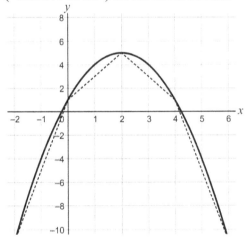

7. *a. For Example I explain why the function has positive concavity over its entire domain (from what we can tell). Then explain to a partner how you can "see" the graph curving upwards as *x* increases.

   b. For Example II explain why the function has positive concavity over its entire domain (from what we can tell). Then explain to a partner how you can "see" the graph curving upwards as *x* increases.

*c. For Example III explain why the function has negative concavity over its entire domain (from what we can tell). Then explain to a partner how you can "see" the graph curving down as x increases.

d. For Example IV explain why the function has negative concavity over its entire domain (from what we can tell). Then explain to a partner how you can "see" the graph curving down as x increases.

8. Return to the graphs in Exercise #6. Identify the interval(s) over which the function graphs are "concave up" and "concave down".

9. Graph each of the following functions using a graphing calculator or graphing software. For each, do the following.
   i. Identify the interval(s) over which the function's graph is "concave up". *It's okay to estimate.*
   ii. Identify the interval(s) over which the function's graph is "concave down". *It's okay to estimate.*

   a. $f(x) = x^3$

   b. $g(x) = -2x^2 + 4x - 1$

   c. $h(x) = -x^3 + 6x$

   d. $j(x) = 3^x$

*10. At 5:00 pm Karen started walking from the grocery store back to her house.
   a. Fill in the table by determining the number of feet Karen is from home, d. Then use the information in the table to determine the average rate of change of the number of feet Karen is from home with respect to time (measured in minutes since Karen started walking) on the specified intervals.

Change in the number of minutes since Karen started walking Δt	Number of minutes since Karen started walking t	Number of feet Karen is from home d	Change in the number of feet Karen is from home Δd	Average rate of change of Karen's distance with respect to time
	0	118		
			−1.5	
	0.5			
			−3.2	
	1			
			−6.5	
	1.5			
			−7.1	
	2			

b. Sketch a graph of the number of meters Karen is from home in terms of the number of minutes since Karen started walking. (*Be sure to label your axes.*)

c. Does this function have positive concavity ("concave up"), negative concavity ("concave down"), or some combination of both on the interval $0 < t < 2$? Make sure you can justify your answer.

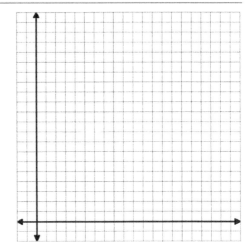

d. Describe how the quantities *number of minutes since Karen started walking* and the *number of meters Karen is from home* change together.

11. a. The function h is defined by $h(x) = \log_4(x)$. Use h to complete the table.

Δx	x	$h(x)$	$\Delta h(x)$	Average rate of change of $h(x)$ with respect to x
	1	0		
	2	0.5		
	4	1		
	8	1.5		
	16	2		

b. Is h an increasing or decreasing function (or a combination of the two)?

c. Does h have positive concavity ("concave up") throughout its domain, negative concavity ("concave down") throughout its domain, or a combination of the two? How do you know?

d. Is $j(x) = \log_{0.5}(x)$ an increasing or decreasing function (or a combination of the two)?

e. Does $j(x) = \log_{0.5}(x)$ have positive concavity throughout its domain ("concave up"), negative concavity ("concave down") throughout its domain, or a combination of the two? How do you know?

*1. Regal Theatre puts on community theatre productions each season. After several years of gathering data, they noted some trends between the length of the plays they produced and the number of tickets they sold for Friday evening shows. They created the model shown below.

play length (hours) x	number of tickets sold to Friday evening shows (according to the model) $g(x)$
1	119
1.5	139
1.75	145
2	149
2.25	150
2.5	149
3	139
3.5	119
4	89

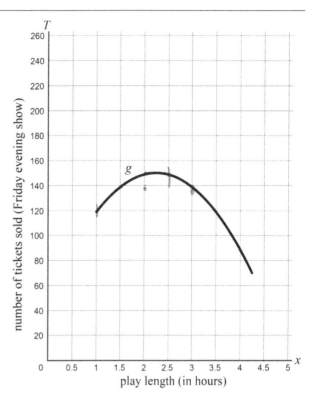

a. What does the ordered pair (3, 139) represent in the context of this situation?

b. Determine the function's average rate of change over each of the following intervals. Make sure to describe how to interpret the meaning of the average rate of change in each case.
   i. $1 \le x \le 2.25$
   ii. $2.5 \le x \le 4$

c. Does the function have positive concavity or negative concavity (or a combination of the two)? What does this tell you about the situation?

© 2018 Carlson, Oehrtman, and Moore

*2. Regal Theatre contacted a similar theatre in another city (Player Productions). Player Productions said their model was virtually identical to the model created by Regal Theatre. The only difference is that they sold 30 fewer tickets each Friday night compared to Regal Theatre.

   a. Complete the table of values for Player Productions's model.

   b. Describe how the outputs of functions g and h compare for any input value x.

play length (hours) x	number of tickets sold to Friday evening shows (according to the model) $h(x)$
1	
1.5	
1.75	
2	
2.25	
2.5	
3	
3.5	
4	

   c. Draw a graph of h on the axes given in Exercise #1.

   d. How does the average rate of change of h on the intervals $1 \le x \le 2.25$ and $2.5 \le x \le 4$ compare to the average rate of change of g on the same intervals? Why?

   e. Use function notation to express the outputs of h in terms of the outputs of g.

*3. A third theatre company (Actor's Guildhouse) found a similar trend, however they sell 1.5 times as many tickets to their Friday shows compared to the Regal Theatre.

   a. Complete the given table of values for Actor's Guildhouse's model.

   b. Describe how the outputs of functions g and f compare for any input value x.

play length (hours) x	number of tickets sold to Friday evening shows (according to the model) $f(x)$
1	
1.5	
1.75	
2	
2.25	
2.5	
3	
3.5	
4	

   c. Draw a graph of f on the axes given in Exercise #1.

   d. How does the average rate of change of f on the intervals $1 \le x \le 2.25$ and $2.5 \le x \le 4$ compare to the average rate of change of g on the same intervals? Why?

   e. Use function notation to express the outputs of f in terms of the outputs of g.

*4. The number of tickets to a Friday performance in terms of the play length (in hours) for a fourth theatre company (Stage Left) is modeled by function j.

    a. If $j(x) = g(x - 0.5)$, how do the ticket sales for a Friday performance compare at Stage Left and Regal Theatre? [*Hint: Which function needs a larger input value to produce the same output value?*] How would the graphs of the functions compare?

    b. If instead $j(x) = 2g(x) - 15$, how do the ticket sales for a Friday performance compare at Stage Left and Regal Theatre? How would the graphs of the functions compare?

*5. The graph of h is given. Draw the graph of g if $g(x) = -h(x + 3)$.

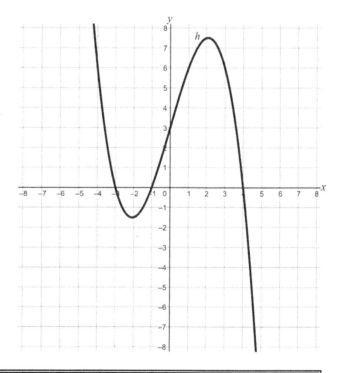

Many of the functions we have worked with in this module (and that we will continue to work with in the next few investigations) are **polynomial functions**.

Polynomial Functions

When expressed as a formula, a polynomial function will be of the form
$f(x) = a_n x^n + a_{n-1} x^{n-1} + a_{n-2} x^{n-2} + \ldots + a_2 x^2 + a_1 x + a_0$ where n, $n-1$, etc. are natural numbers and a_n, a_{n-1}, etc. are real numbers. *Note that the coefficients could have a value of zero.*

Examples of polynomial function formulas include $f(x) = 4x^3 + 8.2x^2 - 3x + 1.7$ and $g(x) = -5x^6 + 13x^2$. Quadratic functions and linear functions are examples of polynomials.

---

*6. Define each function in terms of the other.
  a.   i. Express the outputs of g in terms of the outputs of f.

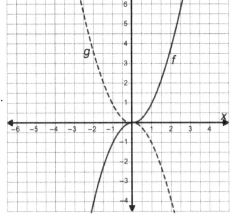

   ii. Express the outputs of f in terms of the outputs of g.

  b.   i. Express the outputs of g in terms of the outputs of f.

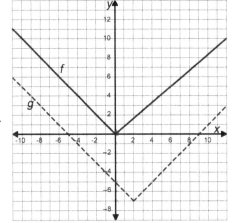

   ii. Express the outputs of f in terms of the outputs of g.

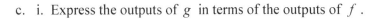

  c.   i. Express the outputs of g in terms of the outputs of f.

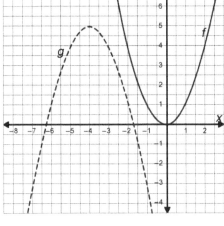

   ii. Express the outputs of f in terms of the outputs of g.

  d.   Which of the functions in parts (a) through (c) could be polynomial functions?

*1. The function f is defined by $f(x) = (x+1)(x-3)^2$.

    a.   Use algebraic methods to find the roots (x-intercepts) of f.

    b.   What do the roots of a polynomial function represent?

    c.   Explain why a polynomial function's roots occur where one of the factors has a value of zero.

    d.   Draw a number line representing values of x and highlight each of the following:
       i.   the intervals of x where f 's output is positive

       ii.   the intervals of x where f 's output is negative

    e. Construct a rough sketch of the graph of f.

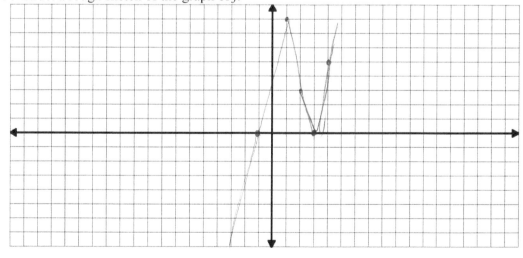

2.   How do the functions f and h compare, given that $f(x) = (x+1)(x-3)^2$ and $h(x) = 2(x+1)(x-3)^2$?

*3. How do the functions h and k compare, given that $h(x) = 2(x+1)(x-3)^2$ and $k(x) = -2(x+1)(x-3)^2$?

*4. Let $f(x) = x^3$, $g(x) = x^5$, $h(x) = x^2$, $j(x) = x^8$. (A function of the form $p(x) = ax^n$, given that a and n are real numbers, is called a **power function**. Note that n must be a non-negative integer for p to be a polynomial function.)

   a. Describe how each power function varies as:

      i. x increases without bound (also written $x \to \infty$)

         $x \to \infty$, $f(x) \to$ _____ $x \to \infty$, $g(x) \to$ _____

         $x \to \infty$, $h(x) \to$ _____ $x \to \infty$, $j(x) \to$ _____

      ii. x decreases without bound (also written $x \to -\infty$)

         $x \to -\infty$, $f(x) \to$ _____ $x \to -\infty$, $g(x) \to$ _____

         $x \to -\infty$, $h(x) \to$ _____ $x \to -\infty$, $j(x) \to$ _____

   b. What general statements can you make about how the exponent on a power function impacts the behavior of the function?

   c. What changes if each function changes to have a coefficient of –2 (for example, $f(x) = x^3$ changes to become $f(x) = -2x^3$)?

*5. Given $f(x) = x^3 + 4x^2 - 6x - 12$ and $g(x) = x^3$, do the following.

   a. Graph the functions with a window size ranging from $x = -5$ to $x = 5$ and from $y = -20$ to $y = 20$. Do the functions have similar behavior?

   b. Graph the functions with a window size ranging from $x = -50$ to $x = 50$ and from $y = -10,000$ to $y = 10,000$. Do the functions have similar behavior?

   c. If your answers are different to parts (a) and (b), why are they different?

A Polynomial Function's Leading Term

For a polynomial function f represented by a formula, the leading term is the term containing the largest exponent. For example, given $f(x) = 5x^4 + 7x^3 + 5x + 100$, the leading term is $5x^4$, and given $g(x) = 5 - 4x^3$, the leading term is $-4x^3$.

It's important to be able to identify the leading term for a polynomial function because the leading term dictates the function's **end behavior** (the behavior of $f(x)$ as $x \to \pm\infty$, or as x increases or decreases without bound). This is because of the power of repeated multiplication with very large numbers – larger exponents create huge discrepancies in the relative size of each term in the long-run.

For example, consider the function $f(x) = 5x^4 + 7x^3 + 5x + 100$. $f(10,000) = 50,007,000,000,050,100$, but how does each term contribute to this function value?

- $5(10,000)^4 = 50,000,000,000,000,000$, which is 99.986% of the value of $f(10,000)$
- $7(10,000)^3 = 7,000,000,000,000$, which is 0.014% of the value of $f(10,000)$
- $5(x) = 50,000$, which is 0.0000000001% of the value of $f(10,000)$
- 100 is 0.0000000000002% of the value of $f(10,000)$

As x continues to increase without bound, the value of $f(x)$ is virtually indistinguishable from the value of $5x^4$. Thus, the value (and behavior) of $f(x)$ can be well-estimated by $5x^4$ as $x \to \pm\infty$.

6. For each polynomial function, identify the leading term.
    *a. $h(x) = -4x^3 + x^2 - 900x + 5$ *b. $f(x) = 9x^2 - 4x - 2x^4$ c. $g(x) = -7(x-5)(x^2+1)$

Since a polynomial function behaves like its leading term we can use notation to communicate this. Returning to $f(x) = 5x^4 + 7x^3 + 5x + 100$, we might write "As $x \to \pm\infty$, $f(x) \to 5x^4$." The arrow is read as "approaches" or "tends to".

However, we also know (or can easily determine) the end behavior of $y = 5x^4$. As $x \to \infty$, $5x^4 \to \infty$ and as $x \to -\infty$, $5x^4 \to \infty$. Thus, this is also the end behavior of $f(x)$. So we can say two things.

- As $x \to \pm\infty$, $f(x) \to 5x^4$. Also,
- As $x \to \infty$, $f(x) \to \infty$ and as $x \to -\infty$, $f(x) \to \infty$.

7. Using the same functions from Exercise #6, complete the following statements by first filling in the variable expression that well-estimates the function values and then filling in the end behavior in terms of increasing or decreasing without bound. *Part (a) is done for you.*
    a. $h(x) = -4x^3 + x^2 - 900x + 5$ *b. $f(x) = 9x^2 - 4x - 2x^4$ c. $g(x) = -7(x-5)(x^2+1)$

    As $x \to \pm\infty$, $h(x) \to -4x^3$.   As $x \to \pm\infty$, $f(x) \to$ _____.   As $x \to \pm\infty$, $g(x) \to$ _____.

    As $x \to \infty$, $h(x) \to -\infty$.   As $x \to \infty$, $f(x) \to$ _____.   As $x \to \infty$, $g(x) \to$ _____.

    As $x \to -\infty$, $h(x) \to -\infty$.   As $x \to -\infty$, $f(x) \to$ _____.   As $x \to -\infty$, $g(x) \to$ _____.

---

8. Describe the end behavior for each of the following polynomial functions without graphing. Then check your work by graphing the functions with a graphing calculator or graphing software. *Remember to consider the role of the leading coefficient when determining a function's end behavior.*

   a. $f(x) = -x^3 + 4x^2 - 8$ b. $g(x) = 5x - x^4 + 3x^5$ c. $h(x) = -2(x+1)(x-3)$

9. Answer the following questions given the graph of *g*.
   a. What are the roots of *g*?

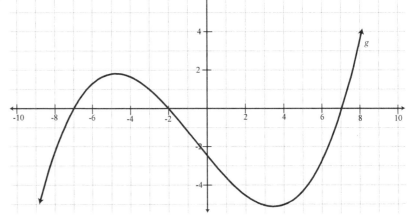

   b. Evaluate $g(0)$.

   c. On what interval(s) of the domain is the function increasing?

   d. On what interval(s) of the domain is the function decreasing?

   e. On what interval(s) of the domain does the function have positive concavity?

   f. On what interval(s) of the domain does the function have negative concavity?

   g. Estimate the location of any inflection points.

   h. Describe the end behavior of the function.

   i. When written as a formula, is the largest exponent an even number or an odd number? How do you know?

*1. Use your graphing calculator to sketch a graph of the following quadratic functions and compare the behavior and properties of these functions. For each of these functions determine the roots (*x*-intercepts) of the function.

a. $f(x) = x^2$

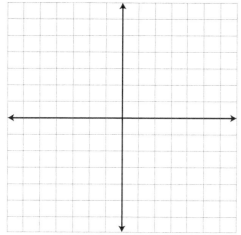

b. $g(x) = 3x^2$

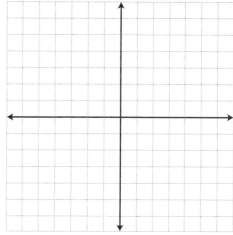

c. $h(x) = 3x^2 - 27$

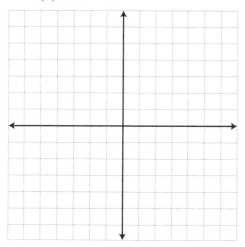

d. $k(x) = -3(x-7)^2$

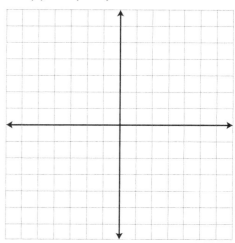

e. $p(x) = (2x-9)(x+4)$

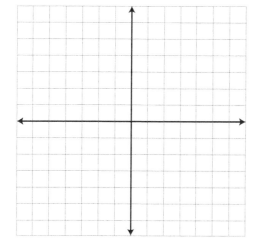

*2. Use your graphs from (1) to answer the following questions.

    a. When a quadratic function f is given in factored form explain why the roots (x-intercepts) occur where each factor has a value of 0. [*Note, if a function is given in factored form such as* $f(x) = (x-3)(x+4)$, *the factors are* $x-3$ *and* $x+4$.]

    b. Is it possible for a quadratic function to have positive concavity over one interval of its domain and negative concavity over some other interval of its domain? Explain.

    c. Does a quadratic function always have a maximum value?

    d. How do you determine if a quadratic function will have positive or negative concavity?

    e. What is the relationship between the x-coordinate where the maximum/minimum function value occurs and the function's roots?

*3. The function f is defined by $f(x) = (x+7)(x-3)$.

    a. Use algebraic methods to determine the roots of f.

    b. Determine the x-coordinate of f's minimum value (also referenced as the x coordinate of the vertex of the parabola generated by graphing f). Then find the function's minimum value.

    c. Find the average rate of change of $f(x)$ with respect to x as x increases from 2 to 7.4.

    d. Evaluate $f(3)$.

It's relatively easy to determine the vertex and real roots (if any) of a quadratic function given in factored form. The roots are the values of x that make one of the factors 0, and the x-value of the vertex is directly in between the roots.

When the function is instead in **standard form** (in the form $f(x) = ax^2 + bx + c$ where a, b, and c are real numbers) the **quadratic formula** can be used to determine the function's roots.

The Quadratic Formula

For a quadratic function of the form $f(x) = ax^2 + bx + c$ where a, b, and c are real numbers*, the **quadratic formula** represents the function's roots (the values of x such that $f(x) = 0$).

$$x = \frac{-b}{2a} \pm \frac{\sqrt{b^2 - 4ac}}{2a}$$

Note that a, b, or c could be 0.

---

4. Use the quadratic formula to determine the roots of each of the following functions (find the exact values and decimal approximations). Then use a graphing calculator to check your work. *It might help to first list the values of a, b, and c to use in the formula.*

   *a. $f(x) = 2x^2 + 5x + 1$

   b. $f(x) = x^2 - 7x + 5$

*5. a. What does $x = \frac{-b}{2a}$ represent in the context of a quadratic function?

   b. What does $f\left(\frac{-b}{2a}\right)$ represent in the context of a quadratic function f ?

   c. What does $\pm \frac{\sqrt{b^2 - 4ac}}{2a}$ represent in the context of a quadratic function f ?

   d. If $\frac{\sqrt{b^2 - 4ac}}{2a} = 0$ for some quadratic function f, what does this tell us about the function?

   e. Assume that for a given quadratic function, f , the solutions to the quadratic formula are $x = -4 \pm 3.25$. Create a possible sketch of this quadratic function and illustrate the vertex and roots of this quadratic function.

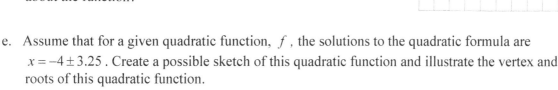

---

*6. An ice cream shop finds that its weekly profit P (measured in dollars) as a function of the price x (measured in dollars) it charges per ice cream cone is given by the function k, defined by
$k(x) = -125x^2 + 670x - 125$ where $P = k(x)$.

   a. Determine the maximum weekly profit and the price of an ice cream cone that produces that maximum profit.

   b. If the cost of the ice cream cone is too low then the ice cream shop will not make a profit. Determine what the ice cream shop needs to charge in order to break even (make a profit of $0.00).

   c. If the cost of the ice cream cone is too high then not enough people will want to buy ice cream. As a result the weekly profit will be $0.00. Determine what the ice cream shop would have to charge for this to happen (the profit to be $0.00).

   d. The profit function for Cold & Creamy (another ice cream shop) is defined by the function g where $g(x) = k(x-2)$. Does the function g have the same maximum value as k? What is the price per ice cream cone that Cold & Creamy ice cream shop must charge to produce a maximum profit? Explain.

   e. Describe the meaning of $h(x) = k(x) - 125$ and then compare/contrast the maximum values for each function.

7. Define the function formula that generates a parabola that has horizontal intercepts at $x = 3$ and $x = -5$, and passes through the point (2, 3).

The Number *i*

Have you ever tried to explain negative numbers to a child? For children, numbers are very concrete concepts – they use numbers to count items and (if they're old enough) perhaps to measure something like an object's height (in some units). In these examples negative numbers don't make much sense since they aren't needed for counting and children don't yet have a concept of directional measurement.

Believe it or not, mathematicians didn't always accept negative numbers. Until about 500 years ago almost every mathematician used geometry to justify their work, and characteristics such as length, area, and volume are represented by positive numbers. So mathematicians threw out any solutions to equations that were negative and believed negative numbers were useless. In this investigation we're going to explore another type of number that comes up when solving quadratic equations. It might be initially strange to think about these numbers, but they have very powerful applications in fields such as science and engineering.

1. Find the solutions to each of the following equations.
    a. $x^2 - 144 = 0$
    b. $x^2 - 49 = 0$

The equations $x^2 - 144 = 0$ and $x^2 - 49 = 0$ each have two real number solutions (one positive and one negative). But the equation $x^2 + 1 = 0$ does not have any real number solutions.

$$x^2 + 1 = 0$$
$$x^2 = -1$$
$$x = ????$$

Initially mathematicians ignored equations such as these because "they do not have a solution." However, eventually some mathematicians defined a new type of number to represent their solutions. They defined the number *i* to a number such that $i^2 = -1$.

If that is the case, then it must be that

$$i^2 = -1$$
$$i = \sqrt{-1}$$

The Number *i*

i is a number such that $i^2 = -1$. Then $i = \sqrt{-1}$, and $x = \pm i$ are the solutions to $x^2 + 1 = 0$.

Based on this idea, we can represent expressions such as $\sqrt{-25}$, $\sqrt{-19}$, and $-\sqrt{-2}$ in terms of this new number.

$\sqrt{-25}$	$\sqrt{-19}$	$-\sqrt{-2}$
$\sqrt{25 \cdot -1}$	$\sqrt{19 \cdot -1}$	$-\sqrt{2 \cdot -1}$
$\sqrt{25} \cdot \sqrt{-1}$	$\sqrt{19} \cdot \sqrt{-1}$	$-\sqrt{2} \cdot \sqrt{-1}$
$5i$	$19i$	$-\sqrt{2}i$

---

2. Rewrite each of the following expressions in terms of *i*.

a. $\sqrt{-4}$ b. $\sqrt{-121}$ c. $\sqrt{-41}$ d. $\sqrt{-13}$

In Exercises #3-5, write the solutions to each equation in terms of the number *i*. Check your answers by substituting the values back into the original equation.

3. $x^2 + 9 = 0$ 4. $x^2 + 36 = 0$ 5. $x^2 + 59 = 0$

Complex Numbers and Arithmetic with the Number *i*

Since mathematicians initially rejected negative numbers, just imagine what some of them thought about the *square root* of a negative number! They thought such "numbers" had no place in serious mathematics. The famous mathematician René Descartes coined the term ***imaginary numbers*** to express his dislike. The name stuck even though we now know that these so-called "imaginary" numbers are actually very useful. It took mathematicians a long time to accept them, but now they are a critical part of modern mathematics.

Expressions involving "imaginary" numbers are called ***complex numbers***.

Complex Numbers

A ***complex number*** is a number of the form ***a + bi*** made up of both a real number portion (*a*) and an imaginary number portion (*bi*).
- If $a = 0$, then the number is called *purely imaginary*.
- If $b = 0$, then the number is a *real number*.

Examples: $3 + 2i$ $5 - 7i$ $7i$ -14

Is it possible to have an expression involving the number *i* that cannot be written in the form $a + bi$? For example, are $i^0 - 6$, $10i^2$, $4 + i^3$, and $11i + 6i^4$ complex numbers? They each have *i* raised to an exponent other than 1. However, since we know that $i^2 = -1$ (and $i^0 = 1$ by definition) we can rewrite each expression as a complex number of the form $a + bi$.

$i^0 - 6$	$10i^2$	$4 + i^3$	$11i + 6i^4$
$1 - 6$	$10(-1)$	$4 + i^2 \cdot i$	$11i + 6(i^2)^2$
-5	-10	$4 + (-1) \cdot i$	$11i + 6(-1)^2$
$-5 + 0i$	$-10 + 0i$	$4 - i$	$11i + 6(1)$
			$6 + 11i$

In Exercises #5-13, rewrite each expression as a complex number of the form $a + bi$.

5. $2+i^3$ 6. $10i^4$ 7. $2i^3 - 8i$ 8. $6i^5 + 4i$ 9. $i^6 - 4i$

10. $5i^{21} - 6i^2$ 11. $6i^{46} + 5i^3$ 12. $i(i^3 - 6i^2)$ 13. $(i^3)^2 + 2i^4 + 4i^3$

The number i follows most of the same basic properties as real numbers. For example, the rules of exponents work the same, as do the commutative and associative properties of addition and multiplication. Therefore we can perform arithmetic with complex numbers and simplify the results.

$$(3+5i)+(6-13i)$$
$$3+5i+6-13i$$
$$3+6+5i-13i$$
$$9-8i$$

$$(1+3i)(7-i)$$
$$(1+3i)(7)+(1+3i)(-i)$$
$$(1)(7)+(3i)(7)+(1)(-i)+(3i)(-i)$$
$$7+21i-i-3i^2$$
$$7+20i-3i^2$$
$$7+20i-3(-1)$$
$$7+20i+3$$
$$10+20i$$

$$(4-3i)^2$$
$$(4-3i)(4-3i)$$
$$(4-3i)(4)+(4-3i)(-3i)$$
$$(4)(4)+(-3i)(4)+(4)(-3i)+(-3i)(-3i)$$
$$16-12i-12i+9i^2$$
$$16-24i+9i^2$$
$$16-24i+9(-1)$$
$$16-24i-9$$
$$7-24i$$

Notice that when we perform operations with complex numbers we end up with complex numbers as the result.

In Exercises #14-24, rewrite each expression as a complex number of the form $a + bi$.

14. $2i(9+4i)$ 15. $(-4+i)+(19-6i)$

16. $3(7-5i)-8(6+3i)$

17. $(1+4i)(5-2i)$

18. $9i+2i(7i^3+3i^2)$

19. $(7-6i)(3-i)$

20. $(3+5i)^2$

21. $(a+bi)(c+di)$

22. $4-\sqrt{-49}$

23. $-2\sqrt{-32}$

24. $\sqrt{3}\cdot\sqrt{-27}$

Geometric Interpretations of Complex Numbers

With real numbers, we know that multiplying by -1 creates a number's opposite, or a number with the same distance from 0 but on the opposite side (such as $4(-1) = -4$).

Thinking about this transformation as a $180°$ rotation centered at 0 yields an identical mapping of 4 to -4.

Since $i^2 = -1$, we can also interpret multiplication by i^2 as a $180°$ rotation centered at 0.

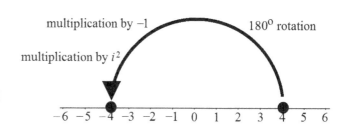

However, since multiplying by i^2 is identical to multiplication by i twice in succession ($4i^2 = 4 \cdot i \cdot i$), mathematicians realized that they could think about multiplication by i as a $90°$ rotation centered at 0 so that doing this twice in a row creates a $180°$ rotation.

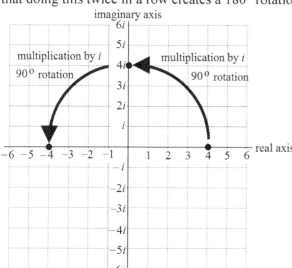 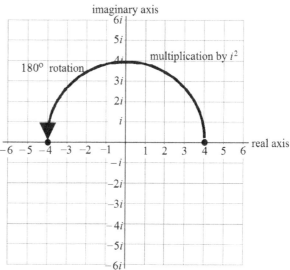

This way of thinking requires three additional ideas. 1) We can imagine that with any real number line there is a second perpendicular number line through 0 representing the imaginary numbers. 2) Multiplication by i is a $90°$ rotation counterclockwise (and multiplication by $-i$ is a $90°$ clockwise rotation).

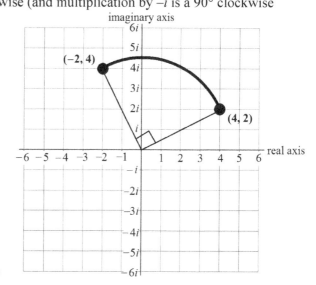

Finally, 3) all complex numbers can be graphed on this **complex plane** with $a + bi$ represented by the point (a, b).

For example, on the complex plane we represent $4 + 2i$ by the point $(4, 2)$. Multiplying by i yields

$$i(4 + 2i)$$
$$4i + 2i^2$$
$$4i + 2(-1)$$
$$-2 + 4i$$

Notice that this is a $90°$ counterclockwise rotation (centered at the intersection point of the axes) of the original point on the complex plane.

25. Represent each of the following complex numbers as points on the complex plane.
    a. $3+5i$
    b. $-6+2i$
    c. $-2-i$
    d. $7-4i$

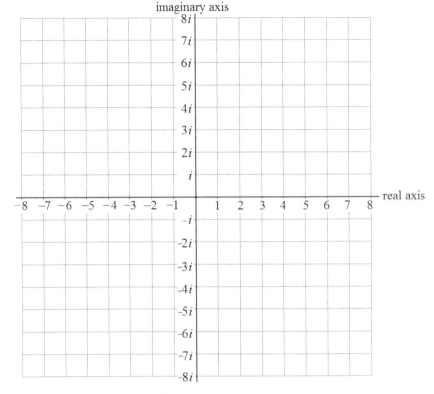

26. Rewrite each of the following products in the form $a + bi$ and plot them as points on the complex plane above. Verify that they are each 90° counterclockwise rotations of the original four points.
    a. $i(3+5i)$ b. $i(-6+2i)$ c. $i(-2-i)$ d. $i(7-4i)$

27 Rewrite each of the following products in the form $a + bi$ and plot them as points on the complex plane above. Verify that they are each 180° rotations of the original four points. *If your graph is getting crowded, you may complete this task on a piece of graph paper.*
    a. $i^2(3+5i)$ b. $i^2(-6+2i)$ c. $i^2(-2-i)$ d. $i^2(7-4i)$

28. Rewrite each of the following products in the form $a + bi$ and plot them as points on the complex plane above. Verify that they are each 90° clockwise rotations of the original four points. *If your graph is getting crowded, you may complete this task on a piece of graph paper.*
    a. $-i(3+5i)$ b. $-i(-6+2i)$ c. $-i(-2-i)$ d. $-i(7-4i)$

1. Use the quadratic formula to find the roots of $f(x) = -3x^2 + x - 4$. Comment on anything important about your solution.

$$x = -\frac{b}{2a} \pm \frac{\sqrt{b^2 - 4ac}}{2a}$$

2. The quadratic formula is supposed to find the zeros of the function. When the zeros are real numbers, they equate to the horizontal intercepts of the function's graph. However, in Exercise #1 the quadratic formula didn't return any real number answers. Graph function f using a calculator and explain what this fact implies about the horizontal intercepts of the graph of f.

3. Use the quadratic formula to find the roots of $f(x) = 2x^2 - 4x + 2$. Comment on anything important about your solution.

4. The quadratic formula was used to find the zeros of each of the following functions.

$f(x) = x^2 + 7x + 25$ $\qquad$ $g(x) = x^2 - 2x - 5$ $\qquad$ $h(x) = 2x^2 + 20x + 50$

$$x = -\frac{7}{2(1)} \pm \frac{\sqrt{(7)^2 - 4(1)(25)}}{2(1)}$$

$$x = -\frac{7}{2} \pm \frac{\sqrt{49 - 100}}{2}$$

$$x = -\frac{7}{2} \pm \frac{\sqrt{-51}}{2}$$

$$x = -\frac{(-2)}{2(1)} \pm \frac{\sqrt{(-2)^2 - 4(1)(-5)}}{2(1)}$$

$$x = -\frac{-2}{2} \pm \frac{\sqrt{4 + 20}}{2}$$

$$x = 1 \pm \frac{\sqrt{24}}{2}$$

$$x = 1 \pm \frac{2\sqrt{6}}{2}$$

$$x = 1 \pm \sqrt{6}$$

$$x = -\frac{20}{2(2)} \pm \frac{\sqrt{(20)^2 - 4(2)(50)}}{2(2)}$$

$$x = -\frac{20}{4} \pm \frac{\sqrt{400 - 400}}{4}$$

$$x = -5 \pm \frac{\sqrt{0}}{4}$$

$$x = -5 \pm 0$$

How many horizontal intercepts does each function have?

5. The expression $b^2 - 4ac$ from the quadratic formula is called the **discriminant** because it discriminates (makes a distinction, or highlights the difference) between functions with zero, one, or two horizontal intercepts.

   a. What is the value of the discriminant ($b^2 - 4ac$) for the functions from Exercise #4?

      For $f(x)$: $b^2 - 4ac =$

      For $g(x)$: $b^2 - 4ac =$

      For $h(x)$: $b^2 - 4ac =$

   b. Why does the value of the discriminant give us enough information to predict the number of horizontal intercepts for a quadratic function?

The Discriminant of a Quadratic Function

Let f be defined by $f(x) = ax^2 + bx + c$ for real numbers a, b, and c. Then the discriminant is the value of

- If _____, then…

- If _____, then…

- If _____, then…

For each of the functions in Exercises #6-9, use the discriminant to determine the number of horizontal intercepts for the function. [*You do not need to find the actual values.*] Graph the functions with a calculator or other graphing software to verify your answer.

6. $f(x) = 2x^2 + 4x + 2$

7. $f(x) = 2x^2 - 7x + 3$

8. $f(x) = x^2 + 3x + 5$

9. $f(x) = 3x^2 - 12x + 12$

When we know that the roots will be complex numbers, we can write them in the form $a + bi$. For example, consider the function $f(x) = x^2 + x + 2.5$. Let's verify that f has only complex roots and then find them. *Note that we will write the complex roots in the form a + bi.*

Solve the equation $f(x) = 0$, or $x^2 + x + 2.5 = 0$, for x.

$$b^2 - 4ac$$
$$(1)^2 - 4(1)(2.5)$$
$$1 - 10$$
$$-9$$
only complex solutions

$$x = -\frac{1}{2(1)} \pm \frac{\sqrt{-9}}{2(1)}$$
$$= -\frac{1}{2} \pm \frac{3i}{2}$$
$$= -\frac{1}{2} \pm \frac{3}{2}i$$

$$\boxed{x = -\tfrac{1}{2} + \tfrac{3}{2}i \quad \text{and} \quad x = -\tfrac{1}{2} - \tfrac{3}{2}i}$$

Remember that roots are input values that produce an output of 0. Let's demonstrate why $x = -\frac{1}{2} + \frac{3}{2}i$ and $x = -\frac{1}{2} - \frac{3}{2}i$ are roots of f.

$$f(-\tfrac{1}{2} + \tfrac{3}{2}i) = (-\tfrac{1}{2} + \tfrac{3}{2}i)^2 + (-\tfrac{1}{2} + \tfrac{3}{2}i) + 2.5$$
$$= \left(\tfrac{1}{4} - \tfrac{3}{2}i + \tfrac{9}{4}i^2\right) + \left(-\tfrac{1}{2} + \tfrac{3}{2}i\right) + \tfrac{5}{2}$$
$$= \tfrac{1}{4} - \tfrac{3}{2}i + \tfrac{9}{4}i^2 - \tfrac{1}{2} + \tfrac{3}{2}i + \tfrac{5}{2}$$
$$= \tfrac{1}{4} + \tfrac{9}{4}(-1) - \tfrac{1}{2} + \tfrac{5}{2}$$
$$= \tfrac{1}{4} - \tfrac{9}{4} - \tfrac{1}{2} + \tfrac{5}{2}$$
$$= \tfrac{1}{4} - \tfrac{9}{4} - \tfrac{2}{4} + \tfrac{10}{4}$$
$$= 0$$

$$f(-\tfrac{1}{2} - \tfrac{3}{2}i) = (-\tfrac{1}{2} - \tfrac{3}{2}i)^2 + (-\tfrac{1}{2} - \tfrac{3}{2}i) + 2.5$$
$$= \left(\tfrac{1}{4} + \tfrac{3}{2}i + \tfrac{9}{4}i^2\right) + \left(-\tfrac{1}{2} - \tfrac{3}{2}i\right) + \tfrac{5}{2}$$
$$= \tfrac{1}{4} + \tfrac{3}{2}i + \tfrac{9}{4}i^2 - \tfrac{1}{2} - \tfrac{3}{2}i + \tfrac{5}{2}$$
$$= \tfrac{1}{4} + \tfrac{9}{4}(-1) - \tfrac{1}{2} + \tfrac{5}{2}$$
$$= \tfrac{1}{4} - \tfrac{9}{4} - \tfrac{1}{2} + \tfrac{5}{2}$$
$$= \tfrac{1}{4} - \tfrac{9}{4} - \tfrac{2}{4} + \tfrac{10}{4}$$
$$= 0$$

In Exercises #10-15, do the following.
   a) Use the discriminant to verify that the function has only complex roots.
   b) Determine the function's roots. Write your final answers in the form $a + bi$.

10. $h(x) = x^2 + 6x + 10$

11. $f(x) = 3x^2 - 9x + 7.5$

12. $f(x) = x^2 + 5x + 9$

13. $f(x) = 4x^2 + 2x + 3$

14. $f(x) = 2x^2 + 5x + 6$

15. $f(x) = -3x^2 + 3x - 4$

I. THE BOTTLE PROBLEM – MODELING CO-VARYING RELATIONSHIPS (TEXT: S2, 3, 4, 5)

1. a. A spherical fish bowl is filling with water. Describe how the height of the water and volume of water in the bowl vary together for equal volumes of water added to the bowl.
    b. Construct a graph that represents the height of the water in the bowl as a function of the volume of water in the bowl.

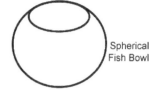
Spherical
Fish Bowl

2. The definition of an ***increasing function*** *f* follows: A function *f* is said to be increasing if
    $f(x_1) < f(x_2)$ whenever $x_1 < x_2$.
    a. Explain what this means in your own words. Use specific examples if it helps you.
    b. Given that *g* is a function defining the height of water in some bottle as a function of the volume of the water in the bottle, *v*, complete the following.
        i.   Why must *g* be an increasing function? (As *v* increases, why must $g(v)$ always increase?)
        ii. Explain the meaning of the statement $g(v_1) < g(v_2)$ whenever $v_1 < v_2$ in this context.
    b. Use mathematical symbols to convey that another function *w* is <u>decreasing</u> for all values of *x*. How does $w(x)$ change as *x* increases?

3. You are given four graphs representing the water height in a bottle as a function of the water volume.
    i.   Describe how the height of the water and volume of water in the bottle vary together for equal amounts of volume of water added to the bottle.
    ii. Construct a careful sketch of the bottle. Include landmarks on both the bottle and graph to show points where the function behavior changes in important ways.

a.

b.

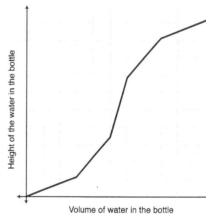

c.

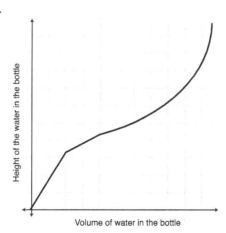

d.

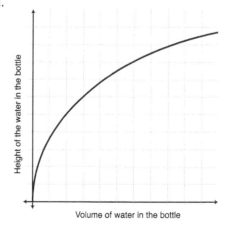

4. For each of the scenarios below, construct a graph of the height of the water in the bottle as a function of the volume of water in the bottle. Then, make an illustration of a bottle that would produce a height-volume graph with that general behavior.
   a. Scenario #1: A bottle in which the height of the water in the bottle increases at a constant rate with respect to the volume of water in the bottle.
   b. Scenario #2: A bottle in which the height of the water in the bottle increases at a constant rate with respect to the volume of water in the bottle, then switches so that equal changes in volume lead to smaller and smaller increases in the height of water in the bottle.
   c. Scenario #3: A bottle in which the height of the water in the bottle increases by larger and larger amounts for equal increases in volume, then increases at a constant rate with respect to the volume of water in the bottle, then increases by smaller and smaller amounts for equal increases in the height of water in the bottle.

5. As a runner is moving around a quarter mile track a radar gun detects the direct distance of the runner from the starting line.
   a. Construct a graph that represents the direct distance (in yards) of the runner from the starting line in terms of the total distance (in yards) the runner has traveled around the track.
   b. At approximately what point(s) around the quarter mile track is the direct distance of the runner from the starting line at its maximum value?
   c. Provide a written description of how the direct distance (in yards) of the runner from the starting line varies with the distance (in yards) the runner has traveled around the track.

6. Watch the video titled "Exploring Co-Varying Quantities" and answer the following questions. (The video can be found in the online textbook, Module 5 p. 7)
   a. What conditions are necessary for there to be a linear relationship between the height of the water and the volume of water in the bottle?
   b. For a cylindrical bottle with shoulders (like the one considered in the video) how does the height of the water in the bottle co-vary with the volume of water in the bottle?
   c. What do sharp corners on a height-volume graph represent?
   d. What is a technique that can be used when analyzing the co-variation of two quantities?

7. Expand the following expressions as much as possible. *Combine like terms to simplify your answer.*
   a. $(x-3)(x+4)$ b. $-(x-7)^2$ c. $(x-4)^2(x-1)$
   d. $3(x-2)^2$ e. $-(3x-2)(x+4)(2x-1)$

II. AVERAGE RATE OF CHANGE AND CONCAVITY (TEXT: S4, 5)

8. For the following functions determine if the average rates of change of the water height with respect to the water volume over successive equal-sized intervals is increasing, decreasing, or constant.

a.

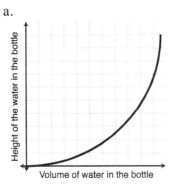

b.

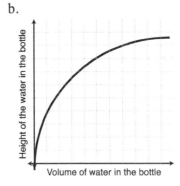

c.

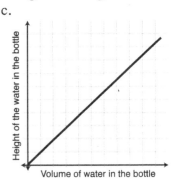

9. When graphing the height of the water in a bottle with respect to the volume of water in the bottle, *inflection points* on the height–volume graph correspond to where the bottle changes from getting narrower to getting wider (or vice-versa).

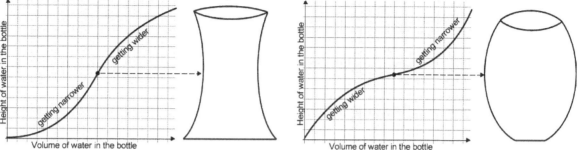

   a. Explain what the inflection point on the height-volume graph for the bottle on the left conveys about the changes in the water height and water volume as the bottle is being filled with water.
   b. Explain what the inflection point on the height-volume graph for the bottle on the right conveys about the changes in the water height and water volume as the bottle is being filled with water.

10. The values in the table below represent the distance (measured in yards) of a dog from a park entrance as a function of the number of seconds since the dog entered the park.

Change in the number of seconds since the dog entered the park	The number of seconds since the dog entered the park	The distance (in yards) of a dog from the park entrance	Change in the distance (in yards) of a dog from the park entrance	Average rate of change of the dog's distance with respect to time
	0	0		
	3	26.25		
	3.2	30.976		
	4.5	77.344		
	7	271.25		

   a. Complete the table of values.
   b. Describe what the average rates of change tell you about how the distance of the dog from the park entrance is changing over the time interval from $t = 0$ to $t = 7$ seconds.

11. For each of the following functions, estimate the intervals on which:
   i.   the function values are increasing   ii. the function values are decreasing
   iii. the function has positive concavity   iv. the function has negative concavity

   a.   b.   c.

 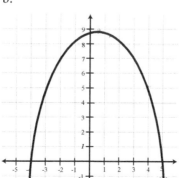 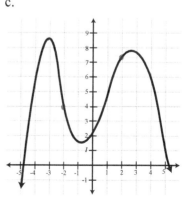

12. Using the functions in Exercise #11, do the following for each of the parts (a) through (c).
    i.   Copy the graph.
    ii. Plot the points $(-2, f(-2))$ and $(3, f(3))$ on the graph.
    iii. Draw a line passing through the two points.
    iv. Find the constant rate of change of the line you drew. *You may have to estimate the function output values.*

Use the following context for Exercises #13-14. Fire pits are frequently used to cook meat. A fire is built to heat the rocks in the bottom of the pit. Once the pit reaches the desired temperature the meat is then put in the pit and covered.

13. The table below represents the air temperature (in degrees Fahrenheit) of a pit in terms of the number of hours that have elapsed since the meat was added to the pit.

Number of hours since meat was added to the pit	Air temperature (in degrees Fahrenheit) of the pit
0	575
2	400
4	320
6	275

a. Using the table of values, do the following.
    i.   Sketch a graph of the air temperature (in degrees Fahrenheit) of the pit in terms of the number of hours since the meat was added to the pit. Be sure to label your axes.
    ii. Represent the changes in the air temperature of the pit from 0 hours to 2 hours; from 2 hours to 4 hours; and from 4 hours to 6 hours.
    iii. What do you notice about the change in the air temperature of the pit for successive equal change is the number of hours since the meat was added to the pit?
b. Let t represent the number of hours since the meat was added to the pit. Determine the average rate of change of the air temperature of the pit on the following time intervals and then describe how to interpret these values.
    i. $0 \le t \le 2$ ii. $2 \le t \le 4$ iii. $4 \le t \le 6$
c. Does this function have positive concavity, negative concavity, or some combination of both on the interval $0 < t < 6$?

14. The table below represents the internal temperature (in degrees Fahrenheit) of the meat in terms of the number of hours that have elapsed since the meat was added to the pit.

Number of hours since meat was added to the pit	Internal temperature (in degrees Fahrenheit) of the meat
0	45
1	80
3	135
10	200

Let *t* represent the number of hours since the meat was added to the pit. Determine the average rate of change of the internal temperature of the meat over the following time intervals and then describe how to interpret these values.
a. $0 \le t \le 1$ b. $1 \le t \le 3$ c. $3 \le t \le 10$

15. $f(t) = 1.5^t$, with $d = f(t)$, represents a car's distance d (measured in feet) from a stop sign in terms of the number of seconds t since the car started to move away from the stop sign.
a. Sketch a graph of this relationship. Be sure to label your axes.
b. Determine the average rate of change of the distance of the car from the stop sign on the following time intervals, then explain how to interpret each value.
    i. $0 \le t \le 2$ ii. $2 \le t \le 4$ iii. $4 \le t \le 6$ iv. $1 \le t \le 5$
c. Does this function have positive concavity, negative concavity, or some combination of both on the interval $0 < t < 6$?

16. Watch the video titled "Co-Varying Quantities and Changing Rate of Change of Non-Linear Polynomial Functions" and answer the following questions. (The video can be found in the online textbook, Module 5 p. 11)
    a. Provide an example of a context in which the values of the output quantity decrease and the average rates of change of the output quantity with respect to the input quantity are increasing as the value of the input quantity increases.
    b. Provide an example of a context in which the values of the output quantity decrease and the average rates of change of the output quantity with respect to the input quantity are decreasing as the value of the input quantity increases.
    c. For the values of r, a, n, and c given in the video is $r < n$ or is $n < r$? Explain your reasoning.
    d. Is -4 greater than or less than -30? Explain.

17. The given graph represents Sally's distance from her house in terms of the number of minutes t since Sally started walking.
    a. Interpret the meaning of the point (20, 1950).
    b. Represent the changes in Sally's distance from her house (in feet) from 0 minutes to 10 minutes; from 10 minutes to 20 minutes; and from 30 minutes to 40 minutes.
    c. What do you notice about the change in Sally's distance from her house for successive equal changes in the number of minutes since Sally started walking?
    d. Describe what these successive changes in Sally's distance from her house for equal change in the number of minutes since Sally started walking tell you about how Sally's distance from her house is changing over the time interval from $t = 0$ to $t = 30$ minutes.
    e. Describe how Sally's speed (in yards per minute) is changing as the number minutes since Sally started walking increases from 0 to 30 minutes.

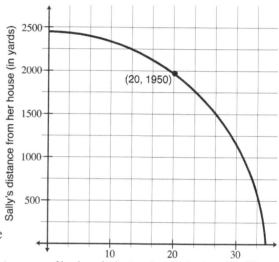

III. TRANSFORMATIONS OF POLYNOMIAL FUNCTIONS (TEXT: S9)

18. The graph of a polynomial function f is given. Sketch a graph of each the following functions.
    a. $g(x) = -f(x)$
    b. $h(x) = f(-x)$
    c. $k(x) = f(x-2)$
    d. $p(x) = f(x) - 2$

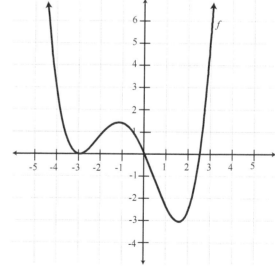

19. A coffee shop models its weekly profit P (measured in dollars) as a function of the price x (measured in dollars per cup) using $f(x) = -2000x^2 + 8000x - 2000$ with $P = f(x)$.
    a. A second coffee shop models its weekly profit as a function of the price it charges per cup using function g where $g(x) = f(x-1)$. Discuss the relationship between the inputs and outputs of functions g and f.
    b. A third coffee shop models its weekly profit as a function of the price it charges per cup using function h where $h(x) = f(x) - 150$. Discuss the relationship between the inputs and outputs of functions h and f.
    c. Do either g or h have the same maximum profits when compared to f? Explain.

20. The graphs of polynomial functions f and g are given below.
    a. How do the input and output pairs for the two functions compare?
    b. Express f in terms of g.
    c. Express g in terms of function f.

21. The graphs of polynomial functions f and g are given.
    a. How do the input and output pairs for the two functions compare?
    b. Express f in terms of g.
    c. Express g in terms of function f.
    d. How does the average rate of change for each function compare on the interval $-1 < x < 3$?

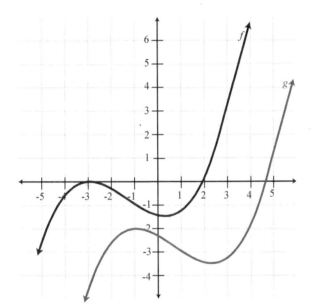

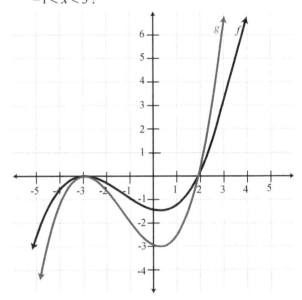

22. Each summer Primo Pizza and Pizza Supreme compete to see who has the larger summer profit. Let f be the function that determines Primo Pizza's profits in terms of the number of days since June 1. Let g be the function that determines Pizza Supreme's profits in terms of the number of days since June 1.
    a. If Primo Pizza's profits each day are two times as large as Pizza Supreme's profits,
        i. express the function f in terms of the function g.
        ii. express the function g in terms of the function f.
    b. If Primo Pizza's profits each day are two hundred dollars more than Pizza Supreme's profits,
        i. express the function f in terms of the function g.
        ii. express the function g in terms of the function f.
    c. If Primo Pizza's profits on a given day are always the same as Pizza Supreme's profits two days later,
        i. express the function f in terms of the function g.
        ii. express the function g in terms of the function f.

23. The function g is defined by $g(x) = 2f(x+3) - 4$. Explain how the behavior of function g compares to the behavior of function f.

24. Factor the following expressions as much as possible.
    a. $-8x^2 - 24x$
    b. $x^2 + 6x - 16$
    c. $2x^2 + 12x + 10$
    d. $2x^2 - 5x - 12$
    e. $3x^2 - 27$
    f. $6x^2 - x - 2$

IV. ROOTS AND END BEHAVIOR OF POLYNOMIAL FUNCTIONS (TEXT: S1, 6, 7, 8)

25. What is the general form of a polynomial function formula? Identify the constant term and leading coefficient.

26. Which of the following are polynomial functions. Justify your answer.
    a. $f(x) = 2^x$
    b. $g(x) = 5$
    c. $h(x) = \frac{5}{x} - 3x^2$
    d. $p(x) = 5x^4 + 3x^2 - 122$
    e. $r(x) = 5^{-2} - 3x$

27. Determine the roots of the following polynomial functions.
    a. $g(x) = 3x(2x - 4)(x + 2)^2$
    b. $h(x) = x^2(x - 4)^2(x^3 - 8)$
    c. $h(x) = x^3 + 6x^2 + 3x$
    d. $k(x) = 2x^2 - 5x - 3$

28. Determine the roots of the following polynomial functions.
    a. $f(x) = 4x^2 + 8x + 2$
    b. $g(x) = x^3 - x^2$
    c. $s(x) = -(2x + 4)(3x - 1)^2(x - 2)$
    d. $n(x) = 2x(x - 7)(3x + 4)$

29. Given the function $f(x) = (x - 3)(x + 1)(x - 2)$, complete the following.
    a. Determine the roots of f.
    b. As x increases without bound, describe the behavior of $f(x)$.
    c. As x decreases without bound, describe the behavior of $f(x)$.
    d. What is the behavior of f on the intervals $-1 < x < 2$ and $2 < x < 3$?
    e. Use your responses in parts (a) through (d) to sketch a graph of f.

30. For the following polynomial functions determine:
    i. the interval(s) on which the output of the function is positive.
    ii. the interval(s) on which the output of the function is negative.
    a. $f(x) = x(3x + 6)(x - 1)$
    b. $g(x) = 2x^3 - 4x^2 + 4x$
    c. $h(x) = 3x(2x - 5)(x + 1)$

31. Define three polynomial functions that have roots at $x = 2$, $x = 4$, and $x = -3$.

32. Define three polynomial functions that have roots at $x = 1$, $x = -1$, and $x = -5$.

33. Find the formula for a polynomial function that has horizontal intercepts (roots) at $x = 2$, $x = 5$, and $x = -4$ and passes through the point (3, 6).

34. For each of the polynomial functions given, identify the leading term of the function and describe the end behavior of the function based on your analysis of the leading term.
    a. $f(x) = 12x^3 - 2x^5 + 3x - 2$
    b. $g(x) = 3x(x-2)(x+4)(-2x+3)^2$
    c. $h(x) = 3x^3 - 4x + 8x^{10} - 3$
    d. $m(x) = -2(4+x)(2x-7)$

35. For each of the polynomial functions given, identify the leading term of the function and describe the end behavior of the function based on your analysis of the leading term.
    a. $f(x) = 3x(x-7)(x+2)(x-4)$
    b. $h(x) = 2x^2(-x+4)(x-7)^2$
    c. $p(x) = 2x(3x-7)(4x+1)$
    d. $s(x) = 3x^2 + 4x - 7x^8 + 6x - 2$

36. For each of the polynomial functions given, identify the leading term of the function and describe the end behavior of the function based on your analysis of the leading term.
    a. $h(x) = 2x(x+5)(x-1)^2$
    b. $k(x) = -(x+3)(x-4)^2$
    c. $g(x) = x^6 - 7x^5 + 13x^4 + 7x^3 - 34x^2 + 4x + 24$
    d. $f(x) = x^3 - 4x^2 + x + 6$

37. Given the function $f(x) = x^2(3x-4)(2x+5)^3$, complete the following.
    a. Determine the roots of f.
    b. Describe whether the graph of f will cross through (change signs from positive to negative or vice versa) or only "bounce off" the horizontal axis at each of the roots.
    c. Evaluate $f(0)$.
    d. Examine the leading term of f to determine the end-behavior of the function.
    e. Determine on what interval(s) of the domain $f(x)$ is positive.
    f. Determine on what interval(s) of the domain $f(x)$ is negative.
    g. Use your responses in part (a) through (f) to sketch a graph of f.

38. Given the function $g(x) = x^3(2x-4)^2(3x-2)(-x+1)^2$, complete the following.
    a. Determine the roots of g.
    b. Describe whether the graph of g will cross through (change signs from positive to negative or vice versa) or only "bounce off" the horizontal axis at each of the roots.
    c. Evaluate $g(0)$.
    d. Examine the leading term of g to determine the end-behavior of the function.
    e. Determine on what interval(s) of the domain $g(x)$ is positive.
    f. Determine on what interval(s) of the domain $g(x)$ is negative.
    g. Use your responses in part (a) through (f) to sketch a graph of g.

Use the graph of f to complete Exercises #39-41.

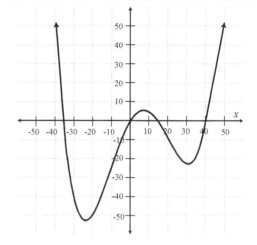

39. a. What is the domain of f ?
    b. What is the range of f ?
    c. Evaluate $f(0)$.
    d. What are the roots of f ?

40. a. On what interval(s) is $f(x)$ increasing?
    b. On what interval(s) is $f(x)$ decreasing?
    c. On what interval(s) does f have positive concavity?
    d. On what interval(s) does f have negative concavity?

41. a. When written as a formula, is the largest exponent an even number or an odd number? Explain your reasoning.
    b. Describe the behavior of $f(x)$ as x increases without bound.
    c. Describe the behavior of $f(x)$ as x decreases without bound.
    d. Are there any roots with an even multiplicity (even exponent)?

Use the graph of g to complete Exercises #42-44.

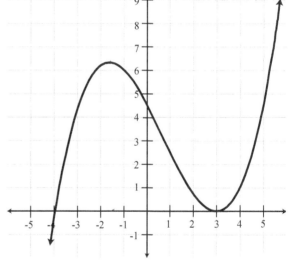

42. a. What is the domain of g?
    b. What is the range of g?
    c. Evaluate $g(0)$.
    d. What are the roots of g?

43. a. On what interval(s) is $g(x)$ increasing?
    b. On what interval(s) is $g(x)$ decreasing?
    c. On what interval(s) does g have positive concavity?
    d. On what interval(s) does g have negative concavity?

44. a. When written as a formula, is the largest exponent an even number or an odd number? Explain your reasoning.
    b. Describe the behavior of $g(x)$ as x increases without bound.
    c. Describe the behavior of $g(x)$ as x decreases without bound.
    d. Are there any roots with an even multiplicity (even exponent)?

45. Evaluate each of the following
    a. $f(x) = (8.5 - 2x)(11 - 2x)x$ when $x = 3.4$
    b. $g(x) = 87.4 - 53x$ when $x = 1.2$
    c. $h(x) = 3x^3 + 2x - 7$ when $x = -3.2$

46. Determine if each of the following are true or false. Provide a brief justification for your answers.
    a. The process of finding zeros of a polynomial function is also referred to as finding the roots of the polynomial function.
    b. We can apply the zero-product property to determine the zeros of a polynomial function in factored form.
    c. The function used to model the box problem in Module 3 has two roots, at $x = 0$ and $x = 4.25$.
    d. The zeros of any function f represent the value(s) of x that when input into the function f return a value of 1 for the output $f(x)$.
    e. Polynomial functions are not always continuous.

47. Watch the video titled "End Behavior of Polynomial Functions" and answer the following questions. (*The video can be found in the online textbook, Module 4 p. 31.*)
    a. How do we represent the phrase "x increases without bound"?
    b. Why is it worthwhile to consider the relative magnitude of each term in a polynomial function?
    c. True or False: When we consider the end behavior of a function we look at how the output values change for input values close to zero. *If the statement is false, rewrite the statement so it is true.*
    d. Given $f(x) = x^3 - 2x^2 + 5x - 100$, what terms dominates the value of $f(x)$ as x increases without bound?

V.   **QUADRATIC FUNCTIONS (TEXT: S9)**

48. Consider the functions $h(x) = x^2$ and $f(x) = 2^x$.
    a. How does the growth of the quadratic function h compare to the growth of the exponential function f?
    b. For large values of x, which of $f(x)$ or $h(x)$ will be larger?
    c. For what value(s) of x is the statement $f(x) = h(x)$ true?

49. Determine the roots of each quadratic function.
    a. $f(x) = (3x - 2)(x + 4)$ b. $g(x) = x^2 - 9$ c. $h(x) = 2x^2 + 5x + 3$ d. $k(x) = -3x^2 + 14x - 16$

50. Determine the vertex of each quadratic function.
    a. $g(x) = (3x - 7)(2x + 6)$ b. $j(x) = x^2 - 16$ c. $p(x) = 4x^2 + 8x + 3$

51. Determine the roots and axis of symmetry of each quadratic function.
    a. $f(x) = x^2 - 6x + 9$ b. $g(x) = (x + 3)(-2x - 5)$ c. $h(x) = -x^2 + 7x - 6$

52. Let $f(x) = x^2$, $g(x) = (x - 4)^2$, $h(x) = (x - 4)^2 + 7$, and $p(x) = 3(x - 4)^2 + 7$.
    a. Determine the roots of each function.
    b. Determine the axis of symmetry for each function.
    c. Sketch a graph of each function.
    d. Compare the graphs (including roots, vertex, and output values) of f, h, g, and p.

53. Given a quadratic function g defined by $g(x) = ax^2 + bx + c$, and the solutions $x = 2 \pm 3.4$ to the quadratic equation $ax^2 + bx + c = 0$, determine the following (if possible).
    a. the roots of g b. the vertex of g

54. Given a quadratic function g defined by $g(x) = ax^2 + bx + c$, and the solutions $x = -4.7 \pm 5$ to the quadratic equation $ax^2 + bx + c = 0$, determine the following (if possible).
    a. the roots of g b. the vertex of g

55. The function f represents the height of a ball h above the ground (measured in feet) in terms of the amount of time t (measured in seconds) since the ball was thrown upward from a bridge. Then $f(t) = -16t^2 + 48t + 120$ with $h = f(t)$.
    a. Approximately how high is the bridge above the ground? Justify your answer.
    b. When does the ball hit the ground? Justify your answer.
    c. Construct a rough sketch of the graph of the function f that relates the height of the ball above the ground and the amount of time since the ball was thrown from the bridge.
       Exercise continues on the next page.
    d. After how many seconds does the ball reach its maximum height above the ground? What is the maximum height above the ground reached by the ball? On the graph you drew in part (c) illustrate the point that represents the ball's maximum height above the ground.
    e. Pick two points on the graph and determine the function's average rate of change over the interval between them. Explain how to interpret this value.

56. A penny is thrown from the top of a 30.48-meter building and hits the ground 3.45 seconds after it was thrown. The penny reached its maximum height above the ground 0.823 seconds after it was thrown.
    a. Define a quadratic function h that expresses the height of the penny above the ground (measured in meters) as a function of the elapsed time (measured in seconds) since the penny was thrown. (*Hint: Determine the zeros of the quadratic function, and then use the height of the building to find the value of the leading coefficient.*)
    b. What is the maximum height of the penny above the ground?

57. A rock is thrown upward from a bridge that is 20 feet above a road. The rock reaches its maximum height above the road 0.91 seconds after it is thrown and contacts the road 2.35 seconds after it was thrown. Use your knowledge of the symmetry of a parabola and the given information to develop a quadratic function that relates the time since the rock was thrown to the height of the rock above the bridge.

58. A coffee shop finds that its weekly profit P (measured in dollars) is determined by the price x (in dollars) that the coffee shop charges for a cup of coffee. The profit P can be determined by the function $f(t) = -4000x^2 + 12000x - 4000$ with $P = f(t)$.
    a. Determine the maximum weekly profit and the price for a cup of coffee that produces the maximum profit.
    b. If $g(x) = f(x - 2)$, describe how the inputs and outputs of g and f are related. Does g have the same maximum profit as f? Explain.
    c. If $h(x) = f(x) - 2$, describe how the inputs and outputs of h and f are related. Does h have the same maximum profit as f? Explain.
    d. If $p(x) = f(x) + 60$, describe how the inputs and outputs of p and f are related.

59. Determine if each of the following are true or false. Provide a brief justification for your answers.
    a. A parabola must have either zero or two x-intercepts.
    b. If $f(x) = ax^2 + bx + c$ with $y = f(x)$, the vertical intercept of function is $y = c$.
    c. The vertex of a parabola is the point where the function values change from increasing to decreasing, or decreasing to increasing.
    d. The zeros of a quadratic function are the horizontal intercept(s) of the function's graph.
    e. The domain of a quadratic function (ignoring contexts) includes all real numbers.
    f. The range of a quadratic function (ignoring contexts) includes all real numbers.
    g. If a quadratic function f has negative concavity on the interval $0 < x < 4$ then the values of $f(x)$ must decrease on this interval.

60. Use the quadratic formula to determine the roots of the following functions.
    a. $f(x) = x^2 + 5x$ b. $g(x) = x^2 + 4x - 3$ c. $k(x) = 10x^2 - 8x - 21$ d. $m(x) = -3x^2 - 2 + 12x$

61. Given the quadratic functions in factored form, write them in an equivalent standard form. Then construct a graph of each function and label its roots and maximum or minimum value.
    a. $h(x) = (2x)(3x - 4)$ b. $m(x) = (x - 5)(2x + 3)$ c. $f(x) = -(3x + 3)(2x - 4)$
62. Given the quadratic functions in standard form, write them in an equivalent factored form. Then construct a graph of each function and label its roots and maximum or minimum value.
    a. $p(x) = 2x^2 - 5x - 3$ b. $h(x) = 3x^2 + 11x - 4$ c. $k(x) = -x^2 + 9x - 14$

63. a. Define the formula for a quadratic function that has horizontal intercepts (roots) at $x = -6$ and $x = 2$ and a graph that passes through the point (0, 5).
    b. What is the parabola's vertex?

64. a. Define the formula for a quadratic function that has horizontal intercepts (roots) at $x = 1$ and $x = 3$ and a graph that passes through the point (0, –10).
    b. What is the parabola's vertex?

65. Use the quadratic formula to solve the following equations for x. (*Hint: First rewrite the equation so that it equals 0. This will allow you to utilize the quadratic formula.*)
    a. $-7x^2 + 13x = -6$ b. $3x^2 - 4x - 4 = 12$ c. $-6x^2 + 22 = 35x$ d. $2x^2 + 5x = 12x - 2$

66. Determine the vertex of each quadratic function by completing the square. (*Note that the product of completing the square only changes the form of a quadratic function. The values represented by the function are unchanged.*)
    a. $f(x) = x^2 - 4x + 1$ b. $h(x) = x^2 + 8x - 7$ c. $k(x) = 2x^2 + 8x - 3$
    d. $p(x) = -2x^2 + 6x - 1$ e. $m(x) = -x^2 + 14x + 3$ f. $p(x) = 3x^2 + 2x + 1$

67. Given the quadratic functions in factored form, write them in equivalent standard form and then complete the square to find the function's maximum or minimum value. Finally construct a graph of each function and label its roots and maximum or minimum value.
    a. $f(x) = (2x + 1)(x - 5)$ b. $h(x) = (x - 7)(-3x + 4)$

68. Why are second order polynomials called quadratics? *You may conduct research on the Internet to determine the answer.*

69. Watch the video titled "Rock Throw Revisited: Creating the Formula" and answer the following questions. (*The video can be found in the online textbook, Module 5 p. 49.*)
    a. Explain how to determine the value of one root of a quadratic function given the other root and the vertex.
    b. Which of the following represents the roots of a function that models the rock throwing problem discussed in the video?
        i. 0.91 ± 1.44 ii. 2.35 ± 2 iii. 2.35 ± 0.53
    c. Why is the factored form of a function useful?
    d. Suppose the zeros of a quadratic function are $x = 2$ and $x = -0.35$ and the graph of the function passes through the point $(0, 2)$. Determine the function's formula.

VI: "IMAGINARY" NUMBERS

In Exercises #70-81, rewrite each expression in terms of i.

70. $\sqrt{-9}$ 71. $\sqrt{-25}$ 72. $\sqrt{-16}$ 73. $\sqrt{-81}$ 74. $\sqrt{-23}$ 75. $\sqrt{-73}$

76. $-\sqrt{-144}$ 77. $\sqrt{-28}$ 78. $\sqrt{-80}$ 79. $-\sqrt{-24}$ 80. $\sqrt{-88}$ 81. $\sqrt{-60}$

In Exercises #82-85, write the solutions to each equation in terms of the number i. Check your answers by substituting the values back into the original equation.

82. $x^2 + 25 = 0$ 83. $x^2 + 121 = 0$ 84. $x^2 + 19 = 0$ 85. $x^2 + 23 = 0$

In Exercises #86-116, rewrite each expression as a complex number of the form $a + bi$.

86. $2 - \sqrt{-64}$ 87. $\sqrt{-144} + 5$ 88. $7 + \sqrt{-99}$ 89. $7\sqrt{-150} + 1$

90. $\sqrt{5} \cdot \sqrt{-20}$ 91 $7 + 2i^3$ 92. $3i^8$ 93. $10i^2 + 3i^5$

94. $9i^7 + i^3$ 95. $i^{16} + 5i^3$ 96. $3i^{53} - 8i^{22}$ 97. $i^{27} + i^{21}$

98. $i(i^5 + 2i^{10})$ 99. $i(4i^{15} + i^{27})$ 100. $(i^5)^3 - 8i^6 + 2i^4$ 101. $(4 + 6i) + (3 + 8i)$

102. $(8 - 2i) + (5 + i)$ 103. $(-6 + 8i) - (2 - 3i)$ 104. $\left(-\dfrac{6}{5} + 5i\right) + \left(\dfrac{9}{2} - \dfrac{16}{3}i\right)$

105. $(n + mi) - (v + ui)$ 106. $3i(2 + 3i)$ 107. $-2i(1 - i)$ 108. $(5 + i)(2 - 2i)$

109. $(-1 - i)(6 + 3i)$ 110. $(3 - 2i)^2$ 111. $(2 - 3i)^2$ 112. $(1 - 2i) - 2(3i)$

113. $\left(1 + \sqrt{2}i\right)\left(4 - \sqrt{3}i\right)$ 114. $\left(\sqrt{7} + 2i\right)\left(\sqrt{7} - 3i\right)$ 115. $i(6i + 4)^2$ 116. $di(p + ni)$

In Exercises #117-122, represent each complex number as a point on the complex plane [recall that $a + bi$ is represented by (a, b)]. *Perform the indicated multiplication and simplify the expression in the form $a + bi$ first if necessary.*

117. a. $2+5i$ b. $i(2+5i)$
     c. $i^2(2+5i)$ d. $-i(2+5i)$

118. a. $-4+6i$ b. $i(-4+6i)$
     c. $i^2(-4+6i)$ d. $-i(-4+6i)$

119. a. $-5-3i$ b. $i(-5-3i)$
     c. $i^2(-5-3i)$ d. $-i(-5-3i)$

120. a. $1-7i$ b. $i(1-7i)$
     c. $i^2(1-7i)$ d. $-i(1-7i)$

121. a. $-6+i$ b. $i(-6+i)$
     c. $i^2(-6+i)$ d. $-i(-6+i)$

122. a. $-3-i$ b. $i(-3-i)$
     c. $i^2(-3-i)$ d. $-i(-3-i)$

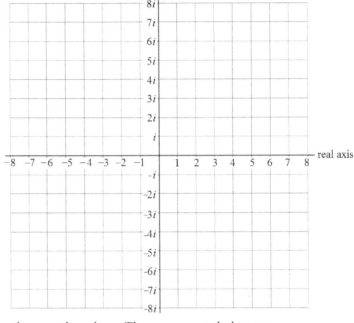

123. Represent $4+2i$ and $3+3i$ as points on the complex plane. Then represent their sum $(4+2i)+(3+3i)$ as a point on the complex plane.

124. Represent $-3+4i$ and $5+i$ as points on the complex plane. Then represent their sum $(-3+4i)+(5+i)$ as a point on the complex plane.

125. Represent $-1-6i$ and $-3+4i$ as points on the complex plane. Then represent their sum $(-1-6i)+(-3+4i)$ as a point on the complex plane.

126. Represent $-2+5i$ and $4-2i$ as points on the complex plane. Then represent their sum $(-2+5i)+(4-2i)$ as a point on the complex plane.

127. How is the location of $(a+bi)+(c+di)$ on the complex plane related to the locations of $a+bi$ and $c+di$?

INVESTIGATION VII: COMPLEX SOLUTIONS TO THE QUADRATIC FORMULA AND THE DISCRIMINANT

In Exercises #128-136, use the discriminant to determine the number of horizontal intercepts for the function. [*You do not need to find the actual values.*] Graph the functions with a calculator or other graphing software to verify your answer.

128. $f(x)=5x^2+3x-1$ 129. $f(x)=2x^2+10x+12.5$ 130. $f(x)=4x^2-14x+12$

131. $f(x)=4x^2+5x+3$ 132. $f(x)=6x^2+x-4$ 133. $f(x)=2.25x^2-6x+4$

134. $f(x) = 0.5x^2 + 4.5x + 10.125$ 135. $f(x) = -0.5x^2 - 3x - 6.125$ 136. $f(x) = -x^2 + x + 0.155$

In Exercises #137-145, do the following.
  a) Use the discriminant to verify that the function has only complex roots.
  b) Determine the function's roots. Write your final answers in the form $a + bi$.

137. $f(x) = x^2 - 2x + 2$ 138. $g(x) = x^2 - 4x + 29$ 139. $h(x) = x^2 + 8x + 25$

140. $f(x) = x^2 + 5x + 26.5$ 141. $h(x) = 2x^2 - 2x + 1$ 142. $f(x) = 3x^2 + 2x + 1$

143. $q(x) = 4x^2 + 53$ 144. $w(x) = -2x^2 - 3x - 2$ 145. $f(x) = -5x^2 + 6x - 7$

This investigation contains review and practice with important skills and procedures you may need in this module and future modules. Your instructor may assign this investigation as an introduction to the module or may ask you to complete select exercises "just in time" to help you when needed. Alternatively, you can complete these exercises on your own to help review important skills.

Simplifying Radicals
Use this section prior to the module or at any point as a spiraled review of skills.

One property of radicals is represented by the statement $\sqrt[n]{a \cdot b} = \sqrt[n]{a} \cdot \sqrt[n]{b}$. Basically, the nth root of a product is equivalent to finding the nth root of each factor and multiplying the results.

Three examples are shown below that demonstrate this property.

$$\sqrt{64} \qquad\qquad \sqrt{100} \qquad\qquad \sqrt[3]{216}$$
$$\sqrt{16 \cdot 4} \qquad\qquad \sqrt{25 \cdot 4} \qquad\qquad \sqrt[3]{27 \cdot 8}$$
$$\sqrt{16} \cdot \sqrt{4} \qquad\qquad \sqrt{25} \cdot \sqrt{4} \qquad\qquad \sqrt[3]{27} \cdot \sqrt[3]{8}$$
$$4 \cdot 2 \qquad\qquad 5 \cdot 2 \qquad\qquad 3 \cdot 2$$
$$8 \qquad\qquad\qquad 10 \qquad\qquad\qquad 6$$

These examples don't demonstrate WHY you would use this property (for example, we already knew that $\sqrt{64} = 8$). This property is most commonly used to rewrite irrational numbers where the number inside can be written as a product of a perfect root and some other number. See the examples below.

$$\sqrt{50} \qquad\qquad \sqrt{192} \qquad\qquad \sqrt[3]{56}$$
$$\sqrt{25 \cdot 2} \qquad\qquad \sqrt{64 \cdot 3} \qquad\qquad \sqrt[3]{8 \cdot 7}$$
$$\sqrt{25} \cdot \sqrt{2} \qquad\qquad \sqrt{64} \cdot \sqrt{3} \qquad\qquad \sqrt[3]{8} \cdot \sqrt[3]{7}$$
$$5\sqrt{2} \qquad\qquad 8\sqrt{3} \qquad\qquad 2\sqrt[3]{7}$$

Take a moment to verify that the expressions at the beginning and end of each process are equivalent. For example, verify that $\sqrt{192}$ and $8\sqrt{3}$ have the same decimal approximation.

In Exercises #1-10 rewrite each expression so that the number inside the radical is as small as possible. *For example, rewrite $\sqrt{18}$ as $2\sqrt{3}$.*

1. $\sqrt{75}$ 2. $\sqrt{28}$ 3. $\sqrt{48}$ 4. $\sqrt{108}$ 5. $\sqrt{45}$

6. $\sqrt{98}$ 7. $\sqrt[3]{54}$ 8. $\sqrt[3]{72}$ 9. $\sqrt[4]{48}$ 10. $\sqrt[4]{162}$

Rewriting Expressions
Use this section prior to the module or with/after Investigations 1 and 2.

In Exercises #11-16 use the distributive property to rewrite each expression.

11. $2x(x^2 - 6)$

12. $-x(10 - x^2)$

13. $4x(x - 3y)$

14. $x^3(2x^4 - \frac{1}{2}x)$

15. $-\frac{2}{3}x(6x + 10)$

16. $-\frac{7}{2}xy(8xy^2 - x^5y^3)$

In Exercises #17-28 rewrite each expression in expanded form. *For example, write* $(x + 2)(2x + 5)$ *in the form* $2x^2 + 9x + 10$.

17. $(x + 4)(x + 5)$

18. $(x - 3)(x + 6)$

19. $(x + 7)(x - 7)$

20. $(x + 10)(x - 8)$

21. $(x - 3)(x - 6)$

22. $(x - 10)(x + 10)$

23. $(x - 1)(x - 4)$

24. $(x + 6)^2$

25. $(x - 5)^2$

26. $(2x + 7)(x + 2)$

27. $(4x - 5)(4x + 5)$

28. $(2x + 3)(3x - 2)$

In the next set of exercises we will factor expressions. A few things to keep in mind when you work on these. First, remember that it can sometimes be helpful to identify common factors. For example, factoring $2x^3 - 16x^2 + 30x$ is easier when we recognize that $2x$ is a common factor of all three terms.

$$2x^3 - 16x^2 + 30x$$
$$2x(x^2 - 8x + 15)$$
$$2x(x-3)(x-5)$$

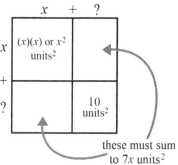

Second, recall the "area model" introduced in an earlier module. This model is often quite helpful for students who are trying to factor trinomial expressions like $x^2 + 7x + 10$. In this case the factored form is $(x+2)(x+5)$.

Third, recall that sometimes a "middle term" can have a value of 0. For example, if you want to factor the expression $x^2 - 25$ you might notice that there is no "x" term (only a term with x^2). However, without changing its value, we can rewrite the expression $x^2 - 25$ as $x^2 + 0 - 25$, or even better as $x^2 + 0x - 25$. The following examples demonstrate this idea.

$x^2 - 25$	$x^2 - 64$	$4x^2 - 9y^2$
$x^2 + 0x - 25$	$x^2 + 0x - 64$	$4x^2 + 0xy - 9y^2$
$(x+5)(x-5)$	$(x+8)(x-8)$	$(2x+3y)(2x-3y)$

29. a. Expand $(x-6)(x+6)$ to show that it is equivalent to $x^2 - 36$.

   b. Expand $(2x-5)(2x+5)$ to show that it is equivalent to $4x^2 - 25$.

In Exercises #30-41 factor each expression. *Use the tips just discussed to help you.*

30. $x^2 + 16x + 60$ 31. $x^2 - 5x - 24$ 32. $x^2 - 100$

33. $5x^3 + 30x^2 + 40x$ 34. $x^2 - 144$ 35. $2x^2 - x - 28$

See instructions on the previous page for Exercises #36-41.

36. $4x^2 - 49$
37. $x^2 - 2xy + y^2$
38. $2x^3 + 5x^2 - 12x$

39. $16x^2 - 36$
40. $3a^2 + 6ab + 3b^2$
41. $6x^3 + 21x^2 + 15x$

Simplifying Rational Expressions
Use this section prior to the module or with/after Investigations 2 and 3.

Sometimes it's possible to factor out the same number from the numerator and denominator of a rational expression. This makes it possible to simplify the expression. For example, the numerator and denominator of $\dfrac{5x + 35}{10}$ both have 5 as a common factor.

$$\frac{5x + 35}{10}$$

$$\frac{5(x + 7)}{5(2)}$$

Since $\frac{a}{b} \cdot \frac{c}{d} = \frac{a \cdot c}{b \cdot d}$ (which is true in "both directions"), we can rewrite this as follows.

$$\frac{5}{5} \cdot \frac{x + 7}{2}$$

$$1 \cdot \frac{x + 7}{2}$$

$$\frac{x + 7}{2}$$

Thus, $\dfrac{5x + 35}{10}$ can be simplified to $\dfrac{x + 7}{2}$. They are equivalent rational expressions. We demonstrate two more examples below.

$$\frac{12x - 15}{3}$$

$$\frac{3(4x - 5)}{3(1)}$$

$$\frac{3}{3} \cdot \frac{4x - 5}{1}$$

$$1 \cdot \frac{4x - 5}{1}$$

$$4x - 5$$

$$\frac{14x + 28}{21}$$

$$\frac{7(2x + 4)}{7(3)}$$

$$\frac{7}{7} \cdot \frac{2x + 4}{3}$$

$$1 \cdot \frac{2x + 4}{3}$$

$$\frac{2x + 4}{3}$$

In Exercises #42-47 simplify the rational expression if possible. If you can't simplify the expression, write "does not simplify".

42. $\dfrac{10x - 20}{10}$

43. $\dfrac{8x - 12}{9}$

44. $\dfrac{21x + 3y}{3}$

45. $\dfrac{8x + 40}{32}$

46. $\dfrac{35x - 5y}{10}$

47. $\dfrac{18x - 72}{45}$

It's also possible to simplify rational expressions when the numerator and denominator have the same variable factors.

$$\frac{2x^2 + 10x}{18x}$$

$$\frac{2x(x + 5)}{2x(9)}$$

$$\frac{2x}{2x} \cdot \frac{x + 5}{9}$$

$$1 \cdot \frac{x + 5}{9}$$

$$\frac{x + 5}{9}$$

Continued on the next page.

HOWEVER, it's important to specify that $\dfrac{2x^2+10x}{18x}$ and $\dfrac{x+5}{9}$ are equivalent only as long as $x \neq 0$.

When $x = 0$ the original expression $\dfrac{2x^2+10x}{18x}$ is undefined. So we say that $\dfrac{2x^2+10x}{18x} = \dfrac{x+5}{9}$ when $x \neq 0$. Two more examples follow.

$$\dfrac{x^2+6x+5}{x+5}$$

$$\dfrac{(x+5)(x+1)}{(x+5)(1)}$$

$$\dfrac{x+5}{x+5} \cdot \dfrac{x+1}{1}$$

$$1 \cdot \dfrac{x+1}{1}$$

$$x+1 \text{ if } x \neq -5$$

$$\dfrac{x^2-7x+12}{x^2-2x-8}$$

$$\dfrac{(x-4)(x-3)}{(x-4)(x+2)}$$

$$\dfrac{x-4}{x-4} \cdot \dfrac{x-3}{x+2}$$

$$1 \cdot \dfrac{x-3}{x+2}$$

$$\dfrac{x-3}{x+2} \text{ if } x \neq 4$$

Notice how we excluded $x = -5$ in the first example because it made the original expression undefined (but not the simplified form). We excluded $x = 4$ in the second example for the same reason.

In Exercises #48-53 simplify the rational expression if possible. If you simplify the rational expression, be sure to list *x*-values we must restrict. If you can't simplify the expression, write "does not simplify".

48. $\dfrac{x^2+5x-14}{x-2}$

49. $\dfrac{x^4+7x^2y}{3x^2}$

50. $\dfrac{x^2-8x-33}{x^2+5x+6}$

51. $\dfrac{x^2-7x+2}{x}$

52. $\dfrac{x+1}{3x^2-x-4}$

53. $\dfrac{x^3}{x^3-2x^2+5x}$

*1. The National Center for Education Statistics (nces.ed.gov) keeps careful records of the number of degrees awarded in the United States. The given table shows the number of PhDs awarded to men and women in the U.S. over time.

- Let $f(t)$ model the number of PhDs awarded to men in terms of the year, t.
- Let $g(t)$ model the number of PhDs awarded to women in terms of the year, t.

a. What is the value of $f(1940)$? $g(1890)$?

year, t	# of PhDs awarded to men in the U.S., $f(t)$	# of PhDs awarded to women in the U.S., $g(t)$	
1880	51	3	
1890	147	2	
1900	359	23	
1920	522	93	
1940	2,861	429	
1960	8,801	1,028	
1980	69,526	26,105	
2000	64,171	55,414	
2010	76,605	81,953	

b. Let h be the function that inputs the year, t, and outputs the value of the ratio $\frac{f(t)}{g(t)}$. That is, $h(t) = \frac{f(t)}{g(t)}$. What is the value of $h(1880)$ and what does it represent in this context?

c. As t varies from 1890 to 1900, does the value of h increase or decrease? Why?

d. Using the given axes, label the axes based on the input and output quantities for h and then plot the points $\left(1880, h(1880)\right)$, $\left(1890, h(1890)\right)$, and $\left(1900, h(1900)\right)$. *Note: We have drawn the horizontal axis as a "broken" axis – you can allow the first tick mark to represent 1870.*

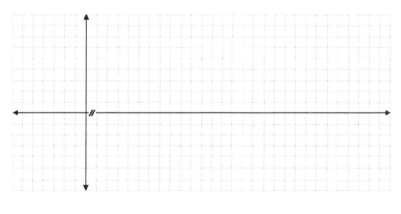

e. What must be true in this context if $h(t) = 3$ for some value of t? If $h(t) = 1$?

f. Is it possible for the output of h to be less than 1 in this context? Explain.

h. Is it possible for the output of h to be negative in this context? Explain.

i.   Must there be a maximum value for $h(t)$ in this context? Explain your thinking.

j.   Use the empty column on the previous page to record values of $h(t)$ and then plot each of the entries in the column as points on your graph. With a partner or as a class, describe the general behavior of h and what that behavior indicates about this context.

Function Outputs as Ratio Values

In Exercise #1 the outputs of function h represented the value of a ratio of two other varying quantities. Function h's output didn't tell us how many PhDs were awarded to men or women – it told us about the <u>relative size</u> of these quantities.

This presents interesting scenarios. For example, it's possible for the number of PhDs awarded to men and women to both increase but for the value of the ratio to decrease. When working with a function whose output is a ratio of two values we <u>must</u> pay careful attention to *how* the two quantities change and how this affects their relative size if we want to be able to understand the meaning of the output values and understand the function's behavior.

---

*2. Consider the function $f(x) = \frac{2}{x}$. What happens to the value of the function when x gets close to 0? Use the given tables to help you formulate your response.

x	$f(x) = \frac{2}{x}$
-2	
-1	
-0.1	
-0.01	
-0.001	

x	$f(x) = \frac{2}{x}$
0.001	
0.01	
0.1	
1	
2	

"Approaches" Notation

In Exercise #2 we thought about the value of x getting close to $x = 0$ from values less than 0 and from values greater than 0.

When x approaches 0 from values less than 0 (increasing towards 0) we say that "x approaches 0 from the left" and write this in notation as $x \to 0^-$ (*because the direction comes from the negative end of the number line*).

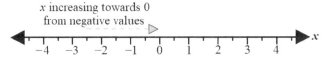

When x approaches 0 from values greater than 0 (decreasing towards 0) we say that "x approaches 0 from the right" and write this in notation as $x \to 0^+$ (*because the direction comes from the positive end of the number line*).

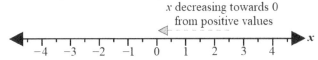

---

3. The following sequences represent varying values of *x*. Use "approaches" notation to describe the trend you observe.

  *a. 6, 5, 4.6, 4.55, 4.51, 4.5001, 4.500001, ...   b. 9, 9.9, 9.99, 9.999, 9.9999, ...

  *c. $-6, -5.5, -5.1, -5.01, -5.001, ...$ d. $-1, -1.5, -1.9, -1.99, -1.999, ...$

*4. Determine whether the following sequences of numbers are increasing or decreasing (*Note: A sequence of all negative numbers is increasing if successive numbers are getting closer to 0.*)

  a. $\frac{1}{100}, \frac{1}{200}, \frac{1}{320}, \frac{1}{450}, \frac{1}{1089}$ b. $\frac{2}{100}, \frac{5}{40}, \frac{10}{35}, \frac{15}{9}, \frac{50}{6}$

  c. $\frac{100}{2}, \frac{40}{5}, \frac{35}{10}, \frac{9}{15}, \frac{6}{50}$ d. $\frac{-1}{100}, \frac{-1}{200}, \frac{-1}{320}, \frac{-1}{450}, \frac{-1}{1089}$

*5. If $f(x) = \frac{x}{x-8}$, complete the following.

  a. Complete the following table of values. *Pay attention the value of the numerator and denominator as you perform your calculations.*

x	*f(x)*		*x*	*f(x)*
7			8.001	
7.5			8.01	
7.9			8.1	
7.99			8.5	
7.999			9	

  b. What do you notice as *x* approaches 8 from the left (from values less than 8, written $x \rightarrow 8^-$)? Why does this happen?

  c. What do you notice as *x* approaches 8 from the right (from values greater than 8, written $x \rightarrow 8^+$)? Why does this happen?

  d. Using a calculator, graph *f*. Discuss with a group or as a class how the graph supports your answers in parts (b) and (c).

Vertical Asymptotes

A *vertical asymptote* occurs at a real number $x = a$ if
- as $x \to a^-$ (as x approaches a from the left, or from values less than a) the value of $f(x)$ increases or decreases without bound

and

- as $x \to a^+$ (as x approaches a from the right, or from values greater than a) the value of $f(x)$ increases or decreases without bound

Note that the examples in Exercises #2 and #5 were functions whose output values represented a ratio of two polynomial functions. Mathematicians call these type of functions *rational functions*.

Rational Functions

If p and r are polynomial functions, then a function whose output values represent a ratio of the values of these functions (such as $f(x) = \frac{p(x)}{r(x)}$) is called a *rational function*.

---

6. Suppose $f(x) = \frac{p(x)}{r(x)}$ where p and r are polynomial functions.
   a. For what value(s) of x is $f(x)$ undefined?   b. For what value(s) of x does $f(x) = 0$?

*7. Five gallons of liquid flavoring are poured into a large vat. Water will be added to the vat and mixed with the flavoring to produce a drink that will be bottled and sold.
   a. Suppose water is added until the total mixture is 7 gallons. What is the ratio of flavoring to water? What does this ratio represent? (Hint: *How many times as large…*)

   b. Suppose water is added until the total mixture is 18 gallons. What is the ratio of flavoring to water?

   c. Define a function f that determines the ratio, R, of flavoring to water in the mixture in terms of the total volume of the mixture x (in gallons). What is the practical domain of this function?

   d. What does it mean to say "as $x \to 5^+$"?

   e. What happens to the value of $f(x)$ as $x \to 5^+$? Why does this make sense?

8. The graphs of $y = p(x)$ and $y = r(x)$ are given below. The rational function h is defined by $h(x) = \frac{p(x)}{r(x)}$.
   Let's explore the behavior of h by thinking about the behavior of p and r.

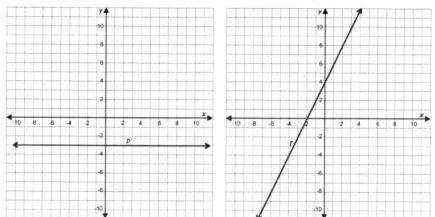

a. As x increases from -10 to -2, describe whether the value of each function is 1) positive or negative and 2) constant, increasing or decreasing.
   i. The value of $p(x)$ is...   ii. The value of $r(x)$ is...   iii. The value of $h(x)$ is...

b. Evaluate $h(-2)$.

c. As x increases from -10 to -2, describe whether the value of each function is 1) positive or negative and 2) constant, increasing or decreasing.
   i. The value of $p(x)$ is...   ii. The value of $r(x)$ is...   iii. The value of $h(x)$ is...

d. Evaluate $h(0)$.

e. As x increases from $x = 0$ to $x = 5$, describe the behavior of h.

f. Sketch a graph of the function h.

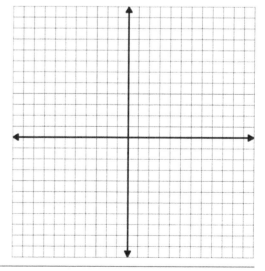

9. For each of the following functions, predict where a vertical asymptote will exist. Then test your prediction using a graphing calculator.

a. $f(x) = \dfrac{8}{x+1}$

b. $g(x) = \dfrac{x}{2x-8}$

*c. $h(x) = \dfrac{6x^2 - 24}{2(x-3)(x+1)}$

d. $m(x) = \dfrac{x+3}{x^2 + 4x - 5}$

*e. $n(x) = \dfrac{x^5 + 1}{x^2 + 1}$

*f. $c(x) = \dfrac{2(x+6)}{x+6}$

10. Write an explanation describing how to determine the vertical asymptotes of a rational function and *why* this approach works.

*1. Interpret the meaning of each of the following.

    a. $x \to 4^+$ b. $x \to 6^-$ c. $x \to \infty$ d. $f(x) \to -\infty$

In Module 5 we explored the long-term behavior (or end behavior) of polynomial functions. We know that as x increases or decreases without bound the leading term is the largest magnitude term in the polynomial. Therefore, the behavior of the function is well-estimated by the behavior of the leading term.

If $f(x) = x^2 - 10x + 5$, then as $x \to \pm\infty$ (as x increases or decreases without bound), f behaves indistinguishably from $y = x^2$. Thus, we might say the following.

$$\text{As } x \to \pm\infty, \; f(x) \to x^2.$$

How might this help us understand the long-term behavior of rational functions?

*2. Given $f(x) = \frac{2x^2-6x+1}{x-5}$ (where $2x^2 - 6x + 1$ and $x - 5$ are polynomials), complete the following.

    a. As x increases or decreases without bound (as $x \to \pm\infty$), what expression can we use to estimate the behavior of $2x^2 - 6x + 1$?

    b. As $x \to \pm\infty$, what expression can we use to estimate the behavior of $x - 5$?

    c. As $x \to \pm\infty$, what expression do you think we can use to estimate the behavior of $f(x) = \frac{2x^2-6x+1}{x-5}$? [*Simplify the expression if possible.*]

    d. Using a graphing calculator or graphing software, graph function f along with $y = \#\#$ on the same set of axes, where "$\#\#$" is the expression you determined in part (c).
       i. When x is relatively close to 0 (from $x = -10$ to $x = 10$, for example), do the two functions behave similarly?

       ii. Zoom out on the graph. As you zoom out, what do you notice?

       iii. What do your answers to parts (i) and (ii) tell us about the rational function f?

3. For each of the following rational functions, create an expression that estimates the function's end behavior (its behavior as $x \to \pm\infty$). Simplify your answer and then use a graphing calculator to check your work (see Exercise #2 part (d)).

    a. $f(x) = \frac{4x+8}{2x-9}$ b. $g(x) = \frac{x^3+x-20}{x+4}$ c. $h(x) = \frac{x^2-6x+5}{x^3+2}$

4. A small airport is considering selling jet fuel at its airport. There is an initial investment of $3,200,000 to install tanks for the fuel. The price the airport pays for fuel is $3.90 per gallon. The function $f(x) = 3,200,000 + 3.90x$ models the total cost (in dollars) for the airport to purchase x gallons of fuel (including the startup cost and per-gallon cost).

   a. The average cost per gallon of fuel can be modeled by the function g where $g(x) = \dfrac{f(x)}{x} = \dfrac{3,200,000 + 3.90x}{x}$. Determine the values of $g(500)$ and $g(1,000,000)$ and explain what they represent in this context.

   b. Use the function g to determine the average cost per gallon the airport owner invests to supply the number of gallons of fuel x given in the table below.

x	Cost $f(x)$ (dollars)	Average Cost $g(x)$ (dollars per gallon)
1,000		
10,000		
100,000		
1,000,000		
10,000,000		
100,000,000		

   c. As the number of gallons of fuel supplied increases, how does the average cost per gallon of fuel change?

   d. What is the change in the average cost per gallon as the number of gallons of fuel supplied increases from 1,000,000 to 10,000,000?

   e. What value does the output of g approach as the number of gallons supplied increases without bound? What does this information convey about the co-variation of quantities in the context of the problem?

   f. If the number of gallons of fuel supplied by the jet fuel company continues to increase, will the average cost per gallon reach a minimum value? Explain.

*5. *Recall the following context from Investigation 1 of this module.* Five gallons of liquid flavoring is poured into a large vat. Water will be added to the vat and mixed with the flavoring to produce a drink that will be bottled and sold.

We defined a function f to relate the ratio of flavoring to water $R = f(x)$ in the mixture to the total volume of the mixture x in gallons by $f(x) = \frac{5}{x-5}$.

a. How does the ratio of flavoring to water change as $x \to \infty$ (as x increases without bound)?

b. Is there a minimum value for the ratio of flavoring to water $f(x)$? If so, state the minimum value. If not, explain why there is no minimum value.

c. Use a calculator or graphing software to graph f. With your group or as a class, discuss how the graph supports your answer to (b).

d. Complete the following statement. As $x \to \infty$, $f(x) \to$ _____.

6. A national park research team noticed a dramatic reduction in the deer population in a 150,000-acre protected area. In order to increase the population of deer, the park services introduced 125 additional deer into the area. The researchers' population model predicts that the expected number of deer $f(t)$ is modeled by the function f, defined by $f(t) = \frac{50(2t+16)}{0.0075t+4}$ where t, the time since the 125 deer were introduced, is measured in years.

a. What was the deer population previous to the addition of the 125 deer? Explain how you determined this value.

b. Find the population when i) $t = 7$ years; ii) $t = 18$ years; and iii) $t = 110$ years.

c. When will the population of deer reach 760?

d. What expression can be used to estimate the long-term behavior of the function's values?

e. The research team's model predicts that the total number of deer that can be supported by the 150,000-acre area is limited. What is the maximum number of deer that the research team expected the 150,000-acre area to support? Discuss your approach with your group or as a class.

7. Given the function f defined by $f(x) = \frac{1}{x-8}$, complete the following.

   a. Fill in the tables of values.

x	$x-8$	$f(x)=\frac{1}{x-8}$
$-1{,}000{,}000$		
$-10{,}000$		
-100		

x	$x-8$	$f(x)=\frac{1}{x-8}$
100		
$10{,}000$		
$1{,}000{,}000$		

   b. How does the output of f change as $x \to \infty$? Why does this happen?

   c. How does the output of f change as $x \to -\infty$? Why does this happen?

   d. Using a calculator, graph f. Explain how the graph supports your conclusions above.

*8. Given the function f defined by $f(x) = \frac{3x}{x+4}$, answer the questions below.

   a. Fill in the tables of values.

x	$3x$	$x+4$	$f(x)=\frac{3x}{x+4}$
$-1{,}000{,}000$			
$-10{,}000$			
-100			
100			
$10{,}000$			
$1{,}000{,}000$			

   b. As x increases without bound ($x \to \infty$) how does $f(x)$ vary? Explain.

   c. As x decreases without bound ($x \to -\infty$) how does $f(x)$ vary? Explain.

   d. Using a calculator, graph f. Explain how the graph supports your conclusions in parts (b) and (c) above.

> ### Horizontal Asymptotes
>
> A *horizontal asymptote* exists if a horizontal line $y = a$ can be used to estimate the end behavior of a function. If $f(x) \to a$ as $x \to \infty$ or $x \to -\infty$ then we say that $y = a$ is a horizontal asymptote for f.
>
> *Note that there are other possible end behaviors for functions (including rational functions). Not every rational function will have a horizontal asymptote.*

9. Determine any horizontal asymptotes from exercises you have completed thus far. Then discuss with your group or as a class what these asymptotes convey about how x and $f(x)$ change together as $x \to \pm\infty$.

*10. For each given function, do the following.
    i. Write a variable expression that can be used to estimate the function's value as $x \to \pm\infty$. Simplify the expression if possible. Use a form similar to, "As $x \to \pm\infty$, $f(x) \to$ ____."
    ii. Write the function's horizontal asymptote (if one exists).
    iii. Verify your work by graphing the function using a graphing calculator or graphing software.

a. $f(x) = \dfrac{8}{x+1}$

b. $g(x) = \dfrac{x}{2x-8}$

c. $h(x) = \dfrac{6x^2 - 24}{2(x-3)(x+1)}$

d. $m(x) = \dfrac{x+3}{x^2 + 4x - 5}$

e. $n(x) = \dfrac{x^5 + 1}{x^2 + 1}$

f. $c(x) = \dfrac{2(x+6)}{x+6}$

---

*11. Generalizing the reasoning in this investigation, any polynomial expression

$p(x) = a_n x^n + a_{n-1} x^{n-1} + a_{n-2} x^{n-2} + ... + a_1 x + a_0$ can be well-estimated by the variable expression $a_n x^n$

as x increases or decreases without bound. That is, as $x \to \pm\infty$, $p(x) \to a_n x^n$.

   Therefore, a rational function $r(x) = \dfrac{p(x)}{q(x)} = \dfrac{a_n x^n + a_{n-1} x^{n-1} + a_{n-2} x^{n-2} + ... + a_1 x + a_0}{b_m x^m + b_{n-1} x^{m-1} + b_{n-2} x^{m-2} + ... + b_1 x + b_0}$ can be well-

estimated by $\frac{a_n x^n}{b_m x^m}$ as x increases or decreases without bound. That is, as $x \to \pm\infty$, $r(x) \to \frac{a_n x^n}{b_m x^m}$.

   a. Under what conditions does a rational function have no horizontal asymptote? Explain and then give an example.

   b. Under what conditions does a rational function have a horizontal asymptote at $y = 0$? Explain and then given an example.

   c. Under what conditions does a rational function have a horizontal asymptote that is NOT $y = 0$? In this case, how can you determine the horizontal asymptote by looking at the polynomial functions in the numerator and denominator? Explain and give an example.

Use the four rational functions defined in (i-iv) to answer Questions 1-7.

$$\text{i) } f(x) = \frac{x-3}{x+2} \qquad *\text{ii) } g(x) = \frac{3x^2}{(x-1)(x-3)} \qquad *\text{iii) } h(x) = \frac{x^2+1}{x-2} \qquad *\text{iv) } k(x) = \frac{5x}{x^2-4}$$

1. a. Find the real zeros (or roots) of each function.
    i)   ii)   iii)   iv)

    b. Describe your method for determining the zeros and what they represent.

2. a. Determine the vertical intercept of each function and explain what this intercept represents.
    i)   ii)   iii)   iv)

    b. Describe your method for determining the vertical intercepts and what they represent.

3. a. What is the domain of each function?
    i)   ii)   iii)   iv)

    b. For what values of x that are excluded from a function's domain does the graph of the function have a hole instead of a vertical asymptote? Explain how you know that the graph has a hole.

4. a. Using what you learned in Investigation 2, fill in the blanks below.

    i) As $x \to \infty$, $f(x) \to$ _____
        As $x \to -\infty$, $f(x) \to$ _____
        Horizontal Asymptote: _____

    ii) As $x \to \infty$, $g(x) \to$ _____
        As $x \to -\infty$, $g(x) \to$ _____
        Horizontal Asymptote: _____

    iii) As $x \to \infty$, $h(x) \to$ _____
        As $x \to -\infty$, $h(x) \to$ _____
        Horizontal Asymptote: _____

    iv) As $x \to \infty$, $k(x) \to$ _____
        As $x \to -\infty$, $k(x) \to$ _____
        Horizontal Asymptote: _____

b. Use the information from your answers above to sketch a graph of each of the four functions and then check your work with a graphing calculator. (*Remember that if you are ever unclear about how a function behaves on a given interval, you can evaluate the function for values of x.*).

If your sketch was incorrect, think carefully about why your graph was incorrect.

i)
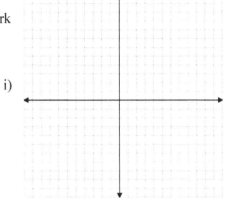

ii)
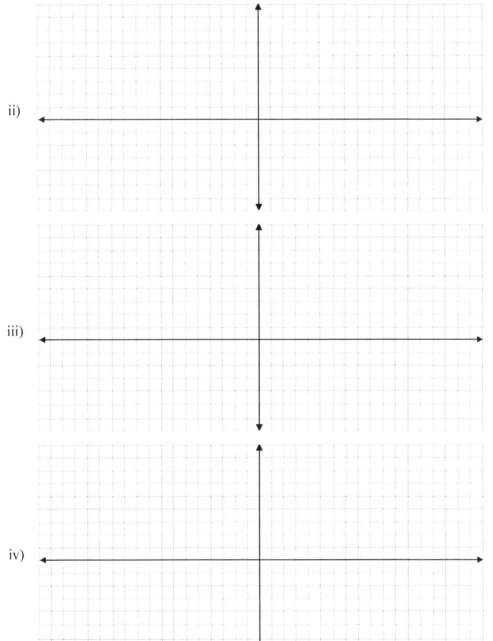

iii)

iv)

5. Sketch a graph of the following rational functions without using a graphing calculator by determining each function's: i) roots; ii) y-intercept; ii) vertical asymptote(s); iii) horizontal asymptote(s); and (iv) the sign of the function on intervals of the function's domain.

(Remember that if you are ever unclear about the value of a function or how the function behaves on a given interval, you can evaluate the function for values of x.).

a. $g(x) = \frac{x+7}{x-5}$

b. $h(x) = \frac{x^2-9}{x+4}$

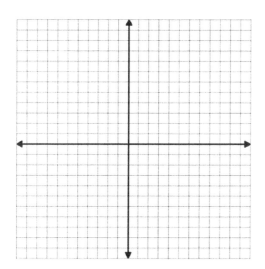
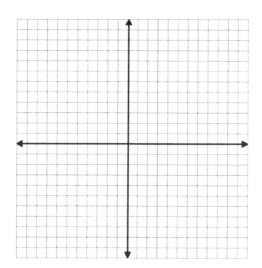

Limit Notation

    Limit Notation is a concise way to communicate behavior about a function. If the output values are approaching a specific value as the input value approaches a specific value (or increases or decreases without bound) we say that value is a *limit* of the function values.

    For example, consider the function $f(x) = \frac{x-3}{x+2}$. As x increases without bound ($x \to \infty$) the function values approach 1. Therefore, we can write "$\lim_{x \to \infty} f(x) = 1$" (read: "As x increases without bound, the function values approach 1.") In addition, as x decreases without bound the function values also approach 1. We can write this as $\lim_{x \to -\infty} f(x) = 1$.

    There is a vertical asymptote at $x = -2$, and by doing a bit of work we can show that $f(x)$ decreases without bound as $x \to -2^-$. Since the output values do not approach a specific value a limit does not exist, or $\lim_{x \to -2^-} f(x)$ DNE. Similarly $\lim_{x \to -2^+} f(x)$ DNE since as $x \to -2^+$, $f(x)$ increases without bound.

---

6. Use the following functions to fill in the blanks below. (Note: If a value does not exist, write DNE)

$f(x) = \frac{x+3}{x+6}$ $g(x) = \frac{3x^2}{(x-1)(x-3)}$ $h(x) = \frac{x^2+1}{x-2}$ $k(x) = \frac{5x}{x^2-4}$

a. $\lim\limits_{x\to\infty} f(x) = $ ____   b. $\lim\limits_{x\to\infty} g(x) = $ ____   c. $\lim\limits_{x\to\infty} h(x) = $ ____   d. $\lim\limits_{x\to-\infty} k(x) = $ ____

$\lim\limits_{x\to-\infty} f(x) = $ ____ $\lim\limits_{x\to1^-} g(x) = $ ____ $\lim\limits_{x\to-\infty} h(x) = $ ____ $\lim\limits_{x\to-2^-} k(x) = $ ____

$\lim\limits_{x\to-6^-} f(x) = $ ____ $\lim\limits_{x\to1^+} g(x) = $ ____ $\lim\limits_{x\to2^-} h(x) = $ ____ $\lim\limits_{x\to2^-} k(x) = $ ____

$\lim\limits_{x\to-6^+} f(x) = $ ____ $\lim\limits_{x\to3^+} g(x) = $ ____ $\lim\limits_{x\to2^+} h(x) = $ ____ $\lim\limits_{x\to2^+} k(x) = $ ____

7. For each part you are given information about a rational function. Use the information to sketch a possible graph of the function.

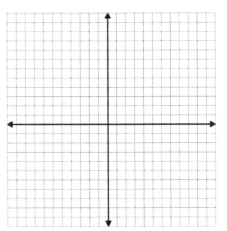

a. $\lim\limits_{x\to\infty} f(x) = -3$

$\lim\limits_{x\to-\infty} f(x) = -3$

$\lim\limits_{x\to2^-} f(x)$ DNE

As $x \to 2^-$, $f(x)$ increases without bound.

$\lim\limits_{x\to2^+} f(x)$ DNE

As $x \to 2^+$, $f(x)$ decreases without bound.

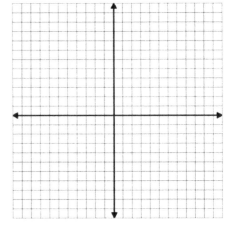

b. $\lim\limits_{x\to\infty} g(x)$ DNE

As $x \to \infty$, $g(x)$ increases without bound.

$\lim\limits_{x\to-\infty} g(x)$ DNE

As $x \to -\infty$, $g(x)$ decreases without bound.

$\lim\limits_{x\to-4^-} g(x)$ DNE

As $x \to 4^-$, $g(x)$ decreases without bound.

$\lim\limits_{x\to-4^+} g(x)$ DNE

As $x \to 4^+$, $g(x)$ increases without bound.

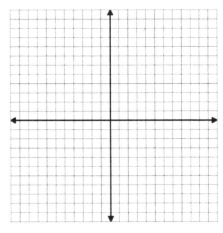

c. $\lim\limits_{x\to\infty} h(x) = 2$ and $\lim\limits_{x\to-\infty} h(x) = 2$

$\lim\limits_{x\to-3^-} h(x)$ DNE

As $x \to -3^-$, $h(x)$ increases without bound.

$\lim\limits_{x\to-3^+} h(x)$ DNE

As $x \to -3^+$, $h(x)$ decreases without bound.

$\lim\limits_{x\to1^-} f(x)$ DNE

As $x \to 1^-$, $h(x)$ decreases without bound.

$\lim\limits_{x\to1^+} f(x)$ DNE

As $x \to 1^+$, $h(x)$ increases without bound.

0. OPTIONAL CONTENT: SYMBOLIC OPERATIONS

In Exercises #1-6, rewrite each function in simplified form and then describe the function's domain.

1. $f(x) = \frac{x^2-5x+6}{3x^2-15x+18}$

2. $f(x) = \frac{3x^4-9x^2}{9x^3+27x^2}$

3. $f(x) = \frac{x^3+x^2-2x}{-2+x^2+x}$

4. $f(x) = \frac{4y^2-20y-56}{2y^2-22y+56}$

5. $f(x) = \frac{2x^2+7x-15}{2x^2-x-3}$

6. $f(x) = \frac{-x^2+6x-8}{x^2-x-12}$

In Exercises #7-12, perform the specified arithmetic operations and simplify the result if possible.

7. $\frac{4x}{x+4} + \frac{x-6}{x-9}$

8. $\frac{5x^2}{x^3+1} + \frac{1}{x}$

9. $\frac{x^2-1}{x-8} - \frac{x+8}{7}$

10. $\frac{x^2}{(x+8)^4} \cdot \frac{(x+8)^6}{x^3(2x-1)}$

11. $\frac{2x^2-x-1}{x+3} \cdot \frac{x+3}{x-1}$

12. $\frac{(4x-2)^3}{(x+3)^2} \div \frac{(4x-2)^5}{(x-3)^2}$

In Exercises #13-18, rewrite the sums and differences as products by factoring the polynomials. For example, given $4(x+6)+(x^2-2)(x+6)$, both terms have $x+6$ as a common factor, so we can rewrite it as $(x+6)\big((4)+(x^2-2)\big)$ by factoring out $x+6$, or $(x+6)(4+x^2-2)$ or $(x+6)(x^2+2)$ simplified.

13. $10(x+14)-2x(x+14)$

14. $x^2(x^2-1)+13(x^2-1)$

15. $3x(x^2+5x-14)-(x^2+5x-14)$

16. $(2x^2+6)^2(x^2-2x)^3+(2x^2+6)^3(x^2-2x)^2$

17. $(x+1)^2(x+2)^3(x+3)^4+(x+1)^3(x+2)^4(x+3)^5$

18. $(2x)^{1/2}-(2x)^{5/2}$

I. INTRODUCTION TO RATIONAL FUNCTIONS AND VERTICAL ASYMPTOTES (Text: S1, 2, 4, 6)

19. The given table shows values of two functions. Function f inputs the year and outputs the average annual compensation (in dollars) for corporate CEOs in the U.S. Function g inputs the year and outputs the average annual compensation (in dollars) for non-manager corporate employees. *Note that the values are adjusted for inflation. Data collected from the Economy Policy Institute.*

year, t	average CEO compensation (dollars) $f(t)$	average non-manager compensation (dollars) $f(t)$ $g(t)$
1965	819,000	39,500
1973	1,069,000	46,400
1978	1,463,000	47,200
1989	2,724,000	44,700
1995	5,768,000	45,600
2000	20,172,000	47,900
2010	12,466,000	52,700
2013	15,175,000	52,100

    a. Evaluate $f(2000)$ and $g(1989)$ and explain what they represent.

    b. The output of function h is the value of the ratio $\frac{f(t)}{g(t)}$. That is, $h(t) = \frac{f(t)}{g(t)}$. Evaluate $h(1978)$ and $h(1995)$ and explain what the values represent in this context.

    c. As t increases from 1978 to 1995, did the values of $f(t)$ and $g(t)$ increase, decrease, or remain constant? What does that tell us about this context?

    d. As t increases from 1978 to 1995, did the value of $h(t)$ increase, decrease, or remain constant? What does that tell us about this context?

    e. What would it mean for $h(t) = 10$ for some value of t? What would it mean for $h(t) = 1$ for some value of t?

    f. Is it possible for $h(t)$ to be less than 1 for some value of t?

    e. Use the information in the table to create a table of values for function h. Describe the behavior of h as t increases and what that tells you about this context.

20. A weight loss center is so confident in their program that they created a special pricing plan. Joining the program costs a one-time fee of $49.99, and members don't have to pay anything more unless they lose weight. However, members pay the center $2.99 per pound they lose while in the program.
    a. Define a function f to express the cost C for someone joining the program and losing x pounds. What is the practical domain of this function?
    b. Suppose we are interested in determining the average cost per pound lost for someone in the program. (*Note that average cost is NOT an average rate of change.*) Describe how to determine the average cost per pound lost when x pounds are lost by a member in the program. (*What calculation determines the average cost and why?*)
    c. Complete the given table and then determine the average cost per pound lost for a member losing x pounds while in the program.
    d. Define a function g that relates the member's average cost per pound lost (measured in dollars) as a function of the number of pounds lost.
    e. When x is positive and getting very close to 0 (which we write as $x \to 0^+$), what happens to the average cost per pound? Why?
    f. Does the average cost per pound have a maximum value? Explain.

x	Cost $f(x)$	Average Cost $g(x)$
0.01		
0.1		
1		
10		
100		

21. A beverage company has just completed brewing a large batch of tea (1500 gallons). They will add sweetening to the tea, then bottle it and prepare it for distribution.
    a. Suppose 10 gallons of corn syrup is added to the mixture as a sweetener. What is the ratio of tea to corn syrup in the mixture? What if 50 gallons of corn syrup is added instead? 200 gallons?
    b. Define a function f whose input x is the amount of corn syrup added (in gallons) and whose output R is the ratio of tea to corn syrup in the mixture.
    c. What is the practical domain for the function you defined?
    d. Complete the given table of values for this function.
    e. What happens to R as $x \to 0^+$? Why does this make sense?

x	$R = f(x)$
0.001	
0.01	
0.1	
1	

22. A cylindrical container is designed to carry liquid that must be insulated (*see diagram*). The interior cylinder will hold the liquid, and the insulation must be 2 inches thick.
    a. If the radius of the entire container (interior cylinder and insulation) is 4.5 inches, what is the radius of the interior cylinder? What if the radius of the entire container is 5.9 inches? x inches?
    b. The formula for the volume of a cylinder is given by $V = \pi r^2 h$. Suppose the container must hold exactly 200 in³ of liquid. How tall must the container be if the radius of the entire container is 4.5 inches and the interior cylinder holds exactly 200 in³? What if the radius of the entire container is 5.9 inches?
    c. Define a function f whose input x is the radius of the entire package (in inches) and whose output h is the height of the package (in inches) necessary so that the interior container holds 200 in³ of liquid.
    d. What happens to the value of h as $x \to 2^+$? What does this mean in the context of this problem?

INSULATION — Interior Cylinder — 2 inches

x	$R = f(x)$
1.01	
1.1	
1.5	
2	

23. Given that $f(x) = \frac{x}{x-9}$, answer the questions below.
    a. Complete the given tables of values. Show the calculations that provided your answers.
    b. How do the output values of f change as $x \to 9^-$? Why?
    c. How do the output values of f change as $x \to 9^+$? Why?
    d. Using a calculator, graph f. Explain how the graph supports your conclusions above.
    e. What changes if the definition of f becomes $f(x) = \frac{x}{x-9}$? Why does this happen?
    f. What changes if the definition of f becomes $f(x) = \frac{x}{x-9}$? Why does this happen?

x	$f(x)$
8	
8.9	
8.99	
8.999	

x	$f(x)$
9.001	
9.01	
9.1	
10	

24. Given that $f(x)=\frac{2}{x+7}$, complete the following.

   a. How do the output values of f change as $x \to -7^-$?
   b. How do the output values of f change as $x \to -7^+$?
   c. Using a calculator, graph f. Explain how the graph supports your conclusions in parts (a) and (b).
   d. What changes if the definition of f becomes $f(x)=-\frac{2}{x+7}$? Why does this happen?

25. Given that $g(x)=\frac{5x}{(x+1)(x-3)}$, complete the following.

   a. How do the output values of g change as $x \to -1^-$? As $x \to -1^+$?
   b. How do the output values of g change as $x \to 3^-$? As $x \to 3^+$?
   c. Using a calculator, graph f. Explain how the graph supports your conclusions in parts (a) and (b).

26. For each of the following functions, predict where a vertical asymptote will exist and then test your prediction using a graphing calculator.

   a. $f(x)=\frac{x-10}{x+10}$ b. $g(x)=\frac{x^2}{5x-9}$ c. $h(x)=\frac{x}{x^2+2}$ d. $m(x)=\frac{6}{x^2-1}$ e. $n(x)=\frac{5x+5}{x+1}$ f. $p(x)=\frac{6-x}{(x-4)(x-5)}$

II. END BEHAVIOR OF RATIONAL FUNCTIONS (Text: S1, 2, 3, 5)

27. A beverage company has just completed brewing a large batch of tea (1500 gallons). They will add corn syrup to the tea, then bottle it and prepare it for distribution. The function f relates the ratio R of tea to corn syrup in the beverage when x gallons of corn syrup are added and is defined by $f(x)=\frac{1500}{x}$ with $R=f(x)$.

x	$R=f(x)$
100	
10,000	
1,000,000	
10,000,000	

   a. Complete the given table of values for this function.
   b. What happens to R as x increases without bound?
   c. Is it practical in this context to allow x to increase without bound? Explain.

28. A cylindrical container is being designed to carry liquid that must be insulated (see diagram below). The interior cylinder will hold the liquid, and the insulation must be 2 inches thick. Function f is defined by $f(x)=\frac{200}{\pi(x-2)^2}$ with $h=f(x)$ where x

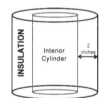

x	$h=f(x)$
10	
100	
1,000	
10,000	

is the radius of the entire package (in inches) and h is the height of the package (in inches) necessary so that the interior container holds 200 in³ of liquid.
   a. Complete the given table of values.
   b. What happens to the value of h as x increases without bound? What does this mean in the context of this problem?

29. Clark's Soda Company incurred a start-up cost of $1276 for equipment to produce a new soda flavor. The cost of producing the drink is $0.26 per can. The company sells the soda for $0.75 per can. *(Assume that Clark's Soda Company is able to sell every can produced.)*
   a. Define a function f to determine the cost (including the start-up cost) measured in dollars to produce x cans of soda.
   b. Define a function g to determine the revenue (measured in dollars) generated from selling x cans of soda.
   c. Define a function h to determine the profit (measured in dollars) from selling x cans of soda (recall that profit = revenue – cost).
   d. Define a function A to determine the average cost per can of producing the soda.
   e. How does A change as the number of cans produced gets larger and larger? Will the average cost function A ever reach a minimum value? Explain.

30. A salt cell is cleaned using a mixture of water and acid. There are currently 10 liters of water in a bucket. A technician adds varying amounts of acid to the 10 liters of water.
    - Let x = the number of liters of acid added to the 10 liters of water
    - Let A = the level of acidity of the mixture (or the percentage of the solution that is acid)
    a. Complete the given table of the mixture's acidity (*measured as a percentage of the total*) as acid is added to the 10 liters of water.
    b. Define a function to determine the acidity of the mixture (measured as a percentage) in terms of the number of liters of acid x that has been added.
    c. Use a calculator to graph f.
    d. Describe how the acidity of the mixture changes as the number of liters of acid added to the solution increases without bound.
    e. Is it possible for the mixture to ever reach 100% acid? Explain.
    f. If the water is too acidic, it can damage the salt cell. If the water is not acidic enough, the mixture will not be practical in cleaning the cell. It turns out the mixture is most efficient if the acidity is between 40% and 60%. What is the range of liters of acid that should be added to the bucket of water so that the mixture is most efficient?
    g. Define a function that accepts the desired percentage of acid as input and determines the number of liters of acid that should be added to the water as output.

liters of acid x	acitidy of mixture, A (as a percent)
0	
0.5	
1.0	
1.5	
2.0	
2.5	
3.0	
3.5	

31. A large mosquito repellent manufacturer produces a repellent using DEET (the most common active ingredient in insect repellents) and a moisturizer lotion. A tank for mixing the repellent is filled with a steady flow of the lotion and DEET. Soon after the filling began, the mixture was sampled and it was determined that there were 97 ounces of lotion and 4 ounces of DEET in the tank (let the time of the first sample be $t = 0$ where time is measured in a number of seconds). Additional readings revealed that the lotion was flowing in at a constant rate of 12 ounces per second and the DEET was flowing in at a constant rate of 6.4 ounces per second. The company needs to monitor the percentage of DEET in their lotion.
    a. Define a function f to determine the number of ounces of DEET in the tank as a function of time (measured in seconds).
    b. Define a function g to determine the *total* number of ounces of the mixture (both lotion and DEET) that are in the tank as a function of time (measured in seconds).
    c. Define a function h to determine the percentage of DEET in the mixture as a function of time (measured in seconds).
    d. Complete the given table. Round your answers to the nearest ten-thousandths.
    e. Describe how the percentage of DEET in the solution changes as time increases. Will the percentage of DEET in the mixture ever reach a maximum? Explain.
    f. Describe the end-behavior (as t increases without bound) of h.
    g. Use a calculator to graph h, then explain how the graph supports your answer in part (f).

Number of seconds elapsed, t	Percentage of DEET in the mixture, $h(t)$
0	
50	
100	
200	
500	

32. For each given function, state the horizontal asymptote (if one exists).
    a. $f(x) = \frac{x}{2x-3}$
    b. $g(x) = \frac{x^2}{x+5}$
    c. $h(x) = \frac{4x+1}{2x-10}$
    d. $m(x) = \frac{x^2-2}{x^2+3x+2}$
    e. $n(x) = \frac{17x+200}{10x^3-100x^2}$

    f. $p(x) = \frac{5x^2}{x(x-4)}$
    g. $q(x) = \frac{2x^3+7}{5x^4-10}$
    h. $r(x) = \frac{4x^2+x+11}{(3x+1)(2x-3)}$
    i. $w(x) = \frac{(x+9)(x-5)}{(x+6)(x+2)(x-3)}$

III. Graphing Rational Functions and Understanding Limits (Text: S3, 4, 5, 6)

33. Which of the following best describes the behavior of the function f defined by $f(x) = \frac{1}{(x-2)^2}$?
    Provide a rationale for your answer.
    a. As the value of x approaches positive infinity, the value of f decreases without bound.
    b. As the value of x approaches positive infinity, the value of f increases without bound.
    c. As the value of x approaches positive infinity, the value of f approaches 0.
    d. As the value of x approaches 2, the value of f approaches 0.
    e. (a) and (c)

In Exercises #34-42, identify the x-intercepts (roots), y-intercept, horizontal asymptotes, vertical asymptotes, and the function's domain. (*State DNE in cases when an intercept or asymptote does not exist.*) Use this information to sketch a graph of the function.

34. $a(x) = \frac{3}{x-7}$ 35. $b(x) = \frac{x}{2x+6}$ 36. $d(x) = \frac{9x}{3x+3}$ 37. $f(x) = \frac{-x+3}{2x-1}$ 38. $g(x) = \frac{9x^2-144}{x^2-1}$

39. $h(x) = \frac{14x}{3x-4}$ 40. $k(x) = \frac{x-11}{x^2-5x+6}$ 41. $p(x) = \frac{x(x+2)}{4x+1}$ 42. $q(x) = \frac{x^2+2x-3}{x^2-1}$

For Exercises #43-44, use the following graph of f.

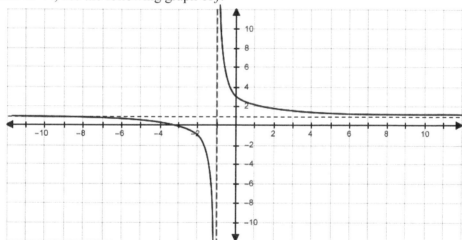

43. Use the graph of f to determine the following limits. If the limit does not exist, write DNE.
    a. $\lim\limits_{x\to\infty} f(x)$ b. $\lim\limits_{x\to-\infty} f(x)$ c. $\lim\limits_{x\to 2^+} f(x)$ d. $\lim\limits_{x\to 2^-} f(x)$

    e. $\lim\limits_{x\to 2} f(x)$ f. $\lim\limits_{x\to-1^+} f(x)$ g. $\lim\limits_{x\to-1^-} f(x)$ h. $\lim\limits_{x\to-1} f(x)$

44. Using the graph of f, identify the vertical and horizontal intercepts, the vertical and horizontal asymptotes, and the domain and range of the function. Then, determine a possible rule for the function f.

For Exercises #45-46, use the following graph of g.

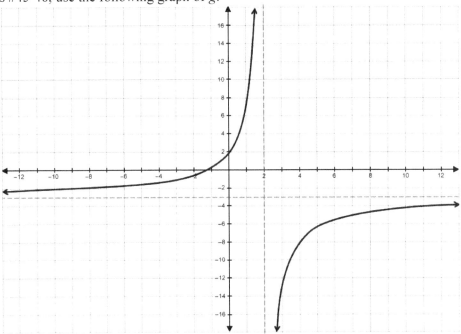

45. Use the graph of g to determine the following limits. If the limit does not exist, write DNE.
    a. $\lim_{x \to \infty} g(x)$
    b. $\lim_{x \to -\infty} g(x)$
    c. $\lim_{x \to 2^+} g(x)$
    d. $\lim_{x \to 2^-} g(x)$

    e. $\lim_{x \to 2} g(x)$
    f. $\lim_{x \to 6^+} g(x)$
    g. $\lim_{x \to 6^-} g(x)$
    h. $\lim_{x \to 6} g(x)$

46. Use the graph of g to identify the vertical and horizontal intercepts, the vertical and horizontal asymptotes, and the domain and range of the function. Then, determine a possible rule for the function g (i.e., represent the function algebraically).

For Exercises #47-48, use the following graph of h.

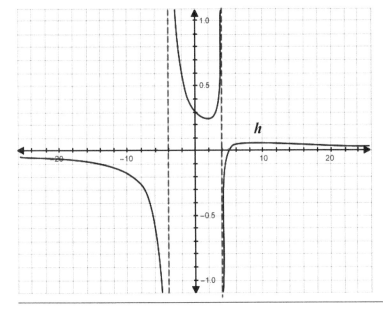

47. Use the graph of h to determine the following limits. If the limit does not exist, write DNE.
    a. $\lim_{x \to \infty} h(x)$
    b. $\lim_{x \to -\infty} h(x)$

    c. $\lim_{x \to -4^+} h(x)$
    d. $\lim_{x \to -4^-} h(x)$

    e. $\lim_{x \to -4} h(x)$
    f. $\lim_{x \to 4^+} h(x)$

    g. $\lim_{x \to 4^-} h(x)$
    h. $\lim_{x \to 4} h(x)$

48. Use the graph of h to identify the vertical and horizontal intercepts, the vertical and horizontal asymptotes, and the domain and range of the function. Then, determine a possible rule for the function h.

For Exercises 49 and 50 using the following table of values for the rational functions f, g, and h.

x	-10000	-1000	-100	100	1000	10000
$f(x)$	-10001.9997	-1001.9970	-101.9694	97.9706	997.9970	9997.9997
$g(x)$	-6.0004	-6.0040	-6.0404	-5.9604	-5.9960	-5.9996
$h(x)$	-0.0005	-0.0050	-0.0506	0.0496	0.0050	0.0005

49. Based on the table of values above, explain the end behavior of each function.
    a. $\lim\limits_{x \to \infty} f(x)$
    b. $\lim\limits_{x \to -\infty} f(x)$
    c. $\lim\limits_{x \to \infty} g(x)$
    d. $\lim\limits_{x \to -\infty} g(x)$
    e. $\lim\limits_{x \to \infty} h(x)$
    f. $\lim\limits_{x \to \infty} h(x)$

50. Consider the rule that defines the functions f, g, and h. How does the degree of the numerator compare to the degree of the denominator (e.g., greater than, less than, or equal to)?

51. Use the given information about function f to complete parts (a) through (d).
    - $\lim\limits_{x \to \infty} f(x) = 0$ and $\lim\limits_{x \to -\infty} f(x) = 0$
    - $\lim\limits_{x \to -6^+} f(x)$ DNE because $f(x)$ increases without bound as $x \to 6^+$
    - $\lim\limits_{x \to 6^+} f(x)$ DNE because $f(x)$ decreases without bound as $x \to 6^-$
    - The y-intercept is $\frac{5}{36}$ (so $\left(0, \frac{5}{36}\right)$ is a point on the graph).
    - The x-intercept is 5 (so $(5, 0)$ is a point on the graph).

    a. Identify the vertical and horizontal asymptotes for f. State DNE if none exist.
    b. What is the domain of f
    c. Find a possible formula for f.
    d. Sketch a graph for f.

52. Use the given information about function g to complete parts (a) through (d).
    - $\lim\limits_{x \to \infty} g(x) = 7$ and $\lim\limits_{x \to -\infty} g(x) = 7$
    - $\lim\limits_{x \to -2^+} g(x)$ DNE because $g(x)$ decreases without bound as $x \to 2^+$
    - $\lim\limits_{x \to -2^-} g(x)$ DNE because $g(x)$ increases without bound as $x \to 2^-$
    - The y-intercept is $\frac{7}{2}$ (so $\left(0, \frac{7}{2}\right)$ is a point on the graph).
    - The x-intercept is -1 (so $(-1, 0)$ is a point on the graph).

    a. Identify the vertical and horizontal asymptotes for g. State DNE if none exist.
    b. What is the domain of g?
    c. Find a possible formula for g.
    d. Sketch a graph for g.

53. Use the given information about function h to complete parts (a) through (d).

   - $\lim\limits_{x \to \infty} h(x)$ DNE because $h(x)$ increases without bound as $x \to \infty$

   - $\lim\limits_{x \to -\infty} h(x)$ DNE because $h(x)$ increases without bound as $x \to -\infty$

   - $\lim\limits_{x \to -(9/2)^+} h(x)$ DNE because $h(x)$ increases without bound as $x \to -(9/2)^+$

   - $\lim\limits_{x \to -(9/2)^-} h(x)$ DNE because $h(x)$ increases without bound as $x \to -(9/2)^-$

   - The y-intercept is $-\frac{10}{9}$ (so $\left(0, -\frac{10}{9}\right)$ is a point on the graph).

   - The x-intercepts are $-\sqrt{5}$ and $\sqrt{5}$ (so $\left(-\sqrt{5}, 0\right)$ and $\left(\sqrt{5}, 0\right)$ are points on the graph).

   a. Identify the vertical and horizontal asymptotes for h. State DNE if none exist.
   b. What is the domain of h?
   c. Find a possible formula for h.
   d. Create a graph for h.

Part 1: The Meaning of Exponents
(Recommended use: Prior to Investigation 4)

1. What does an exponent tell us? For example, what does the expression 3^4 represent?

2. Rewrite each of the following using exponents.
   a. $6 \cdot 6 \cdot 6 \cdot 6 \cdot 6 \cdot 6 \cdot 6$
   b. $x \cdot x \cdot x \cdot x$
   c. $5 \cdot 5 \cdot 5 \cdot 8 \cdot 8 \cdot 8 \cdot 8 \cdot 8$

3. Rewrite each of the following as a product of factors (without using exponents). *Do not simplify your answer.*
   a. $10^2 \cdot 9^3$
   b. $4p^5 t^4$

   c. $\left(5^2\right)^4$
   d. $\left(7x^3 y^2\right)\left(2x^2 y^4\right)$

4. Simplify your results in Exercises #3c and #3d as much as possible.

Part 2: Radicals
(Recommended use: Prior to Investigation 4)

5. What does the square root of a number represent? For example, what is the value of $\sqrt{64}$ and what does it represent?

6. a. Why are there two solutions to the equation $x^2 = 25$?
   b. What are the solutions to the equation $x^2 = 81$? What about $w^2 = 144$?

7. a. Are there also two solutions to the equation $x^3 = 8$? Explain.
   b. What are the solutions to the equation $r^3 = 27$? What about $p^3 = -125$?

8. The *cube root* of a number $\left(\sqrt[3]{\#}\right)$ represents the number that, when raised to an exponent of 3, returns the original number. For example, $\sqrt[3]{8} = 2$ because $2^3 = 8$. Find the value of each of the following.
   a. $\sqrt[3]{64}$
   b. $\sqrt[3]{729}$
   c. $\sqrt[3]{-343}$

9. For some number x, what does each of the following represent?
   a. $\sqrt[5]{x}$
   b. $\sqrt[4]{x}$
   c. $\sqrt[10]{x}$

10. Solve each of the following equations.

    a. $2b^2 = 200$ b. $r^4 = 1,296$ c. $x^7 = -128$

    d. $5x^3 = 320$ e. $64z^8 = 0.25$ f. $12x^5 + 4 = 2,920$

Part 3: Percent Change and Factors
(Recommended use: Prior to Investigation 5)

11. Suppose an item has an original price of \$65 and we purchase it on sale for 20% off.
    a. What number can we multiply \$65 by to find out the discount in dollars? What is the discount in dollars?

    b. Use the result of part (a) to determine the price we are paying.

    c. What percent of the original price are we paying?

    d. What number can we multiply \$65 by to determine the sale price of the item?

12. For each sale described, do the following.
    i) State the number we can multiply the original price by to find the sale price.
    ii) Find the sale price in dollars.
    a. original price: \$150, sale: 40% off   b. original price: \$19, sale: 10% off

    c. original price: \$915.99, sale: 15% off   d. original price: \$22.99, sale: 12.5% off

13. Suppose a store is raising the price of a \$42 item by 15%.
    a. By how many dollars is the price increasing? What number can we multiply \$42 by to determine this?

    b. What is the new price of the item?

    c. What number can we multiply \$42 by to find the new price of the item?

14. For each price increase described, do the following.
    i) State the number we can multiply the original price by to find the new price.
    ii) Find the new price in dollars.
    a. original price: \$52, increase: 10%   b. original price: \$13, increase: 50%

    c. original price: \$14.99, increase: 2.3%   d. original price: \$1,499.99, increase: 100%

15. A city with a population of 480,560 people at the end of the year 2000 grew by 6.2% over 10 years. What was its population at the end of 2010?

16. Student Council reported that attendance at Prom this year was 4.8% less than attendance last year. If 818 people attended Prom last year, how many people attended Prom this year?

A **sequence** in mathematics is an ordered set of objects (usually numbers), such as 2, 4, 6, 8, 10 or 7, 5, 6, 4, 5, 3. The objects in the sequence are called **terms**.

Finite vs. Infinite Sequences

A **finite sequence** is a sequence with a set number of terms. Finite sequences are written like 2, 4, 6, 8, 10 or 2, 4, 6, …, 32.

An **infinite sequence** is a sequence with infinitely many terms where the pattern generating the sequence is repeated without end. Infinite sequences are written like 5, 10, 15, …

---

1. Consider the sequence 1, 2, 4, 8, 16, …
   a. Describe the pattern.

   b. Find the next three terms.

   c. Is it difficult to find the value of the 1000th term? If so, explain why. If not, find its value.

2. Consider the sequence 3, 6, 11, 18, 27, …
   a. Describe the pattern.

   b. Find the next three terms.

   c. Is it difficult to find the value of the 2,500th term? If so, explain why. If not, find its value.

3. Consider the sequence $\frac{2}{1}, \frac{5}{4}, \frac{10}{9}, \frac{17}{16}, \frac{26}{25}, \ldots$
   a. Describe the pattern.

   b. Will any of the following be terms in this sequence? If so, which one(s)?

   $\frac{101}{100}$ $\qquad$ $\frac{116}{115}$ $\qquad$ $\frac{161}{160}$ $\qquad$ $\frac{226}{225}$

   c. Is it difficult to find the value of the 50th term? If so, explain why. If not, find its value.

---

4. Sequences can be thought of as functions in which the input quantity is the ***term position*** [consisting of natural numbers (positive integers)] and the output quantity is the ***term value*** [consisting of the terms of the sequence]. Let's take another look at the sequence in Exercise #3.

input: term position	output: term value	
1	2/1	2
2	5/4	1.25
3	10/9	1.11
4	17/16	1.06
5	26/25	1.04

Like other functions, we can create the graph of a sequence. By convention we track the term position on the horizontal axis and the term value on the vertical axis.

a. Before graphing, consider the following question. When you plot the sequence, should the points be connected? Explain.

b. Graph the sequence. Use at least the first six terms.

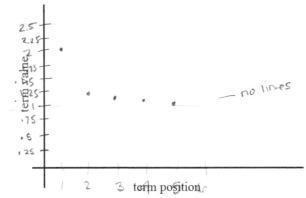

c. What does the graph suggest about the term values as the term position increases?

The Limit of a Sequence

The behavior you noted in Exercise #4 means that this sequence has a ***limit***, or a constant value that the term values approach as the term position increases.[1]

> *Note: Only infinite sequences (sequences with infinitely many terms) are said to have limits. Finite sequences (sequences with a definitive end) do not have a limit.*[2]

In Exercise #4, the *limit is 1*.

---

[1] The formal definition (paraphrased) requires that, for a limit to exist, the term values must be able to get as close as we want to the limiting value as the term position increases for the limit to exist. In other words, if we say that a sequence *has a limit of 4*, it means that at some point the term values must be within (for example) 0.1 of 4, and within 0.003 of 4, and within 0.00000007 of 4, etc. for all remaining terms.

[2] Even if the term values of a finite sequence are getting closer to a constant value, eventually the sequence stops and the last term's value is the closest we can get to this constant. Therefore, the term values can't get arbitrarily close to the constant value. For example, consider the sequence 7.9, 7.99, 7.999, 7.9999. The term values are certainly getting closer to 8, but the final term is 0.0001 away from 8. We could never get within 0.000001 of 8, for example, or within 0.00000003 of 8. Therefore "8" doesn't fit the requirement to be a limit of the sequence.

d. We said that sequences can be thought of as functions. Explain to a partner your understanding of this statement. Then explain how they are different from some of the other functions we have studied.

5. A new sequence is generated by taking the difference of 3 and the term values from the sequence in Exercise #4. For example, the first term of the new sequence is $3-\frac{2}{1}=1$. The second term of the sequence is $3-\frac{5}{4}=\frac{7}{4}$.

a. Graph this new sequence (use at least 6 points).

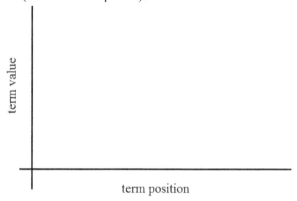

b. Does the sequence appear to have a limit? If so, what is the limit?

c. What is the relationship between the limit of this sequence and the limit of the sequence in Exercise #4? (*That is, is there a mathematical reason why the sequence has term values approaching this limit while the term values of the other sequence approach 1?*)

For Exercises #6-9, do the following.
   a) Examine the pattern and then write the next three terms.
   b) Graph the sequence (use at least six points).
   c) Does the sequence appear to have a limit? If it does, state the limit.

6. 7, 9, 11, 13, ...

7. $1, \frac{1}{2}, \frac{1}{3}, \frac{1}{4}, ...$

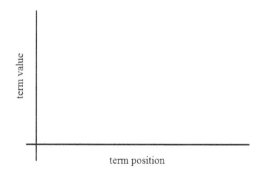

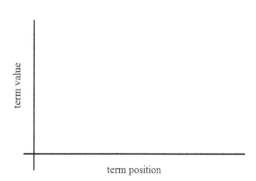

8.   5.1, 4.9, 5.01, 4.99, 5.001, 4.999, ...   9.   1, −1, 2, −2, 4, −4, 8, −8, ...

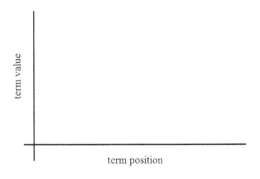

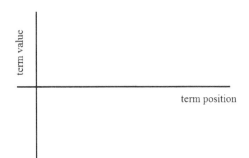

10. A sequence is formed by choosing any real number x to be the first term, then generating the sequence by taking each term value and dividing by 10 to get the next term value.
     a.   Choose a few possible values of x and explore the kinds of sequences produced by following this pattern.

     b.   Do all sequences formed in this manner have a limit? If so, what is the limit? Why does this happen?

     c.   What if the pattern was instead formed by multiplying the term value by 10 to get the subsequent term value? Would sequences formed in this manner have a limit? Explain.

11. Explain, in your own words, what it means for a sequence to have a limit.

In Exercises #1-2, find the indicated term value for the given sequence.

1. $15, 17, 19, 21, 23, 25, 27, \ldots, 73$; find a_6 2. $44, 22, 11, \ldots$; find a_5

3. If a_n represents the value of the nth term in some sequence, how can we represent each of the following?
   a. the value of the term before the nth term   b. the value of the term after the nth term

   c. the value of the term two terms before the nth term

We've seen that a sequence can be thought of as a function where each term position maps to a single term value. Therefore, it's not surprising that we can also write formulas that relate these quantities.

Recursive Formula for a Sequence's Term Values

4. Consider the sequence $17, 23, 29, 35, \ldots, 323$. One of the most common ways to describe this sequence is by saying something similar to "The sequence begins with 17, and the value of every term is 6 more than the value of the previous term."
   a. Using sequence notation, how can you communicate to someone that the value of the first term in the sequence is 17?

   b. Using sequence notation, how can you communicate to someone that the value of any term (such as the nth term) is always 6 more than the value of the previous term?

> **Recursive Formula for a Sequence's Term Values**
>
> A *recursive formula* defines the value of a term a_n based on the value of the previous term or terms.

In Exercises #5-7, use the given formula to write the first four terms of each sequence.

5. $a_1 = 3$
   $a_n = a_{n-1} - 5$

6. $a_1 = 40$
   $a_n = \dfrac{a_{n-1}}{4}$

7. $a_1 = 1$
   $a_2 = 2$
   $a_n = (a_{n-1})(a_{n-2})$

In Exercises #8-9, write a recursive formula to define each sequence, then find a_9.

8. $11, 8, 5, 2, \ldots$

9. $-7, 21, -63, 189, \ldots$

10. John wasn't feeling well, so he went to the doctor yesterday. The doctor gave him a prescription for antibiotics and told him to take one 450 mg dose every 8 hours. John's body metabolizes the drug such that 33% of the medicine remains in his body by the time he takes the next dose.
    a. Why might doctors create a schedule where you take a new dose before the previous dose is completely removed from the body?

    b. Write a recursive formula that will tell you how much medicine is in John's body after taking n doses of the medicine.

    c. Suppose John never stops taking the medicine.
       i. What will happen to the amount of medicine in his body after each dose? Perform some calculations if necessary to explore this question.

       ii. Is there a limit to the maximum amount of antibiotics in John's system? If so, what is the limit?

11. What's the biggest drawback of using a recursive formula to describe a sequence?

12. Consider the following sequence defined recursively. Explain to a partner how determining the values in the sequence are like evaluating function composition expressions such as $f(f(4))$.
    $$a_1 = 7$$
    $$a_n = 3 \cdot a_{n-1} - 10$$

13. Consider the sequence $4, 8, 12, 16, \ldots$. Each term value is exactly 4 times as large as the corresponding term position, so we could think of the sequence as $4(1), 4(2), 4(3), 4(4), \ldots$ and say that $a_n = 4n$. Find the value of the 25th term.

14. Consider the sequence $1, 8, 27, 64, \ldots$. Each term value is the third power of the corresponding term position, so we could think of the sequence as $1^3, 2^3, 3^3, 4^3, \ldots$ and say that $a_n = n^3$. Find the value of the 25th term.

15. How are the formulas $a_n = 4n$ and $a_n = n^3$ different from the recursive formulas we wrote earlier in this investigation?

Explicit Formula for a Sequence's Term Values

An *explicit formula* defines the value of a term a_n based on its position n.

Explicit Formula for a Sequence's Term Values

In Exercises #16-18, find the value of the 12th term in each sequence.

16. $a_n = \dfrac{2}{n}$

17. $b_n = 0.5(n-1)$

18. $c_n = \dfrac{3n}{n+1}$

In Exercises #19-20, write the explicit formula defining the sequence.

19. $12, 24, 36, \ldots, 192$

20. $0, 3, 8, 15, 24, \ldots, 288$

21. How many terms are in the sequences in Exercises #19 and #20?

22. The explicit formulas you wrote Exercises #19 and #20 represent the term value based on its position. Write the inverses for each relationship. (*That is, write the formulas the represent the term's position based on its value.*)

23. When a certain ball is dropped, it bounces back up to ¾ of the distance it fell. Suppose the ball is initially dropped from a height of 12 meters.
    a. Write the first three terms of the sequence describing the height the ball will return to after n bounces.

    b. Write an explicit formula for the sequence that will tell you the height the ball will bounce up to after n bounces.

    c. Is there a limit to this sequence?

Use the following four sequences for Exercises #1-4.
  i) −6, 2, 10, 18, ...   ii) 13, 11, 9, 7, ...   iii) 3.74, 3.79, 3.84, ...   iv) 4.1, 3.3, 2.5, ...

1. Write a recursive formula defining the term values for each sequence.

2. How are the sequences similar to each other?

3. a. How are each of the sequences similar to linear functions?

    b. How are the sequences different from linear functions?

4. Which of the following sequences are similar to the four given sequences? Which are different?
        8, 1, −6, −13, −20, …

        1, 4, 9, 16, 25, …

        3, 6, 12, 24, 48, …

        1, 1.1, 1.2, 1.3, 1.4, …

Arithmetic Sequences

Common Difference:

Arithmetic Sequence:

The Recursive Formula for an Arithmetic Sequence:

Let's take a moment to review formulas for linear functions before thinking about how to write an explicit formula for any arithmetic sequence.

5. Write the formulas for the following linear function relationships.
   a. The constant rate of change of y with respect to x is -2.4 and $(x, y) = (3, 9)$ is one ordered pair for the relationship.

   b. The constant rate of change of y with respect to x is 3 and $(x, y) = (1, 7)$ is one ordered pair for the relationship.

6. Based on her answers to Exercises #3-5, Shelly looked at the following arithmetic sequence and had an idea.
$$7, 10, 13, 16, 19, 22, \ldots$$

   "This sequence is kind of like a linear function with a constant rate of change of 3. I can write $\Delta a_n = 3 \cdot \Delta n$ to think about how this sequence works."

   a. What do you think Shelly understands when she writes $\Delta a_n = 3 \cdot \Delta n$?

   b. We know that the first term in the sequence is 7. We could think about this like the ordered pair $(n, a_n) = (1, 7)$. Based on this idea, answer the following questions.
      i. What is the change in the term position from the 1st term to the 12th term?

    ii. What is the change in term position from the 1st term to the 24th term?

    iii. What is the change in term position from the 1st term to the nth term?

  c. For any change in the term position away from $n = 1$, by how much does the term value change? How you can represent this idea? [For example, when the term position changes from the 1st term to the 12th term, by how much does the term value change? What about from the 1st term to the nth term?]

  d. Knowing that the first term of the sequence is 7 and the common difference is 3, find each of the following term values.
    i. The value of the 54th term.

    ii. The value of the 380th term.

    iii. The value of the nth term for any value of n.

7. Write an explicit formula for the term values in each of the following arithmetic sequences.
    a. 19, 15, 11, 7, …

    b. −56, −41, −26, −11, …

    c. The first term is 5.6 and the common difference is 1.3.

d. The first term is a_1 and the common difference is d.

e. The fifteenth term is 84 and the common difference is 5.

The Explicit Formula for an Arithmetic Sequence

For an arithmetic sequence with a common difference of d, the explicit formula for the term values is…

---

8. a. Each of the following are portions of arithmetic sequences. Fill in the blanks and then write an explicit formula and a recursive formula representing the term values in each sequence.
   i. 15, ____, 20, …   ii. 49, –7, ____, …

b. Find the 6th term in each sequence.

c. For the sequence in part (a) given as 15, ____, 20, …, one of the terms in the sequence is 132.5. What is this term's position?

9. a. Each of the following is a portion of an arithmetic sequence. Fill in the blanks and then write an explicit formula and a recursive formula representing the term values in each sequence.
   i. _____, 32, 40, …   ii. 3, _____, _____, _____, –6, …

   b. Find the 12th term in each sequence.

   c. For the sequence in part (a) given as _____, 32, 40, …, one of the terms in the sequence is 3,472. What is this term's position?

10. Auditoriums are often designed so that there are fewer seats per row for rows closer to the stage. Suppose you are sitting in Row 22 at an auditorium and notice that there are 68 seats in your row. It appears that the row in front of you has 66 seats and the row behind you has 70 seats. Assume this pattern continues throughout the auditorium.
    a. How many seats are in Row 1?

    b. The last row has 100 seats. How many rows are in the auditorium?

    c. Write a recursive formula that defines the value of a_n, the number of seats in row n.

    d. Write an explicit formula that defines the value of a_n, the number of seats in row n.

11. The explicit formula for the term values of a certain sequence is $a_n = 6(n-1) - 27$.

    a. The calculations to determine the 50th term value are given. Answer the questions that go with these calculations.

    $a_n = 6(n-1) - 27$

    $a_{50} = 6(50-1) - 27$ • Step 1

    $a_{50} = 6(49) - 27$ • Step 2

    $a_{50} = 294 - 27$ • Step 3

    $a_{50} = 267$ • Step 4

    i. In Step 1, what does the expression $50 - 1$ represent?

    ii. In Step 2, what does the expression $6(49)$ represent?

    b. [*Inverses*] Solve the formula $a_n = 6(n-1) - 27$ for n and explain what questions this formula helps you to answer.

12. [*Systems of Equations*] The explicit formulas for the term values of two different sequences are $a_n = 4(n-1) + 18$ and $b_n = 6(n-1) - 70$. Is there a term in one sequence that shares the same value and term position as a term in the other sequence? If so, give their value and position.

13. An arithmetic sequence has terms $a_6 = 85$ and $a_{31} = 10$. Write the explicit formula defining the value of a_n.

[Investigation 0 contains review/practice with exponents, the meaning of radical expressions, and how to solve basic equations involving exponents. You can review these concepts as needed.]

Use the following four sequences for Exercises #1-4.

i) $4, 12, 36, ...$ ii) $-\frac{1}{2}, \frac{3}{2}, -\frac{9}{2}, ...$ iii) $6, 2, \frac{2}{3}, ...$ iv) $\frac{10}{3}, -\frac{20}{9}, \frac{40}{27}, ...$

1. Write a recursive formula defining the term values for each sequence.

2. How are the sequences similar to one another?

Geometric Sequences

Common Ratio:

Geometric Sequence:
Recursive Formula for a Geometric Sequence:

---

4. Consider the following sequence.

$$3, 6, 12, 24, 48, \underline{\hspace{1.5cm}}, \underline{\hspace{1.5cm}}, \underline{\hspace{1.5cm}}, ...$$

  a. Verify that this is a geometric sequence and fill in the next three terms.

  b. How does the term value change when the term position changes? Let's explore.
    i. When the term position changes by 1, how does the term value change?

    ii. When the term position changes by 2, how does the term value change?

---

iii. When the term position changes by 3, how does the term value change?

iv. When the term position changes by 7, how does the term value change?

v. When the term position changes by –1, how does the term value change?

c. What is the change in term position from the 1st term to the 40th term? Use your answer to write an expression representing the value of the 40th term in this sequence.

d. What is the change in term position from the 1st term to the 315th term? Use your answer to write an expression representing the value of the 315th term in this sequence.

e. What is the change in term position from the 1st term to the nth term? Use your answer to write an expression representing the value of the nth term in this sequence.

5. Consider the following sequence.

$$4, -12, 36, -108, 324, \underline{\hspace{2cm}}, \underline{\hspace{2cm}}, \underline{\hspace{2cm}}, \dots$$

a. Verify that this is a geometric sequence and fill in the next three terms in the sequence.

b. How does the term value change when the term position changes? Let's explore.
i. When the term position changes by 1, how does the term value change?

ii. When the term position changes by 4, how does the term value change?

iii. When the term position changes by –2, how does the term value change?

iv. When the term position changes by –3, how does the term value change?

c. What is the change in term position from the 1st term to the 24th term? Use your answer to write an expression representing the value of the 24th term in this sequence.

d. What is the change in term position from the 1st term to the 217th term? Use your answer to write an expression representing the value of the 217th term in this sequence.

e. What is the change in term position from the 1st term to the nth term? Use your answer to write an expression representing the value of the nth term in this sequence.

6. Suppose $450 is invested in an account earning 2.8% interest compounded annually. Furthermore, suppose that no additional deposits or withdrawals are made.
    a. To find the account value after the first year we multiply $450 by 1.028. What is the value of the account after 1 year?

    b. If we make a list of the account balance at the end of each year since the initial deposit was made, why will this list form a geometric sequence?

    c. Write a recursive formula for a_n, the value of the account n years since the initial deposit was made.

    d. Write an explicit formula for a_n.

7. If $a_1, a_2, a_3, \ldots$ is a geometric sequence with a common ratio r, what is the explicit formula for the term values in the sequence?

The Explicit Formula for a Geometric Sequence

For a geometric sequence with a common ratio of r, the explicit formula for the term values is...

---

8. Explain what each of the following represents in the explicit formula (be clear and specific).

    a. n b. a_n

    c. $n-1$ d. r^{n-1}

    e. $a_1 \cdot r^{n-1}$

In Exercises #9-12, do the following.
- a) Verify that the series is geometric.
- b) Write a recursive formula for the term values of the sequence and then write an explicit formula for the term values of the sequence.

9. 5, 20, 80, 320, ...   10. 1458, 486, 162, 54, ...

11. −8, 12, −18, 27, ...   12. 15, 6, 2.4, 0.96, ...

13. a. Each of the following is a portion of a geometric sequence. Fill in the blanks and then write an explicit formula for each sequence.

      i. 2, 8, _____ , ...   ii. 81, ___ , 9, ...

    b. Find the value of the 6th term of each sequence.

14. a.   Each of the following is a portion of a geometric sequence. Fill in the blanks and then write an explicit formula for each sequence.

   i.   _____, 60, 15, …   ii.   2, _____, _____, 250, …

   b.   Find the value of the 12th term of each sequence.

15. A pattern is formed according to the following instructions. Beginning with an equilateral triangle the midpoints of the sides are connected forming four smaller equilateral triangles. The middle triangle is then colored black to create the diagram in Stage 2. This process is repeated with all of the white triangles at each stage to form the diagram in the next stage.

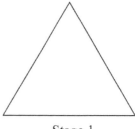

Stage 1

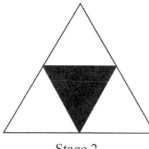

Stage 2

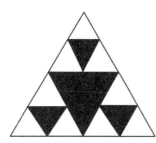

Stage 3

Stage 4   …

   a.   Create a sequence that shows the total number of white triangles a_n at stage n and then write the explicit formula for a_n.

   b.   Does the sequence from part (a) have a limit? What does this represent in the context?

c. Assume that the original white triangle has an area of 8 cm². Write the first several terms b_n of the sequence representing the area of one white triangle at stage n and then write the explicit formula for b_n.

d. Still assuming that the original white triangle has an area of 8 cm², write the first several terms c_n of the sequence representing the total area of all of the white triangles at stage n and then write the explicit formula for c_n.

e. Does the sequence from part (d) have a limit? What represent in the context?

f. The term values of a new sequence are defined by $d_n = 8 - c_n$.
    i. What does this new sequence represent?

    ii. Does this sequence have a limit? What does this represent in the context?

16. A geometric sequence has terms $a_9 = 45,927$ and $a_{15} = 33,480,783$. Write the explicit formula defining the value of a_n.

1. After graduating from college, Andy received job offers from two firms. Firm A offered Andy an initial salary of $52,000 for the first year with a 6% pay raise guaranteed for the first five years. Firm B offered Andy an initial salary of $55,000 with a 4% pay raise guaranteed for the first five years. Andy plans to work for five years and then quit and go to graduate school. He really likes both firms, and the hours and job responsibilities are similar, so he will make his decision based on salary.

   a. *Make a prediction:* Which offer do you think he should accept?

   b. What number do we multiply $52,000 by to find out Andy's salary during his second year if he works for Firm A? What number do we multiply $55,000 by to find out Andy's salary during his second year for Firm B?

   c. Write out the sequences that represent his annual salaries with each firm for the first five years.

Year n	1	2	3	4	5
Salary with Firm A in year n					
Salary with Firm B in year n					

   d. Compare Andy's salary in the fifth year working for each firm. Does this tell him which firm he should choose? Why or why not?

   e. Fill in the following table that keeps track of Andy's total salary after working for 1, 2, 3, 4, and 5 years with each firm.

year	total salary earned while working for Firm A by the end of the year	total salary earned while working for Firm B by the end of the year
1		
2		
3		
4		
5		

   f. Pick one row from the table and explain what it represents.

   g. According to Andy's criteria, which firm should he choose?

Series

Series:

_____

Ex: Given the sequence 3, 6, 9, 12, 15, 18, the corresponding series is

2. Write the corresponding series for each given sequence and give the total sum.
   a. 1, 6, 3, 14, 10, 29   b. −7, −2, 2, 5, 7, 8, 8

When working with series we are often curious about sum of the terms up to a certain point. We call these the *partial sums* and denote them in the form S_n, where S_n is the sum of the first n terms of the sequence.

Partial Sum of a Series

The nth Partial Sum: [represented by S_n] The sum of the terms of a sequence from the first term to the nth term.

_____

Ex: Given the sequence 5, 10, 20, 40, 80, 160,
   a) the third partial sum is given by $S_3 = 5 + 10 + 20 = 35$.
   b) the fifth partial sum is given by $S_5 = 5 + 10 + 20 + 40 + 80 = 155$.
   c) the first partial sum is just the first term, or $S_1 = 5$

In Exercises #3-6, find the indicated partial sum for the given sequence.

3. 10, 8, 6, 4, ..., find S_5 4. $a_n = (n+1)^2 - 3$, find S_3

5. $\frac{1}{3}, \frac{2}{3}, 1, \frac{4}{3}, ...$, find S_7 6. $\begin{aligned} a_1 &= 6 \\ a_n &= 0.5a_{n-1} \end{aligned}$, find S_4

Sequence of Partial Sums

Sequence of Partial Sums: A sequence of partial sums is a sequence where the nth term is the partial sum S_n. In this way, the sequence of partial sums is like a "running total so far" for the terms in the original sequence.

Ex: For the sequence 5, 10, 20, 40, 80, 160, the sequence of partial sums is $S_1, S_2, S_3, S_4, S_5, S_6$, or 5, 15, 35, 75, 155, 315.

---

7. Given the sequence 1, 4, 9, 16, ..., write the first five terms for the sequence of partial sums

8. If $a_n = -7 + \frac{4}{5}(n-1)$, write the first five terms for the sequence of partial sums

9. A basketball tournament is held that includes 64 teams. Each round the teams are paired off and play with the loser being eliminated from the tournament.
    a. The sequence representing the number of games played in each round of the tournament begins 32, 16, ... Complete the sequence and explain why it's a finite sequence.

    b. Turn the sequence into a finite series and find the sum of the series. Explain what this number represents and why it might be useful to the people running the tournament.

    c. Write the sequence of partial sums and explain what it represents in this context.

10. Suppose a pattern is formed using blocks as follows. Let n represent the step number, let a_n represent the number of blocks added at Step n, and let S_n represent the total number of blocks at Step n.

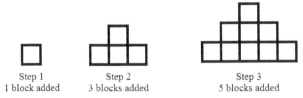

Step 1
1 block added

Step 2
3 blocks added

Step 3
5 blocks added

Then $a_n = 2n - 1$ represents the number of blocks added at Step n.

a. Write the first five terms for a_n and S_n, then explain what the terms of these sequences represent.

b. Write a formula that determines S_n given a step number n.

c. How many blocks will be added at step 9? How many total blocks are in Step 9?

d. Which step number has 225 total blocks?

> ### Finite Arithmetic Series
>
> A *finite arithmetic series* is the sum of the terms of a finite arithmetic sequence.
>
> ---
>
> *Ex:* $-7, -2, 3, 8, 13$ is a finite arithmetic sequence because it has a common difference ($d = 5$) and only finitely many terms. Then $(-7) + (-2) + 3 + 8 + 13$ is the corresponding finite arithmetic series with a sum of 15.

1. a. Is the following series arithmetic? If so, write down the common difference. If not, explain why the series is not arithmetic.

$$1+3+5+7+9+11+13$$

   b. What is the sum of the series?

   c. Starting with the arithmetic series in part (a), suppose we duplicate the series exactly and combine the two series as shown.

$$1+3+5+7+9+11+13+1+3+5+7+9+11+13$$

   How is the sum of *all* of the terms of the two series combined related to the sum of the original series?

   d. Is your answer to part (c) true even if we change the order of terms? For example, is it still true if we write the following?

$$1+3+5+7+9+11+13+13+11+9+7+5+3+1$$

Let's visualize the terms of the arithmetic series as the heights of vertical bars. For example, the terms of the series $1+3+5+7+9+11+13$ are represented below on the left. We have also duplicated the series to the right.

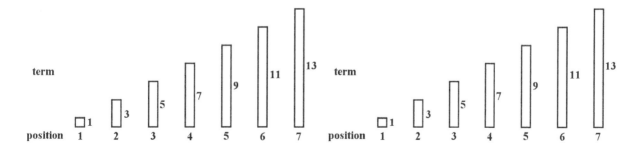

Let's rotate the duplicated terms 180° and then stack them on the terms of the original series.

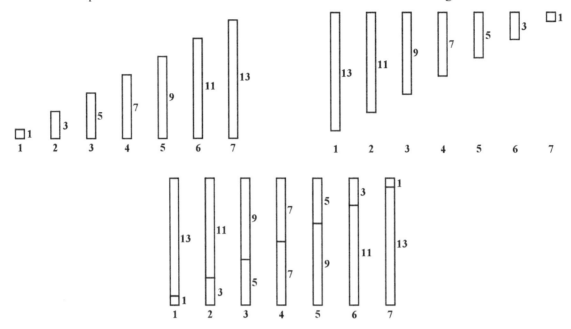

This visualization can help us find the sum of all of the terms in both series together very easily.

2. a. What is the height of each combined bar?   b. How many bars are there?

   c. What is the total sum of all of the terms in both series together and how is this represented in the diagram?

   d. What is the sum of just the original series $1+3+5+7+9+11+13$?

The arithmetic series $1+3+5+7+9+11+13$ is very short and easy to add up on a calculator. However, the reasoning we just explored can really help us when the series get very long. Let's continue to explore this idea.

3. a. The terms in the arithmetic series $2+5+8+11+14+17$ are represented visually below. Imagine duplicating the series and visualizing it as vertical bars rotated 180° and stacked on top of the original diagram. Draw this.

   b. How tall is each bar?

   c. How many bars are there?

   d. What is the total sum of all of the terms in both the original and duplicated series together?

   e. What is the sum of the original arithmetic series $2+5+8+11+14+17$?

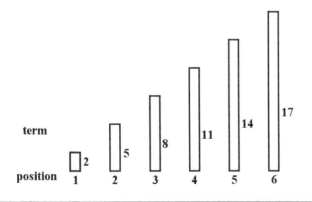

The visualization we've used so far is a really nice geometric argument for the technique we're developing. However, let's repeat the reasoning without the same visual component.

4. a. The series $1+3+5+7+9+11+13$ from Exercises #1-2 is shown below. In addition, the series is duplicated and written in reverse order on the next line. Total each column and put your answers in the given boxes.

$$
\begin{array}{ccccccccccccc}
1 & + & 3 & + & 5 & + & 7 & + & 9 & + & 11 & + & 13 \\
13 & + & 11 & + & 9 & + & 7 & + & 5 & + & 3 & + & 1 \\
\end{array}
$$

$$\boxed{}+\boxed{}+\boxed{}+\boxed{}+\boxed{}+\boxed{}+\boxed{}$$

b. What is the sum of every column and how many columns are there?

c. What is sum of all the terms in both series combined?

d. What is the sum of the arithmetic series $1+3+5+7+9+11+13$?

5. Use the reasoning we've developed to find the sum of each of the following arithmetic series.
   a. $105+141+177+213+249+285+321$ b. $4+7+10+13+16+19+22+25$

   c. $15+13+11+9+7+5+3+1-1-3-5-7$ d. $-126-117-108-99-90-81-72-63-54$

6. Does the technique we've been developing work with non-arithmetic series? Let's find out. Try to use the same reasoning to find the sum of each of the following series. *Note: You should verify that each series is not arithmetic.*
   a. $1+4+9+16+25+36+49$ b. $2+4+8+16+32+64+128$

7. Why does this technique only work with arithmetic series? Create a convincing mathematical argument.

8. a. To develop a general formula we need to think about how to apply the reasoning to ALL arithmetic series. Suppose that $a_1 + a_2 + a_3 + ... + a_{n-2} + a_{n-1} + a_n$ is an arithmetic series with n total terms. Duplicate the series and write it in reverse order below the original series.

$$a_1 \ + \ a_2 \ + \ a_3 \ + \ ... \ + \ a_{n-2} \ + \ a_{n-1} \ + \ a_n$$

   b. What is the sum of each column/pair of terms?

   c. What the total combined sum of all of the terms in both series together?

   d. What is the sum of the original arithmetic series with n terms?

Sum of a Finite Arithmetic Series

If $a_1 + a_2 + a_3 + ... + a_n$ is a finite arithmetic series, then the sum of the series S_n is...

---

9. Recall the following context from Investigation 3. *Auditoriums are often designed so that there are fewer seats per row for rows closer to the stage. Suppose you are sitting in Row 22 at an auditorium and notice that there are 68 seats in your row. It appears that the row in front of you has 66 seats and the row behind you has 70 seats. Assume this pattern continues throughout the auditorium.*
   a. Go back to Investigation 3 and locate the following information: the number of rows, the number of seats in the first row, and the number of seats in the last row.

   b. How many seats are in the auditorium?

10. One method of exercising with weights is to complete 10 repetitions, rest for 30 seconds, and then perform the same exercise completing 9 repetitions. After a 30 second rest, 8 repetitions are completed. This process continues until the person only lifts the weight once. How many total repetitions are completed during such a routine?

11. Shilah recently decided to start jogging each morning and wants to work up to 3.5 miles per day. Tomorrow she will run 0.5 miles, and she will increase the distance she runs by 0.2 miles each day until she reaches 3.5 miles per day.
    a. How many days will she have been jogging when she reaches 3.5 miles per day?

    b. How many total miles will Shilah have run during this time?

In Exercises #12-17, do the following.
  a) Verify that the series is arithmetic. [*Hint: It might help to write out the first several terms of the series if they are not given.*]
  b) If the series is arithmetic, find its sum without simply adding up all of the terms. [*Hint: In most cases you will need to determine the number of terms in the series.*]

12. The sum of integers from 1 to 100.

13. Find the sum of the integers from 1 to 250.

14. $6 + 13 + 20 + ... + 181$

15. $14 + 10 + 6 + ... - 138$

16. the sum of the even numbers from 1 to 300

17. the sum of the positive four-digit multiples of 20

18. Write a finite arithmetic series with a sum of 80 that has 10 terms and a common difference $d \neq 0$. (*Instead of using "guess and check" try to think about a strategy for solving this problem using the ideas you've learned in this investigation.*)

Finite Geometric Series

A *finite geometric series* is the sum of the terms of a finite geometric sequence.

Ex: 1, –2, 4, –8 is a finite geometric sequence because it has a common ratio ($r = -2$) and only finitely many terms. Then $1 + (-2) + 4 + (-8)$ or $1 - 2 + 4 - 8$ is the corresponding finite geometric series with a sum of –5.

For Exercises #1-3, consider the finite geometric series $5 + 15 + 45 + 135 + 405 + 1,215$ with a sum $S_6 = 1,820$.

1. a. Suppose each of the terms of the series is multiplied by 2. Write out the terms of the new series, then find its sum and compare this to the sum of the original series.

    b. Suppose each of the terms of the series is multiplied by 4. Write out the terms of the new series, then find its sum and compare this to the sum of the original series.

2. If we multiply each term of the original series by 3, we get the following new series.
$$3(5) + 3(15) + 3(45) + 3(135) + 3(405) + 3(1,215)$$
$$15 + 45 + 135 + 405 + 1,215 + 3,645$$

    a. How does the sum of this new series compare to the sum of the original series?

    b. Compare the terms of the new series and the terms of the original series. What do you notice?

    c. Why do so many of the terms from the original series reappear in the new series when the term values are multiplied by 3, but not by 2 or 4?

3. Let S_6 represent the sum of the original series and $3 \cdot S_6$ represent the sum of the new series.

    a. What is the value of $S_6 - (3 \cdot S_6)$?

    b. One of your classmates claims that he can calculate $S_6 - (3 \cdot S_6)$ without knowing the sums of the series. He says that $a_1 - 3a_6$ will have the same value as $S_6 - (3 \cdot S_6)$ and shows the following work. Is he correct?

    $$S_6 = 5 + \cancel{15} + \cancel{45} + \cancel{135} + \cancel{405} + \cancel{1,215}$$
    $$-\left(3 \cdot S_6 = \quad \cancel{15} + \cancel{45} + \cancel{135} + \cancel{405} + \cancel{1,215} + 3,645\right)$$
    $$S_6 - 3 \cdot S_6 = 5 - 3,645$$
    $$S_6 - 3 \cdot S_6 = -3,640$$

    c. Use the equation $S_6 - 3 \cdot S_6 = -3,640$ to solve for S_6.

4. Let's practice the technique from Exercise #3 with the finite geometric series $2 + 10 + 50 + 250 + 1,250 + 6,250 + 31,250$ with a sum S_7 and a common ratio $r = 5$. If we multiply the terms of the series by 5 we get the following series with a sum of $5 \cdot S_7$.

    $$2(5) + 10(5) + 50(5) + 250(5) + 1,250(5) + 6,250(5) + 31,250(5)$$
    $$10 + 50 + 250 + 1,250 + 6,250 + 31,250 + 156,250$$

    Complete the steps to find S_7 without actually adding up the terms of the series.

    $$S_7 = 2 + 10 + 50 + 250 + 1,250 + 6,250 + 31,250$$
    $$-\left(5 \cdot S_7 = \quad 10 + 50 + 250 + 1,250 + 6,250 + 31,250 + 156,250\right)$$
    $$S_7 - 5 \cdot S_7 = \underline{\hspace{4cm}}$$

    $$\underline{\hspace{1.5cm}} S_7 = \underline{\hspace{3cm}}$$

    $$S_7 = \underline{\hspace{3cm}}$$

Sum of a Finite Geometric Series

If S_n is the sum of a finite geometric series with a first term a_1, a last term a_n, and a common ratio r, then

We then solve the equation for S_n to find the sum.

This technique allows us to find the sum
- without adding up all of the term values and
- even if we don't know all of the term values or the number of terms.

In Exercises #5-10, find the sum of each finite geometric series.

5. $2 + 4 + 8 + \ldots + 2{,}048$

6. $1 + 6 + 36 + \ldots + 10{,}077{,}696$

7. The series begins $2 - 6 + 18 - \ldots$ and there are 11 terms.

8. $\frac{1}{16} - \frac{1}{4} + 1 - \ldots - 1024$

9. $4 + \frac{4}{3} + \frac{4}{9} + \frac{4}{27} + \ldots + \frac{4}{2,187}$

10. Rising healthcare costs are a constant issue facing families and businesses. Suppose the cost of insuring an individual is \$8,900 this year and is expected to increase by 7% per year for the next 9 years. How much do we expect it to cost to cover this person over the entire 10-year period?

So far we have written series in a form like $4+7+10+13+16$. However, this form has shortcomings. Series with many terms are very common in math, and in these cases we'd need to either write out the entire long series or shorten it (like writing $12+17+22+...+122$) which can hide important information. Mathematicians needed a way to write the sum of long series in a condensed way that also provides maximum information. Their solution was *sigma notation*.

The best way to introduce sigma notation is through an example. Consider the series $4+7+10+13+16$. This series is made up of the terms of the sequence $4, 7, 10, 13, 16$ described with the explicit formula $a_n = 4+3(n-1)$. The first term is $a_1 = 4$. The last term is $a_5 = 16$. We use the capital Greek letter sigma (Σ) to mean *sum of*.

We want to represent the statement "the sum of the terms of the sequence a_n from a_1 to a_5" in some way other than $4+7+10+13+16$. We can write this series in sigma notation as $\sum_{n=1}^{5}\left[4+3(n-1)\right]$.

Here are two important points about sigma notation.

I) $\sum_{n=1}^{5} a_n = a_1 + a_2 + a_3 + a_4 + a_5$. We can translate sigma notation into the expanded form by substituting $n=1$, then continuing to substitute values of n until we reach the index value written above sigma (in this case $n=5$).

II) The number written above sigma is **not** intended to represent *the number of terms*. For example, consider $\sum_{n=5}^{8} a_n$ (4 terms) and $\sum_{n=2}^{3} a_n$ (2 terms).

$$\sum_{n=5}^{8} a_n = a_5 + a_6 + a_7 + a_8 \qquad\qquad \sum_{n=2}^{3} a_n = a_2 + a_3$$

In Exercises #1-4 , write out the terms of the series and find the sum.

1. $\sum_{n=1}^{4}\left[22-2(n-1)\right]$

2. $\sum_{n=1}^{5} 4(3)^{n-1}$

3. $\sum_{n=1}^{3} 2^{n+2}$

4. $\sum_{n=3}^{7} \dfrac{n^2}{2}$

In Exercises #5-8, write each series in sigma notation. (*Hint: You might first need to determine the number of terms in the series.*)

5. $3 + 15 + 75 + 375 + 1,875 + 9,375$

6. $2 + 6 + 10 + 14 + ... + 90$

7. $1 + \frac{4}{3} + \frac{5}{3} + 2 + ... + 33$

8. $\frac{1}{2^3} + \frac{1}{2^4} + \frac{1}{2^5} + ... + \frac{1}{2^{10}}$

9. Represent the sum of the first 150 odd positive integers using sigma notation. *Hint: It might help to write out the first several terms of the series first.*

10. Represent the sum of all of the numbers from 1 to 400 that are evenly divisible by 5. *Hint: It might help to write out the first several terms of the series first.*

11. Recall the following context from Investigations 3 and 6. *Auditoriums are often designed so that there are fewer seats per row for rows closer to the stage. Suppose you are sitting in Row 22 at an auditorium and notice that there are 68 seats in your row. It appears that the row in front of you has 66 seats and the row behind you has 70 seats. Assume this pattern continues throughout the auditorium.*

    Represent the total number of seats in the auditorium using sigma notation. *(You can refer back to Investigations 3 and 6 to find any additional information you may need.)*

12. Recall the following context from Investigation 5. *A basketball tournament is held that includes 64 teams. Each round the teams are paired off and play with the loser being eliminated from the tournament. The sequence representing the number of games played in each round of the tournament begins 32, 16, ...*

    Represent the total number of games played in the tournament using sigma notation. *(You can refer back to Investigation 5 to find any additional information you may need.)*

13. *Recall the following context from Investigation 7. Rising healthcare costs are a constant issue facing families and businesses. Suppose the cost of insuring an individual is $8,900 this year and is expected to increase by 7% per year for the next 9 years.*

    Represent the expected cost to cover this person over the entire 10-year period using sigma notation.

In Exercises #14-17, do the following.
  a) State whether the series is arithmetic, geometric, or neither.
  b) If the series is arithmetic or geometric, give the common difference or common ratio.
  c) Write down the first and last terms of the series.

14. $\sum_{n=1}^{14}[3+2n]$

15. $\sum_{n=1}^{6}7^n$

16. $\sum_{n=1}^{11}\frac{1}{n^2}$

17. $\sum_{n=5}^{9}[4-6(n-1)]$

For Exercises #18-21, find the sum of the series.

18. $\sum_{i=1}^{10}4(3)^{i-1}$

19. $\sum_{n=1}^{105}[6-4(n-1)]$

20. $\sum_{n=1}^{5}\left[n^2-6\right]$

21. $\sum_{n=1}^{40}3(n-3)$

22. When writing a series using sigma notation we use the explicit formula and not the recursive formula. For example, $12+17+22+...+122$ is written as $\sum_{n=1}^{28}[12+5(n-1)]$ and not as $\sum_{i=1}^{28}[a_{n-1}+5]$. What are the advantages of using the explicit formula for the term values instead of the recursive formula in sigma notation?

1. Explain what it means for a sequence to have a limit.

2. Explain what the sequence of partial sums represents for a series.

3. Explain what each of the following represents.

    a. $\sum_{n=6}^{10} [3n+2]$

    b. $\sum_{n=1}^{\infty} [40+n^2]$

4. Using a ruler, draw a square on a piece of paper. Make sure that the square is reasonably large – at least 4 inches per side. We'll call the area of this square "one square unit." Now consider the series
    $$\tfrac{1}{2}+\tfrac{1}{4}+\tfrac{1}{8}+\tfrac{1}{16}+...$$
    Let's imagine these terms each represent areas (in square units).
    a. Write the first six terms of the sequence of partial sums.

    b. Cut your square in half parallel to one of the sides. You are now holding two rectangles, each with an area of ½ square unit. Set one of these to the side. This represents the value of the first term in your sequence of partial sums.
        Take the second rectangle and cut it in half. You are now holding two squares, each with an area of ¼ square unit. Set one of these aside next to the rectangle with an area of ½ square unit. Repeat this process several more times. How does this activity represent the sequence of partial sums?

    c. Does the sequence of partial sums have a limit? If so, what is the limit?

5. Consider the series $6+2+\frac{2}{3}+\frac{2}{9}+....$ This time, let's imagine the terms represent lengths.

    a. Write the first six terms in the sequence of partial sums.

    b. On the line below, a bolded line segment is drawn measuring 6 units. This represents the first term in the sequence of partial sums. Extend this line segment to generate a segment whose length is the second term in the sequence of partial sums.

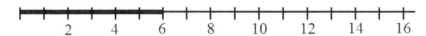

    c. Repeat part (b) to represent the next several terms in the sequence of partial sums.

    d. Does the sequence of partial sums have a limit? If so, what is the limit?

For Exercises #6-11, do the following.
    a) State whether the series is arithmetic or geometric and identify the common difference or common ratio.
    b) Graph the first six terms of the sequence that makes up the series. Does there appear to be a limit? If so, what is it?
    c) Generate and graph the first six terms of the sequence of partial sums for the series.
    d) Does the sequence of partial sums appear to have a limit? If so, what is it?

6. $\displaystyle\sum_{n=1}^{\infty} 2^{n+3}$

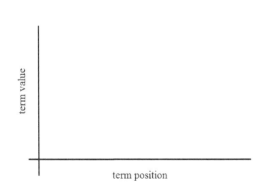

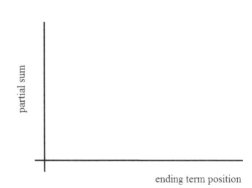

7. $-1+2+5+...$

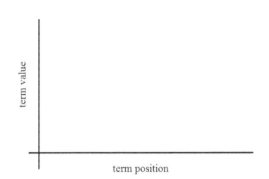

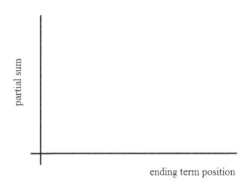

8. $\displaystyle\sum_{n=1}^{\infty}3\left(-\tfrac{1}{3}\right)^{n-1}$

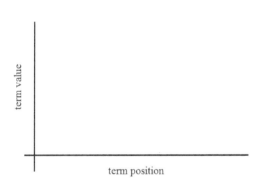

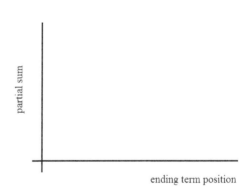

9. $\displaystyle\sum_{n=1}^{\infty}-2n+6$

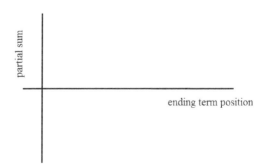

10. $3 + \frac{3}{2} + \frac{3}{4} + \frac{3}{8} + \ldots$

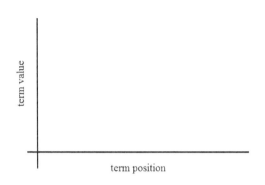

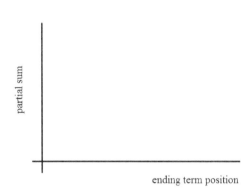

11. $4 - 8 + 16 - 32 + \ldots$

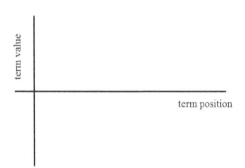

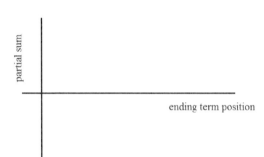

12. What does it mean when the sequence of partial sums for an infinite series has a limit? (In other words, why is part (d) important in Exercises #4-9?)

13. TRUE or FALSE: For an infinite geometric series with a common ratio $r \neq 0$ and $a_1 \neq 0$, the sequence of partial sums always has a limit. Justify your answer.

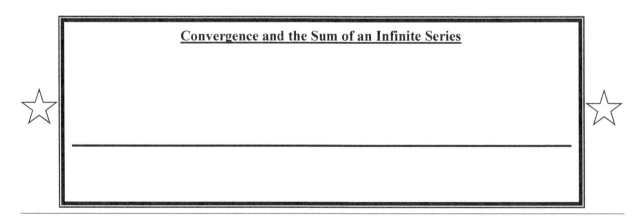

Convergence and the Sum of an Infinite Series

> ### Sum of an Infinite Geometric Series
>
> If S is the sum of an infinite geometric series with a first term a_1 and a common ratio r, then
>
> We solve the equation for S to find the sum.
>
> *Remember:*
> - The sum of an infinite series is the limit of the sequence of partial sums.
> - An infinite geometric series will only have a sum if $|r| < 1$.

In Exercises #1-3, find the sum if possible.

1. $\displaystyle\sum_{n=1}^{\infty} 24\left(\tfrac{2}{3}\right)^{n-1}$ 2. $\displaystyle\sum_{n=1}^{\infty} (1.2)^{n}$ 3. $\displaystyle\sum_{n=1}^{\infty} 7(-0.4)^{n-1}$

4. A pendulum is made up of a string or solid arm with a weight attached to the end. Because of outside factors such as air resistance and gravity, each swing of a pendulum is a little shorter than the previous one. Suppose the length of the pendulum's swing follows a geometric sequence with the first swing being 100 cm long and the second swing length being 99% of the previous swing length.

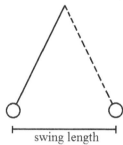

swing length

    a. What is the common ratio for the sequence of pendulum swing lengths? Write out the first several terms of the sequence of swing lengths.

    b. Suppose an infinite series is formed from this sequence. Find the sum of the series (if possible).

    c. Does the sum of the series have a real-world meaning? If so, describe the meaning. If not, explain your thinking.

For Exercises #5-8, do the following.
  a) Write the series in sigma notation.
  b) Find the sum of the series (if possible).

5. $120 + 30 + \frac{30}{4} + \frac{30}{16} + \dots$

6. $-10 + 5 - 2.5 + 1.25 - \dots$

7. $1.25 - 2.5 + 5 - 10 + \dots$

8. $1 + x + x^2 + x^3 + \dots$ where $-1 < x < 1$

In Exercises #9-11, create a series that meets the stated requirements. Write the series using sigma notation. (*Note: Do not use any of the series we have provided in this investigation.*)

9. an infinite geometric series with a negative common ratio that has a sum

10. an infinite geometric series that does not have a sum

11. an infinite geometric series with a sum between 0 and 1

12. A doctor prescribes a pain reliever to a patient with severe back pain. The doctor tells the patient to take a 500 mg does every 8 hours and that she will reevaluate the patient in the future. After some research about the medication, the patient learns that his body likely eliminates 90% of the drug in his system over the course of 8 hours.
   a. How much of the drug is in the patient's system right after he takes the second dose? Show the expression that calculates this value.

   b. How much of the drug is in the patient's system right after he takes the third dose? Show the expression that calculates this value.

   c. How much of the drug is in the patient's system right after he takes the fourth dose? Show the expression that calculates this value.

   d. Explain how the amount of drug in the patient's system after the nth dose forms a geometric series.

   e. Suppose the patient stays on the medication indefinitely. What eventually happens to the amount of drug in his system when he takes a new dose?

13. Suppose the doctor prescribes an ibuprofen regimen to another patient to alleviate problems with swollen joints. The doctor tells the patient to take 600 mg of ibuprofen every 12 hours, and during each 12-hour period the patient's body eliminates 85% of the drug in the patient's system.
    a. Find the amount of drug in the patient's system right after taking the 7th dose.

    b. Suppose the patient stays on the medication indefinitely. What eventually happens to the amount of drug in his system?

© 2018 Carlson, Oehrtman, and Moore

INVESTIGATION 1: SEQUENCES AND THE LIMITS OF SEQUENCES

For Exercises #1-6, do the following.
    a) Describe the pattern.
    b) Complete the table showing the relationship between the term positions and the term values.

input: term position	output: term value
1	
2	
3	
4	
5	
6	

    c) Graph the sequence (use at least six points).
    d) Does the sequence appear to have a limit? If so, what is it?

1. $40, 52, 64, \dots$
2. $15, 5, \frac{5}{3}, \dots$
3. $1, \frac{2}{3}, \frac{4}{9}, \dots$
4. $-6, -7.8, -9.6, \dots$
5. $0, 1, 4, 9, \dots$
6. $6, 9, 10.5, 11.25, \dots$

7. A sequence is formed by choosing any real number x to be the first term, and then generating the sequence by taking each term value and dividing by 2 to get the next term value.
    a. Choose a few possible values of x and explore the kinds of sequences produced by following this pattern.
    b. Do all sequences formed in this manner have a limit? If so, what is the limit? Why does this happen?

8. A sequence is formed by choosing any real number x to be the first term, then generating the sequence by taking each term value and multiplying by 3.5 to get the subsequent term value.
    a. Choose a few possible values of x and explore the kinds of sequences produced by following this pattern.
    b. Do all sequences formed in this manner have a limit? If so, what is the limit? Why does this happen?

9. A pyramid is formed from blocks according to the given pattern. Write the next three terms in the sequence showing the total number of blocks in the pyramid at each stage.

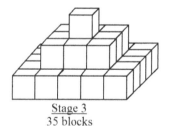

Stage 1   Stage 2   Stage 3
1 block   10 blocks   35 blocks

10. A sequence is formed by determining the number of diagonals that can be drawn inside of regular polygons as shown below. (A diagonal is a line segment drawn inside of the figure from one vertex to another.) Determine the pattern formed by this sequence and write the next three terms of the sequence.

Stage 1   Stage 2   Stage 3   Stage 4

0 diagonals   2 diagonals   5 diagonals   ??? diagonals

11. An infinite sequence begins 40, 60, ...
    a. Determine a possible pattern for this sequence such that the sequence *will not have a limit*. Write the next three terms using this pattern.
    b. Determine another possible pattern for this sequence such that sequence *will not have a limit*. Write the next three terms using this pattern.
    c. Determine another possible pattern for this sequence such that sequence *will* have a limit. Write the next three terms using this pattern.

12. An infinite sequence begins $-8, -3$, ...
    a. Determine a possible pattern for this sequence so that the sequence *will not have a limit*. Write the next three terms using this pattern.
    b. Determine another possible pattern for this sequence so that sequence *will not have a limit*. Write the next three terms using this pattern.
    c. Determine another possible pattern for this sequence so that sequence *will* have a limit. Write the next three terms using this pattern.

INVESTIGATION 2: FORMULAS FOR SEQUENCES

In Exercises #13-16, find the indicated term value for the given sequence.
13. $1, -3, 9, ...$; find a_5
14. $104, 107, 110, ...$; find a_6
15. $\frac{1}{2}, \frac{1}{3}, \frac{1}{4}, ...$; find a_{10}
16. $1, -5, 25, -125, 625, ...$; find a_5

17. If a_n represents the value of the nth term in some sequence, how could you represent each of the following?
    a. the value of the term three term positions before the nth term
    b. the value of the term two term positions after the nth term
    c. the term position one term prior to the nth term

18. If a_n represents the value of the nth term in some sequence, how could you represent each of the following?
    a. the term position four terms after the nth term
    b. the value of the term five term positions before the nth term
    c. the value of the term three term positions after the nth term

In Exercises #19-24, use the given formula to write the first four terms of each sequence.

19. $a_1 = -2, \quad a_n = a_{n-1} + 3$
20. $a_1 = 360, \quad a_n = \frac{a_{n-1}}{3}$
21. $a_1 = 10, \quad a_n = -2a_{n-1} + 4$

22. $a_1 = 4, \quad a_n = \frac{128}{a_{n-1}}$
23. $a_1 = -1, \ a_2 = 4$
    $a_n = a_{n-1} + a_{n-2}$
24. $a_1 = 1, \ a_2 = 2, \ a_3 = 4$
    $a_n = 2a_{n-3} + 3a_{n-2}$

In Exercises #25-28, write a recursive formula to define each sequence.
25. $25, 30, 35, ...$
26. $1, -7, -15, ...$
27. $3, 18, 108, ...$
28. $1, -\frac{1}{8}, \frac{1}{64}, ...$

In Exercises #29-30, write the first four terms of the sequence.
29. $a_n = \frac{5(n-1)}{4n}$
30. $a_n = 7(-3)^n$

In Exercises #31-32, find the value of the 15th term in the sequence.

31. $a_n = -4 - 15(n-1)$

32. $a_n = \dfrac{14}{(n+3)^2}$

In Exercises #33-34, write the explicit formula defining the sequence and then find the number of terms in the given sequence.

33. $1, 4, 9, 16, 25, ..., 225$

34. $10, 13, 16, 19, ..., 178$

In Exercises #35-38 you are given the explicit formula for a sequence. Write the inverses for each relationship. (*That is, write the formulas the represent the term's position based on its value.*)

35. $a_n = 3n + 6$ 36. $a_n = -2(n-1) + 8$ 37. $a_n = n^2 + 7$ 38. $a_n = \frac{6n-12}{5}$

39. After a car is purchased its value generally decreases over time. Suppose a car's original purchase price is $24,679 and that is the value of the car in any given year is always 0.85 times as large as the value of the car the year before.
    a. Write a sequence showing the car's value at the end of each of the first five years since its original purchase.
    b. Write a recursive formula for the sequence in part (a).
    c. Write an explicit formula for the sequence in part (b).

40. Suppose we have 57 micrograms of a particular bacteria population in a petri dish. We place this petri dish in an incubator and the bacteria grows in such a way that its mass triples each day.
    a. Write a sequence showing the bacteria's mass at the end of each of the first five days since it was placed in the incubator.
    b. Write a recursive formula for the sequence in part (a).
    c. Write an explicit formula for the sequence in part (b).

INVESTIGATION 3: ARITHMETIC SEQUENCES

41. Your friends learned about sequences in another class and don't understand how or why the explicit formula for arithmetic sequences $(a_n = a_1 + d(n-1)$ or $a_n = d(n-1) + a_1)$ works to find any term value (they just memorized the formula for a test). Explain to your friends what each of the following represents in the formula. *Hint: Think about linear functions.*
    a. n b. d c. a_n d. $n-1$ e. $d(n-1)$ f. $a_1 + d(n-1)$ or $d(n-1) + a_1$

42. The explicit formula for the term values of a certain sequence is $a_n = 4(n-1) + 19$. The calculations to determine the value of the 33rd term are given. Answer the questions that go with these calculations.

$a_n = 4(n-1) + 19$

$a_{33} = 4(33-1) + 19$ • Step 1

$a_{33} = 4(32) + 19$ • Step 2

$a_{33} = 128 + 19$ • Step 3

$a_{33} = 147$ • Step 4

a. What do "4" and "19" represent?

b. In Step 1, what does the expression 33 – 1 represent?

c. In Step 2, what does the expression 4(32) represent?

For Exercises #43-50, do the following.
   a) Write the recursive formula for the arithmetic sequence.
   b) Write the explicit formula for the arithmetic sequence.
   c) Determine the number of terms in the arithmetic sequence.

43. $13, 15, 17, ..., 251$

44. $14, 13.7, 13.4, ..., -10.6$

45. $62, 63.1, 64.2, ..., 124.7$

46. $-30, -26.5, -23, ..., 488$

47. $-33, -41, -49, ..., -825$

48. $1077, 1077.1, 1077.2, ..., 1085.4$

49. All of the 3-digit multiples of 7

50. All of the 5-digit multiples of 25

51. Interior angles of convex polygon are formed by two adjacent sides of the polygon opening into the interior of the figure. The sum of the measures of all of the interior angles of a polygon follow the pattern shown below.

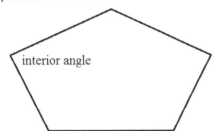

number of sides n	sum of the measures of the interior angles a_n
3	180°
4	360°
5	540°
6	720°

   a. We can think of the sequence beginning with a_3 instead of a_1. Write the recursive formula for the sequence.
   b. Write the explicit formula for the sequence.
   c. Regular polygons are polygons where all of the interior angles are congruent and all of the sides are the same length. What is the measure of *each* interior angle in a regular polygon with 18 sides?

52. Auditoriums are often designed so that there are fewer seats per row for rows closer to the stage. Suppose you are sitting in Row 18 at an auditorium and notice that there are 73 seats in your row. It appears that the row in front of you has 70 seats and the row behind you has 76 seats. Suppose this pattern continues throughout the auditorium.
   a. How many seats are in the first row?
   b. How many seats are in the 30th row?
   c. Write an explicit formula for the sequence where a_n is the number of seats in the nth row.

In Exercises #53-54, solve the given explicit formula for n and explain what questions this new version of the formula helps you to answer.

53. $a_n = 6(n-1) - 27$

54. $a_n = 6(n-1) - 27$

[*Systems of Equations*] In Exercises #55-56 you are given the explicit formulas for the term values of pairs of sequences. For each pair, is there a term in one sequence that shares the same value and term position as a term in the other sequence? If so, give their value and position.

55. $a_n = -3(n-1) + 30$ and $b_n = 2(n-1) - 25$

56. $a_n = 4(n-1) + 25$ and $b_n = 6(n-1) - 78$

57. In this module we've seen that it's possible for an infinite sequence to have a limit. However, infinite arithmetic sequences with $d \neq 0$ never have a limit. Explain why this is true.

58. An arithmetic sequence has the following two terms: $a_{13} = 58$ and $a_{28} = 140.5$. Write the explicit formula defining the value of the nth term a_n.

59. An arithmetic sequence has the following two terms: $a_6 = 13.5$ and $a_{24} = 51.3$. Write the explicit formula defining the value of the nth term a_n.

60. A finite arithmetic sequence has the following two terms: $a_9 = 52.9$ and $a_{27} = 121.3$. The value of the final term is 934.5. How many terms are in the sequence?

61. A finite arithmetic sequence has the following two terms: $a_5 = 71.6$ and $a_{23} = 33.8$. The value of the final term is -167.8. How many terms are in the sequence?

INVESTIGATION 4: GEOMETRIC SEQUENCES

In Exercises #62-63 you are given diagrams intended to help a person visualize how the term values of a geometric sequence compare to one another. For each diagram, estimate the value of the common ratio and the values of a_2, a_3, a_4, and a_5.

62.

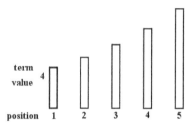

63.

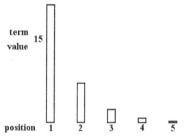

64. Draw a diagram for an arithmetic sequence similar to the diagrams in Exercise #62-63. Compare the diagrams for arithmetic sequences to the diagrams for geometric sequences.

For Exercises #65-70, do the following.
    a) Write the recursive formula for the geometric sequence.
    b) Write the explicit formula for the geometric sequence.
    c) Determine if the sequence has a limit. If so, state the limit.

65. $3, 6, 12, 24, \ldots$ 66. $38, 19, 9.5, 4.75, \ldots$ 67. $-15, 60, -240, 960, \ldots$

68. $88, -11, \frac{11}{8}, \ldots$ 69. $90, 30, 10, \frac{10}{3}, \ldots$ 70. $12, 18, 27, 40.5, \ldots$

71. Inflation describes the tendency of prices for goods to rise over time. Historically, prices of goods have risen about 3% per year. Suppose a loaf of bread costs $2.99 in January 2012 and that its cost will rise by 3% per year over the next several years.
    a. Write a recursive formula for the cost of a loaf of bread a_n in dollars n years since January 2012.
    b. Write an explicit formula for the cost of a loaf of bread a_n in dollars n years since January 2012.
    c. Assuming this pattern continues, what do you expect to be the cost of a loaf of bread in 2025?

72. In 2010, a university's budgeting committee decided that they would set the annual tuition rate at $14,000 per year and that they would raise this rate by 2.5% each year following the 2010-2011 school year.
    a. Write a recursive formula for the tuition rate a_n in dollars n years since the 2010-2011 school year.
    b. Write an explicit formula for the tuition rate a_n in dollars n years since the 2010-2011 school year.
    c. Assuming this pattern continues, what do you expect to be the tuition rate for the 2018-2019 school year?

For Exercises #73-76, do the following.
   a) Fill in the blanks to make the sequence arithmetic.
   b) Fill in the blanks to make the sequence geometric.
73. 12, 36, _____   74. _____, 1, − 4, ...   75. 14, _____, 224, ...   76. 20, _____, 45, ...

77. A geometric sequence has the following two terms: $a_3 = 72$ and $a_7 = 93,312$. Write the explicit formula defining the value of the nth term a_n.

78. A geometric sequence has the following two terms: $a_5 = 2048$ and $a_8 = 131,072$. Write the explicit formula defining the value of the nth term a_n.

79. A finite geometric sequence has the following two terms: $a_7 = 288$ and $a_{12} = 9,216$. The last term in the sequence is $37,748,736$. How many terms are in the sequence?

80. A finite geometric sequence has the following two terms: $a_4 = 250$ and $a_8 = 156,250$. The last term in the sequence is 2,441,406,250. How many terms are in the sequence?

INVESTIGATION 5: INTRODUCTION TO SERIES AND PARTIAL SUMS

Suppose a series is formed using the terms from the sequences defined in Exercises #81-84 below. For each, find the given partial sum.
81. 103, 206, 309, ..., find S_4 82. 9, 16, 25, 36, ..., find S_6
83. $a_n = \dfrac{(8-n)^2}{n^3}$, find S_1 84. $a_1 = 64$, $a_n = \frac{1}{4}a_{n-1}$, find S_5

In Exercises #85-88, suppose a series is formed using the terms from the given sequence. Write the first five terms for the sequence of partial sums.

85. $a_n = 20 - 6n$ 86. $3, \frac{9}{2}, \frac{27}{4}, ...$ 87. $a_1 = 2.5$, $a_n = 6 \cdot a_{n-1} - 2$ 88. $\begin{aligned} a_1 &= 1, \ a_2 = 1 \\ a_n &= a_{n-2} + a_{n-1} \end{aligned}$

89. The table below shows the terms of a sequence where a_n is the power bill (in dollars) for a single family home during the nth month of 2011.

n	a_n	S_n	n	a_n	S_n
1	53.15		7	212.63	
2	52.90		8	175.10	
3	57.44		9	118.02	
4	73.80		10	68.98	
5	98.17		11	56.65	
6	152.82		12	53.70	

   a. Fill in the column showing the partial sums S_n.
   b. Explain what the partial sums are keeping track of in this context.

90. The table below shows the terms of a sequence where a_n is the number of DWI (Driving While Intoxicated) tickets given out in Travis County for the nth month of 2012.

n	a_n	S_n
1	62	
2	48	
3	55	
4	41	
5	54	
6	62	

n	a_n	S_n
7	67	
8	70	
9	63	
10	59	
11	56	
12	48	

   a. Fill in the column showing the partial sums S_n.
   b. Explain what the partial sums are keeping track of in this context.

In Exercises #91-93 below you are given information about the terms of arithmetic series and the sequence of partial sums for each series. Complete the tables.

91.

n	a_n	S_n
1		
2		
3	11	
4	15	
5	19	
6		
7		

92.

n	a_n	S_n
1		
2		
3		
4		
5		5
6		0
7		−7

93.

n	a_n	S_n
1		
4		
5		
10	23.5	
13	31	
16		
18		

In Exercises #94-96 below you are given information about the terms of geometric series and the sequence of partial sums for each series. Complete the tables.

94.

n	a_n	S_n
1		
2		
3	54	
4	162	
5		

95.

n	a_n	S_n
1		−20
2		10
3		
4		
5		

96.

n	a_n	S_n
1		
4		
5		
10	2,048	
13	16,384	

INVESTIGATION 6: FINITE ARITHMETIC SERIES

97. a. Draw vertical bars with heights that represent the terms of the series $2+4+6+8+10+12+14$. [*See Exercises #1 and #2 in Investigation 6.*]
   b. Duplicate the diagram and combine it with your diagram in part (a) to demonstrate the total combined sum of the two series. [*See Exercises #1 and #2 in Investigation 6.*]
   c. What is the height of each combined bar and how many bars are there?
   d. What is the total combined sum of the two series?
   e. What is the sum of the original series?

98. Repeat Exercise #97 for the series $1+4+7+10+13+16+19+22$.

99. The series $-4+(-1)+2+5+8+11+14+17$ is shown below. In addition, the series is duplicated and written in reverse order on the next line. Total each column and explain how this can help you determine the sum of the original series.

$$(-4)+ \ (-1)+ \ \ 2 \ + \ 5 \ + \ 8 \ + 11 + \ 14 + \ 17$$
$$\ \ 17 \ + \ 14 \ + 11 \ + \ 8 \ + \ 5 \ + \ \ 2 + (-1) \ + (-4)$$

$$\boxed{}+\boxed{}+\boxed{}+\boxed{}+\boxed{}+\boxed{}+\boxed{}+\boxed{}$$

100. Repeat Exercise #99 for the series $-10+(-6)+(-2)+2+6+10+14+18+22$.

For Exercises #101-102, find the sum of the series.

101. $121+128+135+...+233$ (17 terms)

102. $83+81+79+...-19$ (52 terms)

For Exercises #103-106, do the following for each finite arithmetic series.
   a. Find the number of terms in the series.
   b. Find the sum of the series.

103. $17+21+25+...+89$

104. $223+214+205+...+(-56)$

105. $6+6.3+6.6+...+25.2$

106. $-10+(-8.2)+(-6.4)+...+42.2$

For Exercises #107-108, do the following for each finite arithmetic series.
   a. Give the first three terms of the series and the last term of the series.
   b. Find the number of terms in the series.
   c. Find the sum of the series.

107. the sum of all 4-digit numbers

108. the sum of the 3-digit multiples of 2

109. Auditoriums are often designed so that there are fewer seats per row for rows closer to the stage. Suppose you are sitting in Row 23 at an auditorium and notice that there are 65 seats in your row. It appears that the row in front of you has 63 seats and the row behind you has 67 seats. Suppose this pattern continues throughout the auditorium. You count a total of 42 rows in the auditorium. How many seats does the auditorium contain?

110. A child builds a pyramid out of multiple decks of playing cards. As he starts from the bottom-up, the layers are numbered starting at the base. Suppose he creates the sixth layer by using 12 cards. His friend notes that the fifth layer is made out of 16 cards, and the boy is planning to use 8 cards to create the seventh layer. Suppose this pattern continues throughout the entire pyramid. The boy who is building says that his pyramid will have a total of eight layers. How many cards does it take to build the pyramid?

111. A finite arithmetic series has 73 terms with $a_7=21.4$ and $a_{13}=32.8$. What's the sum of the series?

112. A finite arithmetic series has 90 terms with $a_5=182$ and $a_{86}=291.6$. What's the sum of the series?

113. A finite arithmetic series has a sum of 81,674 with a first term of 912 and a final term of -70. How many terms are in the series?

114. A finite arithmetic series has a sum of 104,030 with a first term of -12 and a final term of 1042. How many terms are in the series?

115. Write a finite arithmetic series with a sum of 200 that has 8 terms with a common difference $d \neq 0$. (*Instead of using "guess and check" try to think about a strategy for solving this problem using the ideas you've learned in this investigation.*)

116. Write a finite arithmetic series with a sum of 540 that has 12 terms with a common difference $d \neq 0$. (*Instead of using "guess and check" try to think about a strategy for solving this problem using the ideas you've learned in this investigation.*)

INVESTIGATION 7: FINITE GEOMETRIC SERIES

117. The finite geometric series $10 + 40 + 160 + \ldots + 163,840$ has 8 terms and a sum S_8. Show the process of multiplying the sum by the common ratio and finding the difference of S_8 and $r \cdot S_8$ to find the sum. (In other words, justify why $S_n - r \cdot S_n = a_1 - r \cdot a_n$ is true for finite geometric series.)

118. The finite geometric series $3 + 9 + 27 + \ldots + 2,187$ has 7 terms and a sum S_7. Show the process of multiplying the sum by the common ratio and finding the difference of S_7 and $r \cdot S_7$ to find the sum. (In other words, justify why $S_n - r \cdot S_n = a_1 - r \cdot a_n$ is true for finite geometric series.)

In Exercises #119-124, find the sum of each finite geometric series.

119. $5 + 25 + 125 + \ldots + 390,625$ 120. $-3 + 6 - 12 + \ldots - 786,432$ 121. $4 + 12 + 36 + \ldots + 78,732$

122. $-128 + 64 - 32 + \ldots + 1$ 123. $1 + \frac{1}{10} + \frac{1}{100} + \ldots + \frac{1}{100,000,000}$ 124. $36 + 12 + 4 + \ldots + \frac{4}{2,187}$

125. The local power company plans to raise rates to cover the increased costs of producing power. In a recent newsletter, they notified their customers to expect power costs to increase by 4.2% per year for the next 10 years (including this year). (The power costs one year are 1.042 times as large as the costs in the previous year.)
   a. If you paid a total of $1031.60 for power last year, what do you expect to pay for power over the next 10 years (assuming you continue to live in your current residence and that your power usage does not change)?
   b. How does this compare to the total price if power costs remained the same over the next 10 years?

126. A bouncing ball reaches heights of 16 cm, 12.8 cm, and 10.24 cm on three consecutive bounces.
   a. If the ball was dropped from a height of 25 cm, how many times has it bounced when it reaches a height of 16 cm? 10.24 cm?
   b. Write the first five terms of the sequence representing the bounce height after n bounces.
   c. How much total distance *in the downward direction only* has the ball traveled after five bounces? (*Be careful!*)
   d. How much total distance *in the upward direction only* has the ball traveled after five bounces (and reaching the top of its fifth bounce)?
   e. What is the *total distance* traveled by the ball when it reaches the top of its fifth bounce?

127. Suppose you had the option of receiving $100 today, $200 tomorrow, $300 the next day, and so on for a month, or choosing to get $0.01 today, $0.02 tomorrow, $0.04 the next day, $0.08 the day after that, and so. Which would you choose? How much more money do you get with your chosen option? (*Assume "one month" means "30 days"*).

INVESTIGATION 8: SIGMA NOTATION FOR SERIES

In Exercises #128-131, write out the terms of each series.

128. $\sum_{n=1}^{7} 5(2)^{n+1}$ 129. $\sum_{n=1}^{5} \frac{n^2 - 3}{10}$ 130. $\sum_{n=4}^{8} \frac{4^n + n}{3n}$ 131. $\sum_{n=2}^{4} \left(2(5)^n + 3(4)^{n-2} \right)$

In Exercises #132-135, write each series using sigma notation. (*Hint: You might first need to determine the number of terms in the series.*)

132. $10+16+22+28+34+40+46+52$

133. $3-12+48-192+768-3072$

134. $-6+(-4)+(-2)+...+142$

135. $5+20+80+...+5,242,880$

136. Represent the sum of the numbers from 1 to 300 that are evenly divisible by 3 using sigma notation. *Hint: It might help to write out the first several terms of the series first.*

137. Represent the sum of the numbers from 1 to 1000 that are evenly divisible by 25 using sigma

INVESTIGATION 9: INFINITE SERIES

For Exercises #138-141 do the following.
 a) State whether the series is arithmetic or geometric and identify the common difference or common ratio.
 b) Graph the first six terms of the sequence that makes up the series. Does there appear to be a limit? If so, what is it?
 c) Generate and graph the first six terms of the sequence of partial sums for the series.
 d) Does the sequence of partial sums appear to have a limit? If so, what is it?

138. $\sum_{n=1}^{\infty} 7\left(\frac{4}{3}\right)^{n-1}$

139. $\sum_{n=1}^{\infty} -0.3n+7$

140. $-1+0.2+(-0.04)+0.008+(-0.0016)+0.00032$

141. $\frac{16}{4}, 5, \frac{25}{4}, \frac{125}{16}, \frac{625}{64}, \frac{3125}{256}$

INVESTIGATION 10: INFINITE GEOMETRIC SERIES

In Exercises #142-144, find the sum if possible.

142. $\sum_{n=1}^{\infty} 28\left(-\frac{5}{4}\right)^{n-1}$

143. $\sum_{n=1}^{\infty} \left(\frac{5}{8}\right)^{n}$

144. $\sum_{n=1}^{\infty} -5(0.95)^{n-1}$

For Exercises #145-148 do the following.
 a) Write the series in sigma notation.
 b) Find the sum of the series (if possible).

145. $-12+(-6)+(-3)+(-1.5)+...$

146. $2-2.5+3.125-\frac{125}{32}+...$

147. $2.1-2.1x+2.1x^2-2.1x^3+...$; where $1<x<1.2$

148. $4.5+4.5a+4.5a^2+...$; where $|a|<1$

In Exercises #149-154, create a series that meets the stated requirements. Write the series using sigma notation. (*Note: Do not use any of the series we have provided in the investigations.*)

149. an infinite geometric series with a positive common ratio that does not have a sum

150. an infinite geometric series that has a negative common ratio and does not have a sum

151. an infinite geometric series with a positive common ratio that does have a sum

152. an infinite geometric series with a negative common ratio that does have a sum

153. an infinite geometric series with a sum between 0 and 1

154. an infinite geometric series with a sum between 0 and -1